A TREASURY OF

Stephen Leacock

By Stephen Leacock

AUTOBIOGRAPHY

The Boy I Left Behind Me (1946)

BIOGRAPHY

Mark Twain (1932)

Charles Dickens: His Life and Work (1933)

DRAMA

'Q': A Farce in One Act [with Basil Macdonald] (1915)

ECONOMICS

Economic Prosperity in the British Empire (1930)

Back to Prosperity: The Great Opportunity of the Empire Conference (1932)

The Gathering Financial Crisis in Canada: A Survey of the Present Critical Situation (1936)

EDUCATION

The Pursuit of Knowledge: A Discussion of Freedom and Compulsion in Education (1934)

Too Much College, or Education Eating Up Life (1939)

HISTORY

Baldwin, Lafontaine, Hincks: Responsible Government (1907)

Adventures of the Far North: A Chronicle of the Frozen Seas (1914)

The Dawn of Canadian History: A Chronicle of Aboriginal Canada and the Coming of the White Man (1914)

The Mariner of St. Malo: A Chronicle of the Voyages of Jacques Cartier (1914)

Mackenzie, Baldwin, Lafontaine, Hincks (1926)

Lincoln Frees the Slaves (1934)

The British Empire: Its Structure, Its History, Its Strength (1940)

Canada: The Foundations of Its Future (1941)

Our Heritage of Liberty: Its Origin, Its Achievement, Its Crisis: A Book for War Time (1942)

Montreal: Seaport and City (1942)

Canada and the Sea (1944)

HUMOUR

Literary Lapses (1910)

Nonsense Novels (1911)

Sunshine Sketches of a Little Town (1912)

Behind the Beyond, and Other Contributions to Human Knowledge (1913)

Arcadian Adventures with the Idle Rich (1914)

Moonbeams from the Larger Lunacy (1915)

Further Foolishness: Sketches and Satires on the Follies of the Day (1916)

Frenzied Fiction (1918)

The Hohenzollerns in America; with the Bolsheviks in Berlin, and Other Impossibilities (1919)

Winsome Winnie, and Other New Nonsense Novels (1920)

My Discovery of England (1922)

College Days (1923)

Over the Footlights (1923)

The Garden of Folly (1924)

Winnowed Wisdom (1926)

Short Circuits (1928)

The Iron Man and the Tin Woman, with Other Such Futurities (1929)

Wet Wit and Dry Humour: Distilled from the Pages of Stephen Leacock (1931)
The Dry Pickwick and Other Incongruities (1932)
Afternoons in Utopia: Tales of the New Time (1932)
Hellements of Hickonomics in Hiccoughs of Verse Done in Our Social Planning Mill (1936)
Funny Pieces: A Book of Random Sketches (1936)
Here Are My Lectures (1937)
Model Memoirs, and Other Sketches from Simple to Serious (1938)
My Remarkable Uncle and Other Sketches (1942)
Happy Stories Just to Laugh At (1943)
Last Leaves (1945)

LITERARY CRITICISM

Essays and Literary Studies (1916)
Humour: Its Theory and Technique (1935)
The Greatest Pages of American Humor (1936)
Humour and Humanity: An Introduction to the Study of Humour (1937)
How to Write (1943)

POLITICAL SCIENCE

Elements of Political Science (1906)
The Unsolved Riddle of Social Justice (1920)
My Discovery of the West: A Discussion of East and West in Canada (1937)
While There Is Time: The Case against Social Catastrophe (1945)

A TREASURY OF Stephen Leacock

Three Complete and Unabridged Canadian Classics

STEPHEN LEACOCK

A DIVISION OF CHAPTERS INC.

Canadian Cataloguing in Publication Data

Leacock, Stephen, 1859-1944
A treasury of Stephen Leacock

Contents: Literary lapses–Sunshine sketches–Winnowed wisdom.
ISBN 1-55267-282-4

I. Title.

PS8523.E15L43 1999 C813'.52 C99-930975-7
PR9199.3.L367L43 1999

The publisher gratefully acknowledges the support of the Canada Council for the Arts and the Ontario Arts Council for its publishing program

Canadä

We acknowledge the financial support of the Government of Canada through the Book Publishing Industry Development Program (BPIDP) for our publishing activities.

This edition produced for Prospero Books, a division of Chapters Inc., 90 Ronson Drive, Etobicoke, Ontario M9W 1C1.

Key Porter Books Limited
70 The Esplanade
Toronto, Ontario
Canada M5E 1R2

www.keyporter.com

Design: Peter Maher
Electronic formatting: Jean Peters

Printed and bound in Canada

00 01 02 03 6 5 4 3 2

Contents

Literary Lapses

Contents

My Financial Career

WHEN I go into a bank I get rattled. The clerks rattle me; the wickets rattle me; the sight of the money rattles me; everything rattles me.

The moment I cross the threshold of a bank and attempt to transact business there, I become an irresponsible idiot.

I knew this beforehand, but my salary had been raised to fifty dollars a month and I felt that the bank was the only place for it.

So I shambled in and looked timidly round at the clerks. I had an idea that a person about to open an account must needs consult the manager.

I went up to a wicket marked "Accountant." The accountant was a tall, cool devil. The very sight of him rattled me. My voice was sepulchral.

"Can I see the manager?" I said, and added solemnly, "alone." I don't know why I said "alone."

"Certainly," said the accountant, and fetched him.

The manager was a grave, calm man. I held my fifty-six dollars clutched in a crumpled ball in my pocket.

"Are you the manager?" I said. God knows I didn't doubt it.

"Yes," he said.

"Can I see you," I asked, "alone?" I didn't want to say "alone" again, but without it the thing seemed self-evident.

The manager looked at me in some alarm. He felt that I had an awful secret to reveal.

"Come in here," he said, and led the way to a private room. He turned the key in the lock.

"We are safe from interruption here," he said. "Sit down."

We both sat down and looked at each other. I found no voice to speak.

"You are one of Pinkerton's men, I presume," he said.

He had gathered from my mysterious manner that I was a detective. I knew what he was thinking, and it made me worse.

"No, not from Pinkerton's," I said, seeming to imply that I came from a rival agency.

"To tell the truth," I went on, as if I had been prompted to lie about it, "I am not a detective at all. I have come to open an account. I intend to keep all my money in this bank."

The manager looked relieved but still serious; he concluded now that I was a son of Baron Rothschild or a young Gould.

"A large account, I suppose," he said.

"Fairly large," I whispered. "I propose to deposit fifty-six dollars now and fifty dollars a month regularly."

The manager got up and opened the door. He called to the accountant.

"Mr. Montgomery," he said unkindly loud, "this gentleman is opening an account, he will deposit fifty-six dollars. Good morning."

I rose.

A big iron door stood open at the side of the room.

"Good morning," I said, and stepped into the safe.

"Come out," said the manager coldly, and showed me the other way.

I went up to the accountant's wicket and poked the ball of money at him with a quick convulsive movement as if I were doing a conjuring trick.

My face was ghastly pale.

"Here," I said, "deposit it." The tone of the words seemed to mean, "Let us do this painful thing while the fit is on us."

He took the money and gave it to another clerk.

He made me write the sum on a slip and sign my name in a book. I no longer knew what I was doing. The bank swam before my eyes.

"Is it deposited?" I asked in a hollow, vibrating voice.

"It is," said the accountant.

"Then I want to draw a cheque."

My idea was to draw out six dollars of it for present use. Someone gave me a cheque-book through a wicket and someone else began telling me how to write it out. The people in the bank had the impression that I was an invalid millionaire. I wrote something on the cheque and thrust it in at the clerk. He looked at it.

"What! are you drawing it all out again?" he asked in surprise. Then I realised that I had written fifty-six instead of six. I was too far gone to reason now. I had a feeling that it was impossible to explain the thing. All the clerks had stopped writing to look at me.

Reckless with miser, I made a plunge.

"Yes, the whole thing."

"You withdraw your money from the bank?"

"Every cent of it."

"Are you not going to deposit any more?" said the clerk, astonished.

"Never."

An idiot hope struck me that they might think something had insulted me while I was writing the cheque and that I had changed my mind. I made a wretched attempt to look like a man with a fearfully quick temper.

The clerk prepared to pay the money.

"How will you have it?" he said.

"What?"

"How will you have it?"

"Oh"—I caught his meaning and answered without even trying to think—"in fifties."

He gave me a fifty-dollar bill.

"And the six?" he asked dryly.

"In sixes," I said.

He gave it me and I rushed out.

As the big door swung behind me I caught the echo of a roar of laughter that went up to the ceiling of the bank. Since then I bank no more. I keep my money in cash in my trousers pocket and my savings in silver dollars in a sock.

Lord Oxhead's Secret

A Romance in One Chapter

It was finished. Ruin had come. Lord Oxhead sat gazing fixedly at the library fire. Without, the wind soughed (or sogged) around the turrets of Oxhead Towers, the seat of the Oxhead family. But the old earl heeded not the sogging of the wind around his seat. He was too absorbed.

Before him lay a pile of blue papers with printed headings. From time to time he turned them over in his hands and replaced them on the table with a groan. To the earl they meant ruin—absolute, irretrievable ruin, and with it the loss of his stately home that had been the pride of the Oxheads for generations. More than that—the world would now know the awful secret of his life.

The earl bowed his head in the bitterness of his sorrow, for he came of a proud stock. About him hung the portraits of his ancestors. Here on the right an Oxhead who had broken his lance at Crécy, or immediately before it. There McWhinnie Oxhead who had ridden madly from the stricken field of Flodden to bring to the affrighted burghers of Edinburgh all the tidings that he had been able to gather in passing the battlefield. Next him hung the dark half Spanish face of Sir Amyas Oxhead of Elizabethan days whose pinnace was the first to dash to Plymouth with the news that the English fleet, as nearly as could be judged from a reasonable distance, seemed about to grapple with the Spanish Armada.

Below this, the two Cavalier brothers. Giles and Everard Oxhead, who had sat in the oak with Charles II. Then to the right again the portrait of Sir Ponsonby Oxhead who had fought with Wellington in Spain, and been dismissed for it.

Immediately before the earl as he sat was the family escutcheon emblazoned above the mantelpiece. A child might read the simplicity of its proud significance—an ox rampant quartered in a field of gules with a pike dexter and a dog intermittent in a plain parallelogram right centre, with the motto, "Hic, haec, hoc, hujus, hujus, hujus."

"Father!"—The girl's voice rang clear through the half light of the wainscoted library. Gwendoline Oxhead had thrown herself about the earl's neck. The girl was radiant with happiness. Gwendoline was a beautiful girl of thirty-three, typically English in the freshness of her girlish innocence. She wore one of those charming walking suits of brown holland so fashionable among the aristocracy of England, while a rough leather belt encircled her waist in a single sweep. She bore herself with that sweet simplicity which was her greatest charm. She was probably more simple than any girl of her age for miles around. Gwendoline was the pride of her father's heart, for he saw reflected in her the qualities of his race.

"Father," she said, a blush mantling her fair face, "I am so happy, oh, so happy; Edwin has asked me to be his wife, and we have plighted our troth—at least if you consent. For I will never marry without my father's warrant," she added, raising her head proudly; "I am too much of an Oxhead for that."

Then as she gazed into the old earl's stricken face, the girl's mood changed at once. "Father," she cried, "father, are you ill? What is it? Shall I ring?" As she spoke Gwendoline reached for the heavy bell-rope that hung beside the wall, but the earl, fearful that her frenzied efforts might actually make it ring, checked her hand. "I am, indeed, deeply troubled," said Lord Oxhead, "but of that anon. Tell me first what is this news you bring. I hope, Gwendoline, that your choice has been worthy of an Oxhead, and that he to whom you have plighted your troth will be worthy to bear our motto with his own." And, raising his eyes to the escutcheon before him, the earl murmured half unconsciously, "Hic, haec, hoc, hujus, hujus, hujus," breathing perhaps a prayer as many of his ancestors had done before him that he might never forget it.

"Father," continued Gwendoline, half timidly, "Edwin is an American."

"You surprise me indeed," answered Lord Oxhead; "and yet," he continued, turning to his daughter with the courtly grace that marked the nobleman of the old school, "why should we not respect and admire the Americans? Surely there have been great names among them. Indeed, our ancestor Sir Amyas Oxhead was, I think, married to Pocahontas—at least if not actually married"—the earl hesitated a moment.

"At least they loved one another," said Gwendoline simply.

"Precisely," said the earl, with relief, "they loved one another, yes, exactly." Then, as if musing to himself, "Yes, there have been great Americans. Bolivar was an American. The two Washingtons—George and Booker—are both Americans. There have been others, too, though for the moment I do not recall their names. But tell me, Gwendoline, this Edwin of yours—where is his family seat?"

"It is at Oshkosh, Wisconsin, father."

"Ah! Say you so?" rejoined the earl, with rising interest. "Oshkosh is, indeed, a grand old name. The Oshkosh are a Russian family. An Ivan Oshkosh came to England with Peter the Great and married my ancestress. Their descendant in the second degree once removed, Mixtup Oshkosh, fought at the burning of Moscow and later at the sack of Salamanca and the treaty of Adrianople. And Wisconsin, too," the old nobleman went on, his features kindling with animation, for he had a passion for heraldry, genealogy, chronology, and commercial geography; "the Wisconsins, or better, I think, the Guisconsins, are of old blood. A

Guisconsin followed Henry I to Jerusalem and rescued my ancestor Hardup Oxhead from the Saracens. Another Guisconsin..."

"Nay, father," said Gwendoline, gently interrupting, "Wisconsin is not Edwin's own name: that is, I believe, the name of his estate. My lover's name is Edwin Einstein."

"Einstein," repeated the earl dubiously—"an Indian name perhaps; yet the Indians are many of them of excellent family. An ancestor of mine..."

"Father," said Gwendoline, again interrupting, "here is a portrait of Edwin. Judge for yourself if he be noble." With this she placed in her father's hand an American tin-type, tinted in pink and brown. The picture represented a typical specimen of American manhood of that Anglo-Semitic type so often seen in persons of mixed English and Jewish extraction. The figure was well over five feet two inches in height and broad in proportion. The graceful sloping shoulders harmonised with the slender and well-poised waist, and with a hand pliant and yet prehensile. The pallor of the features was relieved by a drooping black moustache.

Such was Edwin Einstein, to whom Gwendoline's heart, if not her hand, was already affianced. Their love had been so simple and yet so strange. It seemed to Gwendoline that it was but a thing of yesterday, and yet in reality they had met three weeks ago. Love had drawn them irresistibly together. To Edwin, the fair English girl with her old name and wide estates possessed a charm that he scarcely dared to confess to himself. He determined to woo her. To Gwendoline there was that in Edwin's bearing, the rich jewels that he wore, the vast fortune that rumour ascribed to him, that appealed to something romantic and chivalrous in her nature. She loved to hear him speak of stocks and bonds, corners and margins, and his father's colossal business. It all seemed so noble and so far above the sordid lives of the people about her. Edwin, too, loved to hear the girl talk of her father's estates, of the diamond-hilted sword that the Saladin had given, or had lent, to her ancestor hundreds of years ago.

Her description of her father, the old earl, touched something romantic in Edwin's generous heart. He was never tired of asking how old he was, was he robust, did a shock, a sudden shock, affect him much? And so on. Then had come the evening that Gwendoline loved to live over and over again in her mind, when Edwin had asked her in his straightforward, manly way, whether—subject to certain written stipulations to be considered later—she would be his wife: and she, putting her hand confidingly in his hand, answered simply, that—subject to the consent of her father and pending always the necessary legal formalities and inquiries—she would.

It had all seemed like a dream: and now Edwin Einstein had come in person to ask her hand from the earl, her father. Indeed, he was at this moment in the outer hall testing the gold leaf in the picture-frames with his pen-knife while waiting for his affianced to break the fateful news to Lord Oxhead.

Gwendoline summoned her courage for a great effort. "Papa," she said, "there is one other thing that it is fair to tell you. Edwin's father is in business."

The earl started from his seat in blank amazement. "In business!" he repeated. "The father of the suitor of the daughter of an Oxhead in business! My daughter the stepdaughter of the grandfather of my grandson! Are you mad, girl? It is too much, too much!"

"But, father," pleaded the beautiful girl in anguish, "hear me. It is Edwin's father—Sarcophagus Einstein, senior—not Edwin himself. Edwin does nothing. He has never earned a penny. He is quite unable to support himself. You have only to see him to believe it. Indeed, dear father, he is just like us. He is here now, in this house, waiting to see you. If it were not for his great wealth..."

"Girl," said the earl sternly, "I care not for the man's riches. How much has he?"

"Fifteen million, two hundred and fifty thousand dollars," answered Gwendoline. Lord Oxhead leaned his head against the mantelpiece. His mind was in a whirl. He was trying to calculate the yearly interest on fifteen and a quarter million dollars at four and a half per cent reduced to pounds, shillings, and pence. It was bootless. His brain, trained by long years of high living and plain thinking, had become too subtle, too refined an instrument for arithmetic....

At this moment the door opened and Edwin Einstein stood before the earl. Gwendoline never forgot what happened. Through her life the picture of it haunted her—her lover upright at the door, his fine frank gaze fixed inquiringly on the diamond pin in her father's necktie, and he, her father, raising from the mantelpiece a face of agonised amazement.

"You! You!" he gasped. For a moment he stood to his full height, swaying and groping in the air, then fell prostrate his full length upon the floor. The lovers rushed to his aid. Edwin tore open his neckcloth and plucked aside his diamond pin to give him air. But it was too late. Earl Oxhead had breathed his last. Life had fled. The earl was extinct. That is to say, he was dead.

The reason of his death was never known. Had the sight of Edwin killed him? It might have. The old family doctor, hurriedly summoned, declared his utter ignorance. This, too, was likely. Edwin himself could explain nothing. But it was observed that after the earl's death and his marriage with Gwendoline he was a changed man; he dressed better, talked much better English.

The wedding itself was quiet, almost sad. At Gwendoline's request there was no wedding breakfast, no bridesmaids, and no reception, while Edwin, respecting his bride's bereavement, insisted that there should be no best man, no flowers, no presents, and no honeymoon.

Thus Lord Oxhead's secret died with him. It was probably too complicated to be interesting anyway.

Boarding-House Geometry

Definitions and Axioms

ALL boarding-houses are the same boarding-house.

Boarders in the same boarding-house and on the same flat are equal to one another.

A single room is that which has no parts and no magnitude.

The landlady of a boarding-house is a parallelogram—that is, an oblong angular figure, which cannot be described, but which is equal to anything.

A wrangle is the disinclination of two boarders to each other that meet together but are not in the same line.

All the other rooms being taken, a single room is said to be a double room.

Postulates and Propositions

A pie may be produced any number of times.

The landlady can be reduced to her lowest terms by a series of propositions.

A bee-line may be made from any boarding-house to any other boarding-house.

The clothes of a boarding-house bed, though produced ever so far both ways, will not meet.

Any two meals at a boarding-house are together less than two square meals.

If from the opposite ends of a boarding-house a line be drawn passing through all the rooms in turn, then the stovepipe which warms the boarders will lie within that line.

On the same bill and on the same side of it there, should not be two charges for the same thing.

If there be two boarders on the same flat, and the amount of side of the one be equal to the amount of side of the other, each to each, and the wrangle between one boarder and the landlady be equal to the wrangle between the landlady and the other, then shall the weekly bills of the two boarders be equal also, each to each.

For if not, let one bill be the greater.

Then the other bill is less than it might have been—which is absurd.

The Awful Fate of Melpomenus Jones

SOME people—not you nor I, because we are so awfully self-possessed—but some people, find great difficulty in saying good-bye when making a call or spending the evening. As the moment draws near when the visitor feels that he is fairly entitled to go away he rises and says abruptly, "Well, I think I..." Then the people say, "Oh, must you go now? Surely it's early yet!" And a pitiful struggle ensues.

I think the saddest case of this kind of thing that I ever knew was that of my poor friend Melpomenus Jones, a curate—such a dear young man, and only twenty-three! He simply couldn't get away from people. He was too modest to tell a lie, and too religious to wish to appear rude. Now it happened that he went to call on some friends of his on the very first afternoon of his summer vacation. The next six weeks were entirely his own—absolutely nothing to do. He chatted awhile, drank two cups of tea, then braced himself for the effort and said suddenly:

"Well, I think I..."

But the lady of the house said, "Oh, no! Mr. Jones, can't you really stay a little longer?"

Jones was always truthful. "Oh, yes," he said, "of course, I—er—can stay."

"Then please don't go."

He stayed. He drank eleven cups of tea. Night was falling. He rose again.

"Well, now," he said shyly, "I think I really..."

"You must go?" said the lady politely. "I thought perhaps you could have stayed to dinner...."

"Oh, well, so I could, you know," Jones said, "if..."

"Then please stay, I'm sure my husband will be delighted."

"All right," he said feebly, "I'll stay," and he sank back into his chair, just full of tea, and miserable.

Papa came home. They had dinner. All through the meal Jones sat planning to leave at eight-thirty. All the family wondered whether Mr. Jones was stupid and sulky, or only stupid.

After dinner mamma undertook to "draw him out," and showed him photographs. She showed him all the family museum, several gross of them—photos of papa's uncle and his wife, and mamma's brother and his little boy, an awfully interesting photo of papa's uncle's friend in his Bengal uniform, an awfully well-taken photo of papa's grandfather's partner's dog, and an awfully wicked one of papa as the devil for a fancy-dress ball.

At eight-thirty Jones had examined seventy-one photographs. There were about sixty-nine more that he hadn't. Jones rose.

"I must say good night now," he pleaded.

"Say good night!" they said, "why, it's only half-past eight! Have you anything to do?"

"Nothing," he admitted, and muttered something about staying six weeks, and then laughed miserably.

Just then it turned out that the favourite child of the family, such a dear little romp, had hidden Mr. Jones's hat; so papa said that he must stay, and invited him to a pipe and a chat. Papa had the pipe and gave Jones the chat, and still he stayed. Every moment he meant to take the plunge, but couldn't. Then papa began to get very tired of Jones, and fidgeted and finally said with jocular irony, that Jones had better stay all night, they could give him a shake-down. Jones mistook his meaning and thanked him with tears in his eyes, and papa put Jones to bed in the spare room and cursed him heartily.

After breakfast next day, papa went off to his work in the City, and left Jones playing with the baby, broken-hearted. His nerve was utterly gone. He was meaning to leave all day, but the thing had got on his mind and he simply couldn't. When papa came home in the evening he was surprised and chagrined to find Jones still there. He thought to jockey him out with a jest, and said he thought he'd have to charge him for his board, he! he! The unhappy young man stared wildly for a moment, then wrung papa's hand, paid him a month's board in advance, and broke down and sobbed like a child.

In the days that followed he was moody and unapproachable. He lived, of course, entirely in the drawing-room, and the lack of air and exercise began to tell sadly on his health. He passed his time in drinking tea and looking at the photographs. He would stand for hours gazing at the photographs of papa's uncle's friend in his Bengal uniform—talking to it, sometimes swearing bitterly at it. His mind was visibly failing.

At length the crash came. They carried him upstairs in a raging delirium of fever. The illness that followed was terrible. He recognised no one, not even papa's uncle's friend in his Bengal uniform. At times he would start up from his bed and shriek, "Well, I think I . . ." and then fall back upon the pillows with a horrible laugh. Then, again, he would leap up and cry, "Another cup of tea and more photographs! More photographs! Har! Har!"

At length, after a month of agony, on the last day of his vacation, he passed away. They say that when the last moment came, he sat up in bed with a beautiful smile of confidence playing upon his face, and said, "Well—the angels are calling me; I'm afraid I really must go now. Good afternoon."

And the rushing of his spirit from its prison-house was as rapid as a hunted cat passing over a garden fence.

A Christmas Letter

(In answer to a young lady who has sent an invitation to be present at a children's party)

Mademoiselle,

Allow me very gratefully but firmly to refuse your kind invitation. You doubtless mean well; but your ideas are unhappily mistaken.

Let us understand one another once and for all. I cannot at my mature age participate in the sports of children with such abandon as I could wish. I entertain, and have always entertained, the sincerest regard for such games as Hunt-the-Slipper and Blind-Man's Buff. But I have now reached a time of life, when, to have my eyes blindfolded and to have a powerful boy of ten hit me in the back with a hobby-horse and ask me to guess who hit me, provokes me to a fit of retaliation which could only culminate in reckless criminality. Nor can I cover my shoulders with a drawing-room rug and crawl round on my hands and knees under the pretence that I am a bear without a sense of personal insufficiency, which is painful to me.

Neither can I look on with a complacent eye at the sad spectacle of your young clerical friend, the Reverend Mr. Uttermost Farthing, abandoning himself to such gambols and appearing in the rôle of life and soul of the evening. Such a degradation of his holy calling grieves me, and I cannot but suspect him of ulterior motives.

You inform me that your maiden aunt intends to help you entertain the party. I have not, as you know, the honour of your aunt's acquaintance, yet I think I may with reason surmise that she will organise games—guessing games—in which she will ask me to name a river in Asia beginning with a Z; on my failure to do so she will put a hot plate down my neck as a forfeit, and the children will clap their hands. These games, my dear young friend, involve the use of a more adaptable intellect than mine, and I cannot consent to be a party to them.

May I say in conclusion that I do not consider a five-cent pen-wiper from the top branch of a Xmas tree any adequate compensation for the kind of evening you propose.

I have the honour

To subscribe myself,

Your obedient servant.

How to Make a Million Dollars

I MIX a good deal with the millionaires. I like them. I like their faces. I like the way they live. I like the things they eat. The more we mix together the better I like the things we mix.

Especially I like the way they dress, their grey check trousers, their white check waistcoats, their heavy gold chains, and the signet-rings that they sign their cheques with. My! they look nice. Get six or seven of them sitting together in the club and it's a treat to see them. And if they get the least dust on them, men come and brush it off. Yes, and are glad to. I'd like to take some of the dust off them myself.

Even more than what they eat I like their intellectual grasp. It is wonderful. Just watch them read. They simply read all the time. Go into the club at any hour and you'll see three or four of them at it. And the things they can read! You'd think that a man who's been driving hard in the office from eleven o'clock until three, with only an hour and a half for lunch, would be too fagged. Not a bit. These men can sit down after office hours and read the *Sketch* and the *Police Gazette* and the *Pink Un*, and understand the jokes just as well as I can.

What I love to do is to walk up and down among them and catch the little scraps of conversation. The other day I heard one lean forward and say, "Well, I offered him a million and a half and said I wouldn't give a cent more, he could either take it or leave it——" I just longed to break in and say, "What! what! a million and a half! Oh! say that again! Offer it to me, to either take it or leave it. Do try me once: I know I can: or here, make it a plain million and let's call it done."

Not that these men are careless over money. No, sir. Don't think it. Of course they don't take much account of big money, a hundred thousand dollars at a shot or anything of that sort. But little money. You've no idea till you know them how anxious they get about a cent, or half a cent, or less.

Why, two of them came into the club the other night just frantic with delight: they said wheat had risen and they'd cleaned up four cents each in less than half an hour. They bought a dinner for sixteen on the strength of it. I don't understand it. I've often made twice as much as that writing for the papers and never felt like boasting about it.

One night I heard one man say, "Well, let's call up New York and offer them a quarter of a cent." Great heavens! Imagine paying the cost of calling up New York, nearly five million people, late at night and offering them a quarter of a cent! And yet—did New York get mad? No, they took it. Of course, it's high finance. I don't pretend to understand it. I tried after that to call up Chicago and offer it a cent and a half, and to call up Hamilton, Ontario, and offer it half a dollar, and the operator only thought I was crazy.

All this shows, of course, that I've been studying how the millionaires do it. I have. For years. I thought it might be helpful to young men just beginning to work and anxious to stop.

You know, many a man realises late in life that if when he was a boy he had known what he knows now, instead of being what he is he might be what he won't; but how few boys stop to think that if they knew what they don't know instead of being what they will be, they wouldn't be? These are awful thoughts.

At any rate, I've been gathering hints on how it is they do it.

One thing I'm sure about. If a young man wants to make a million dollars he's got to be mighty careful about his diet and his living. This may seem hard. But success is only achieved with pains.

There is no use in a young man who hopes to make a million dollars thinking he's entitled to get up at 7.30, eat Force and poached eggs, drink cold water at lunch, and go to bed at 10 p.m. You can't do it. I've seen too many millionaires for that. If you want to be a millionaire you mustn't get up till ten in the morning. They never do. They daren't. It would be as much as their business is worth if they were seen on the street at half-past nine.

And the old idea of abstemiousness is all wrong. To be a millionaire you need champagne, lots of it and all the time. That and Scotch whisky and soda: you have to sit up nearly all night and drink buckets of it. This is what clears the brain for business next day. I've seen some of these men with their brains so clear in the morning, that their faces look positively boiled.

To live like this requires, of course, resolution. But you can buy that by the pint.

Therefore, my dear young man, if you want to get moved on from your present status in business, change your life. When your landlady brings your bacon and eggs for breakfast, throw them out the window to the dog and tell her to bring you some chilled asparagus and a pint of Moselle. Then telephone to your employer that you'll be down about eleven o'clock. You will get moved on. Yes, very quickly.

Just how the millionaires make the money is a difficult question. But one way is this. Strike the town with five cents in your pocket. They nearly all do this; they've told me again and again (men with millions and millions) that the first time they struck town they had only five cents. That seems to have given them their start. Of course, it's not easy to do. I've tried it several times. I nearly did it once. I borrowed five cents, carried it away out of town with an awful rush. If I hadn't struck a beer saloon in the suburbs and spent the five cents I might have been rich to-day.

Another good plan is to start something. Something on a huge scale: something nobody ever thought of. For instance, one man I know told me that once he was down in Mexico without a cent (he'd lost his five in striking Central America) and he noticed that they had no power plants. So he started some and made a mint of money. Another man that I know was once stranded in New York, absolutely without a nickel. Well, it occurred to him that what was needed were buildings ten stories higher than any that had been put up. So he built two and sold them right away. Ever so many millionaires begin in some such simple way as that.

There is, of course, a much easier way than any of these. I almost hate to tell this, because I want to do it myself.

I learned of it just by chance one night at the club. There is one old man there, extremely rich, with one of the best faces of the lot, just like a hyena. I never used to know how he had got so rich. So one evening I asked one of the millionaires how old Bloggs had made all his money.

"How he made it?" he answered with a sneer. "Why, he made it by taking it out of widows and orphans."

Widows and orphans! I thought, what an excellent idea. But who would have suspected that they had it?

"And how," I asked pretty cautiously, "did he go at it to get it out of them?"

"Why," the man answered, "he just ground them under his heels, that was how."

Now isn't that simple? I've thought of that conversation often since and I mean to try it. If I can get hold of them, I'll grind them quick enough. But how to get them. Most of the widows I know look pretty solid for that sort of thing, and as for orphans, it must take an awful lot of them. Meantime I am waiting, and if I ever get a large bunch of orphans all together, I'll stamp on them and see.

I find, too, on inquiry, that you can also grind it out of clergymen. They say they grind nicely. But perhaps orphans are easier.

How to Live to be 200

TWENTY years ago I knew a man called Jiggins, who had the Health Habit.

He used to take a cold plunge every morning. He said it opened his pores. After it he took a hot sponge. He said it closed the pores. He got so that he could open and shut his pores at will.

Jiggins used to stand and breathe at an open window for half an hour before dressing. He said it expanded his lungs. He might, of course, have had it done in a shoe-store with a boot-stretcher, but after all it cost him nothing this way, and what is half an hour?

After he had got his undershirt on, Jiggins used to hitch himself up like a dog in harness and do Sandow exercises. He did them forwards, backwards, and hind-side up.

He could have got a job as a dog anywhere. He spent all his time at this kind of thing. In his spare time at the office, he used to lie on his stomach on the floor and see if he could lift himself up with his knuckles. If he could, then he tried some other way until he found one that he couldn't do. Then he would spend the rest of his lunch hour on his stomach, perfectly happy.

In the evenings in his room he used to lift iron bars, cannonballs, heave dumb-bells, and haul himself up to the ceiling with his teeth. You could hear the thumps half a mile.

He liked it.

He spent half the night slinging himself around his room. He said it made his brain clear. When he got his brain perfectly clear, he went to bed and slept. As soon as he woke, he began clearing it again.

Jiggins is dead. He was, of course, a pioneer, but the fact that he dumb-belled himself to death at an early age does not prevent a whole generation of young men from following in his path.

They are ridden by the Health Mania.

They make themselves a nuisance.

They get up at impossible hours. They go out in silly little suits and run Marathon heats before breakfast. They chase around barefoot to get the dew on their feet. They hunt for ozone. They bother about pepsin. They won't eat meat because it has too much nitrogen. They won't eat fruit because it hasn't any. They prefer albumen and starch and nitrogen to huckleberry pie and doughnuts. They won't drink water out of a tap. They won't eat sardines out of a can. They won't use oysters out of a pail. They won't drink milk out of a glass. They are afraid of alcohol in any shape. Yes, sir, afraid. "Cowards."

And after all their fuss they presently incur some simple old-fashioned illness and die like anybody else.

Now people of this sort have no chance to attain any great age. They are on the wrong track.

Listen. Do you want to live to be really old, to enjoy a grand, green, exuberant, boastful old age and to make yourself a nuisance to your whole neighbourhood with your reminiscences?

Then cut out all this nonsense. Cut it out. Get up in the morning at a sensible hour. The time to get up is when you have to, not before. If your office opens at eleven, get up at ten-thirty. Take your chance on ozone. There isn't any such thing anyway. Or, if there is, you can buy a thermos bottle full for five cents, and put it on a shelf in your cupboard. If your work begins at seven in the morning, get up at ten minutes to, but don't be liar enough to say that you like it. It isn't exhilarating, and you know it.

Also, drop all that cold-bath nonsense. You never did it when you were a boy. Don't be a fool now. If you must take a bath (you don't really need to), take it warm. The pleasure of getting out of a cold bed and creeping into a hot bath beats a cold plunge to death. In any case, stop gassing about your tub and your "shower," as if you were the only man who ever washed.

So much for that point.

Next, take the question of germs and bacilli. Don't be scared of them. That's all. That's the whole thing, and if you once get on to that you never need to worry again.

If you see a bacilli, walk right up to it, and look it in the eye. If one flies into your room, strike at it with your hat or with a towel. Hit it as hard as you can between the neck and the thorax. It will soon get sick of that.

But as a matter of fact, a bacilli is perfectly quiet and harmless if you are not afraid of it. Speak to it. Call out to it to "lie down." It will understand. I had a bacilli once, called Fido, that would come and lie at my feet while I was working. I never knew a more affectionate companion, and when it was run over by an automobile, I buried it in the garden with genuine sorrow.

(I admit this is an exaggeration. I don't really remember its name; it may have been Robert.)

Understand that it is only a fad of modern medicine to say that cholera and typhoid and diphtheria are caused by bacilli and germs; nonsense. Cholera is caused by a frightful pain in the stomach, and diphtheria is caused by trying to cure a sore throat.

Now take the question of food.

Eat what you want. Eat lots of it. Yes, eat too much of it. Eat till you can just stagger across the room with it and prop it up against a sofa cushion. Eat everything that you like until you can't eat any more. The only test is, can you pay for it? If you can't pay for it, don't eat it. And listen—don't worry as to whether your food contains starch, or albumen, or gluten, or nitrogen. If you are damn fool enough to want these things, go and buy them and eat all you want of them. Go to a laundry and get a bag of starch, and eat your fill of it. Eat it, and take a good long drink of glue after it, and a spoonful of Portland cement. That will gluten you, good and solid.

If you like nitrogen, go and get a druggist to give you a canful of it at the soda counter, and let you sip it with a straw. Only don't think that you can mix all these things up with your food. There isn't any nitrogen or phosphorus or albumen in ordinary things to eat. In any decent household all that sort of stuff is washed out in the kitchen sink before the food is put on the table.

And just one word about fresh air and exercise. Don't bother with either of them. Get your room full of good air, then shut up the windows and keep it. It will keep for years. Anyway, don't keep using your lungs all the time. Let them rest. As for exercise, if you have to take it, take it and put up with it. But as long as you have the price of a hack and can hire other people to play baseball for you and run races and do gymnastics when you sit in the shade and smoke and watch them—great heavens, what more do you want?

How to Avoid Getting Married

SOME years ago, when I was the Editor of a Correspondence Column, I used to receive heart-broken letters from young men asking for advice and sympathy. They found themselves the object of marked attentions from girls which they scarcely knew how to deal with. They did not wish to give pain or to seem indifferent to a love which they felt was as ardent as it was disinterested, and yet they felt that they could not bestow their hands where their hearts had not spoken. They wrote to me fully and frankly, and as one soul might write to another for relief. I accepted their confidences as under the pledge of a secrecy, never divulging their disclosures beyond the circulation of my newspapers, or giving any hint of their identity other than printing their names and addresses and their letters in full. But I may perhaps without dishonour reproduce one of these letters, and my answer to it, inasmuch as the date is now months ago, and the softening hand of Time has woven its roses—how shall I put it?—the mellow haze of reminiscences has—what I mean is that the young man has gone back to work and is all right again.

Here then is a letter from a young man whose name I must not reveal, but whom I will designate as D. F., and whose address I must not divulge, but will simply indicate as Q. Street, West.

"Dear Mr. Leacock,

"For some time past I have been the recipient of very marked attentions from a young lady. She has been calling at the house almost every evening, and has taken me out in her motor, and invited me to concerts and the theatre. On these latter occasions I have insisted on her taking my father with me, and have tried as far as possible to prevent her saying anything to me which would be unfit for father to hear. But my position has become a very difficult one. I do not think it right to accept her presents when I cannot feel that my heart is hers. Yesterday she sent to my house a beautiful bouquet of American Beauty roses addressed to me, and a magnificent bunch of Timothy Hay for father. I do not know what to say. Would it be right for father to keep all this valuable hay? I have confided fully in father, and we have discussed the question of presents. He thinks that there are some that we can keep with propriety, and others that a sense of delicacy forbids us to retain. He himself is going to sort out the presents into the two classes. He thinks that as far as he can see, the Hay is in class B. Meantime I write to you, as I understand that Miss Laura Jean Libby and Miss Beatrix Fairfax are on their vacation, and in any case a friend of mine who follows their writings closely tells me that they are always full.

"I enclose a dollar, because I do not think it right to ask you to give all your valuable time and your best thought without giving you back what it is worth."

On receipt of this I wrote back at once a private and confidential letter which I printed in the following edition of the paper.

"My dear, dear Boy,

"Your letter has touched me. As soon as I opened it and saw the green and blue tint of the dollar bill which you had so daintily and prettily folded within the pages of your sweet letter, I knew that the note was from someone that I could learn to love, if our correspondence were to continue as it had begun. I took the dollar from your letter and kissed and fondled it a dozen times. Dear unknown boy! I shall always keep that dollar! No matter how much I may need it, or how many necessaries, yes, absolute necessities, of life I may be wanting, I shall always keep *that* dollar. Do you understand, dear? I shall keep it. I shall not spend it. As far as the *use* of it goes, it will be just as if you had not sent it. Even if you were to send me another dollar, I should still keep the first one, so that no matter how many you sent, the recollection of one first friendship would not be contaminated with mercenary considerations. When I say dollar, darling, of course an express order, or a postal note, or even stamps would be all the same. But in that case do not address me in care of this office, as I should not like to think of your pretty little letters lying round where others might handle them.

"But now I must stop chatting about myself, for I know that you cannot be interested in a simple old fogey such as I am. Let me talk to you about your letter and about the difficult question it raises for all marriageable young men.

"In the first place, let me tell you how glad I am that you confide in your father. Whatever happens, go at once to your father, put your arms about his neck, and have a good cry together. And you are right, too, about presents. It needs a wiser head than my poor perplexed boy to deal with them. Take them to your father to be sorted, or, if you feel that you must not overtax his love, address them to me in your own pretty hand.

"And now let us talk, dear, as one heart to another. Remember always that if a girl is to have your heart she must be worthy of you. When you look at your own bright innocent face in the mirror, resolve that you will give your hand to no girl who is not just as innocent as you are and no brighter than yourself. So that you must first find out how innocent she is. Ask her quietly and frankly—remember, dear, that the days of false modesty are passing away—whether she has ever been in jail. If she has not (and if *you* have not), then you know that you are dealing with a dear confiding girl who will make you a life mate. Then you must know, too, that her mind is worthy of your own. So many men to-day are led astray by the merely superficial graces and attractions of girls who in reality possess no mental equipment at all. Many a man is bitterly disillusioned after marriage when he realises that his wife cannot solve a quadratic equation, and that he is compelled to spend all his days with a woman who does not know that x squared plus $2xy$ plus y squared is the same thing, or, I think, nearly the same thing, as x plus y squared.

"Nor should the simple domestic virtues be neglected. If a girl desires to woo you, before allowing her to press her suit, ask her if she knows how to press yours. If she can, let her woo; if not, tell her to whoa. But I see I have written quite as much as I need for this column. Won't you write again, just as before, dear boy?

"STEPHEN LEACOCK."

How to be a Doctor

Certainly the progress of science is a wonderful thing. One can't help feeling proud of it. I must admit that I do. Whenever I get talking to anyone—that is, to anyone who knows even less about it than I do—about the marvellous development of electricity, for instance, I feel as if I had been personally responsible for it. As for the linotype and the aeroplane and the vacuum house-cleaner, well, I am not sure that I didn't invent them myself. I believe that all generous-hearted men feel just the same way about it.

However, that is not the point I am intending to discuss. What I want to speak about is the progress of medicine. There, if you like, is something wonderful. Any lover of humanity (or of either sex of it) who looks back on the achievements of medical science must feel his heart glow and his right ventricle expand with the pericardiac stimulus of a permissible pride.

Just think of it. A hundred years ago there were no bacilli, no ptomaine poisoning, no diphtheria, and no appendicitis. Rabies was but little known, and only imperfectly developed. All of these things we owe to medical science. Even such things as psoriasis and parotitis and trypanosomiasis, which are now household names, were known only to the few, and were quite beyond the reach of the great mass of the people.

Or consider the advance of the science on its practical side. A hundred years ago it used to be supposed that fever could be cured by the letting of blood; now we know positively that it cannot. Even seventy years ago it was thought that fever was curable by the administration of sedative drugs; now we know that it isn't. For the matter of that, as recently as thirty years ago, doctors thought that they could heal a fever by means of low diet and the application of ice; now they are absolutely certain that they cannot. This instance shows the steady progress made in the treatment of fever. But there has been the same cheering advance all along the line. Take rheumatism. A few generations ago people with rheumatism used to have to carry round potatoes in their pockets as a means of cure. Now the doctors allow them to carry absolutely anything they like. They may go round with their pockets full of water-melons if they wish to. It makes no difference. Or take the treatment of epilepsy. It used to be supposed that the first thing to do in sudden attacks of this kind was to unfasten the patient's collar and let him breathe; at present, on the contrary, many doctors consider it better to button up the patient's collar and let him choke.

In only one respect has there been a decided lack of progress in the domain of medicine, that is in the time it takes to become a qualified practitioner. In the good old days a man was turned out thoroughly equipped after putting in two winter sessions at a college and spending his summers in running logs for a sawmill. Some of the students were turned out even sooner. Nowadays it takes anywhere from five to eight years to become a doctor. Of course, one is willing to grant that our young men are growing stupider and lazier every year. This fact will be corroborated at once by any man over fifty years of age. But even when this is said it seems odd that a man should study eight years now to learn what he used to acquire in eight months.

However, let that go. The point I want to develop is that the modern doctor's business is an extremely simple one, which could be acquired in about two weeks. This is the way it is done.

The patient enters the consulting-room. "Doctor," he says, "I have a bad pain." "Where is it?" "Here." "Stand up," says the doctor, "and put your arms up above your head." Then the doctor goes behind the patient and strikes him a powerful blow in the back. "Do you feel that," he says. "I do," says the patient. Then the doctor turns suddenly and lets him have a left hook under the heart. "Can you feel that?" he says viciously, as the patient falls over on the sofa in a heap. "Get up," says the doctor, and counts ten. The patient rises. The doctor looks him over very carefully without speaking, and then suddenly fetches him a blow in the stomach that doubles him up speechless. The doctor walks over to the window and reads the morning papers for a while. Presently he turns and begins to mutter more to himself than to the patient. "Hum!" he says, "there's a slight anæsthesia of the tympanum." "Is that so?" says the patient, in an agony of fear. "What can I do about it, doctor?" "Well," says the doctor, "I want you to keep very quiet; you'll have to go to bed and stay there and keep quiet." In reality, of course, the doctor hasn't the least idea what is wrong with the man; but he *does* know that if he will go to bed and keep quiet, awfully quiet, he'll either get quietly well again or else die a quiet death. Meantime, if the doctor calls every morning and thumps and beats him, he can keep the patient submissive and perhaps force him to confess what is wrong with him.

"What about diet, doctor?" says the patient, completely cowed.

The answer to this question varies very much. It depends on how the doctor is feeling and whether it is long since he had a meal himself. If it is late in the morning and the doctor is ravenously hungry, he says: "Oh, eat plenty, don't be afraid of it; eat meat, vegetables, starch, glue, cement, anything you like." But if the doctor has just had lunch and his breathing is short-circuited with huckleberry-pie, he says very firmly: "No. I don't want you to eat anything at all: absolutely not a bite; it won't hurt you, a little self-denial in the matter of eating is the best thing in the world."

"And what about drinking?" Again the doctor's answer varies. He may say: "Oh, yes, you might drink a glass of lager now and then, or, if you prefer it, a gin and soda or a whisky and Apollinaris, and I think before going to bed I'd take a hot Scotch with a couple of lumps of white sugar and a bit of lemon-peel in it and a good grating of nutmeg on the top." The doctor says this with real feeling, and his eye glistens with the pure love of his profession. But if, on the other hand, the doctor has spent the night before at a little gathering of medical friends, he is very apt to forbid the patient to touch alcohol in any shape, and to dismiss the subject with great severity.

Of course, this treatment in and of itself would appear too transparent, and would fail to inspire the patient with a proper confidence. But nowadays this element is supplied by the work of the analytical laboratory. Whatever is wrong with the patient, the doctor insists on snipping off parts and pieces and extracts of him and sending them mysteriously away to be analysed. He cuts off a lock of the patient's hair, marks it, "Mr. Smith's Hair, October, 1910." Then he clips off the lower part of the ear, and wraps it in paper, and labels it. "Part of Mr. Smith's Ear, October, 1910." Then he looks the patient up and down, with the scissors in his hand, and if he sees any likely part of him he clips it off and wraps it up. Now this, oddly enough, is the very thing that fills the patient up with that sense of personal importance which is worth paying for. "Yes," says the bandaged patient, later in the day to a group of friends much impressed, "the doctor thinks there may be a slight anæsthesia of the prognosis, but he's sent my ear to New York and my appendix to Baltimore and a lock of my hair to the editors of all the medical journals, and meantime I am to keep very quiet and not exert myself beyond drinking a hot Scotch with lemon and nutmeg every half-hour." With that he sinks back faintly on his cushions, luxuriously happy.

And yet, isn't it funny?

You and I and the rest of us—even if we know all this—as soon as we have a pain within us, rush for a doctor as fast as a hack can take us. Yes, personally, I even prefer an ambulance with a bell on it. It's more soothing.

The New Food

I SEE from the current columns of the daily press that "Professor Plumb, of the University of Chicago, has just invented a highly concentrated form of food. All the essential nutritive elements are put together in the form of pellets, each of which contains from one to two hundred times as much nourishment as an ounce of an ordinary article of diet. These pellets, diluted with water, will form all that is necessary to support life. The Professor looks forward confidently to revolutionising the present food system."

Now this kind of thing may be all very well in its way, but it is going to have its drawbacks as well. In the bright future anticipated by Professor Plumb, we can easily imagine such incidents as the following:

The smiling family were gathered round the hospitable board. The table was plenteously laid with a soup-plate in front of each beaming child, a bucket of hot water before the radiant mother, and at the head of the board the Christmas dinner of the happy home, warmly covered by a thimble and resting on a poker chip. The expectant whispers of the little ones were hushed as the father, rising from his chair, lifted the thimble and disclosed a small pill of concentrated nourishment on the chip before him. Christmas turkey, cranberry sauce, plum pudding, mince pie—it was all there, all jammed into that little pill and only waiting to expand. Then the father with deep reverence, and a devout eye alternating between the pill and heaven, lifted his voice in a benediction.

At this moment there was an agonised cry from the mother.

"Oh, Henry, quick! Baby has snatched the pill!" It was too true. Dear little Gustavus Adolphus, the golden-haired baby boy, had grabbed the whole Christmas dinner off the poker chip and bolted it. Three hundred and fifty pounds of concentrated nourishment passed down the œsophagus of the unthinking child.

"Clap him on the back!" cried the distracted mother. "Give him water!"

The idea was fatal. The water striking the pill caused it to expand. There was a dull rumbling sound and then, with an awful bang, Gustavus Adolphus exploded into fragments!

And when they gathered the little corpse together, the baby lips were parted in a lingering smile that could only be worn by a child who had eaten thirteen Christmas dinners.

A New Pathology

IT HAS long been vaguely understood that the condition of a man's clothes has a certain effect upon the health of both body and mind. The well-known proverb, "Clothes make the man," has its origin in a general recognition of the powerful influence of the habiliments in their reaction upon the wearer. The same truth may be observed in the facts of everyday life. On the one hand we remark the bold carriage and mental vigour of a man attired in a new suit of clothes; on the other hand we note the melancholy features of him who is conscious of a posterior patch, or the haunted face of one suffering from internal loss of buttons. But while common observation thus gives us a certain familiarity with a few leading facts regarding the ailments and influence of clothes, no attempt has as yet been made to reduce our knowledge to a systematic form. At the same time the writer feels that a valuable addition might be made to the science of medicine in this direction. The numerous diseases which are caused by this fatal influence should receive a scientific analysis, and their treatment be included among the principles of the healing art. The diseases of the clothes may roughly be divided into medical cases and surgical cases, while these again fall into classes according to the particular garment through which the sufferer is attacked.

Medical Cases

Probably no article of apparel is so liable to a diseased condition as the trousers. It may be well, therefore, to treat first those maladies to which they are subject.

I. *Contractio Pantalunæ, or Shortening of the Legs of the Trousers*, an extremely painful malady most frequently found in the growing youth. The first symptom is the appearance of a yawning space (lacuna) above the boots, accompanied by an acute sense of humiliation and a morbid anticipation of mockery. The application of treacle to the boots, although commonly recommended, may rightly be condemned as too drastic a remedy. The use of boots reaching to the knee, to be removed only at night, will afford immediate relief. In connection with Contractio is often found—

II. *Inflatio Genu, or Bagging of the Knees of the Trousers*, a disease whose symptoms are similar to those above. The patient shows an aversion to the standing posture, and, in acute cases, if the patient be compelled to stand, the head is bent and the eye fixed with painful rigidity upon the projecting blade formed at the knee of the trousers.

In both of the above diseases anything that can be done to free the mind of the patient from a morbid sense of his infirmity will do much to improve the general tone of the system.

III. *Oases, or Patches*, are liable to break out anywhere on the trousers, and range in degree of gravity from those of a trifling nature to those of a fatal character. The most distressing cases are those where the patch assumes a different colour from that of the trousers (dissimilitas coloris). In this instance the mind of the patient is found to be in a sadly aberrated condition. A speedy improvement may, however, be effected by cheerful society, books, flowers, and, above all, by a complete change.

IV. The overcoat is attacked by no serious disorders, except—

Phosphorescentia, or Glistening, a malady which indeed may often be observed to affect the whole system. It is caused by decay of tissue from old age and is generally aggravated by repeated brushing. A peculiar feature of the complaint is the lack of veracity on the part of the patient in reference to the cause of his uneasiness. Another invariable symptom is his aversion to outdoor exercise; under various pretexts, which it is the duty of his medical adviser firmly to combat, he will avoid even a gentle walk in the streets.

V. Of the waistcoat science recognises but one disease—

Porriggia, an affliction caused by repeated spilling of porridge. It is generally harmless, chiefly owing to the mental indifference of the patient. It can be successfully treated by repeated fomentations of benzine.

VI. *Mortificatio Tilis, or Greenness of the Hat*, is a disease often found in connection with Phosphorescentia (mentioned above), and characterised by the same aversion to outdoor life.

VII. *Sterilitas, or Loss of Fur*, is another disease of the hat, especially prevalent in winter. It is not accurately known whether this is caused by a falling out of the fur or by a cessation of growth. In all diseases of the hat the mind of the patient is greatly depressed and his countenance stamped with the deepest gloom. He is particularly sensitive in regard to questions as to the previous history of the hat.

Want of space precludes the mention of minor diseases, such as—

VIII. *Odditus Soccorum, or Oddness of the Socks*, a thing in itself trifling, but of an alarming nature if met in combination with Contractio Pantalunæ. Cases are found where the patient, possibly on the public platform or at a social gathering, is seized with a consciousness of the malady so suddenly as to render medical assistance futile.

Surgical Cases

It is impossible to mention more than a few of the most typical cases of diseases of this sort.

I. *Explosio, or Loss of Buttons*, is the commonest malady demanding surgical treatment. It consists of a succession of minor fractures, possibly internal, which at first excite no alarm. A vague sense of uneasiness is presently felt, which often leads the patient to seek relief in the string habit—a habit which, if unduly indulged in, may assume the proportions of a ruling passion. The use of sealing-wax, while admirable as a temporary remedy for Explosio, should never be allowed to gain a permanent hold upon the system. There is no doubt that a persistent indulgence in the string habit, or the constant use of sealing-wax, will result in—

II. *Fractura Suspendorum, or Snapping of the Braces*, which amounts to a general collapse of the system. The patient is usually seized with a severe attack of Explosio, followed by a sudden sinking feeling and sense of loss. A sound constitution may rally from the shock, but a system undermined by the string habit invariably succumbs.

III. *Sectura Pantalunæ, or Ripping of the Trousers*, is generally caused by sitting upon warm beeswax or leaning against a hook. In the case of the very young it is not unfrequently accompanied by a distressing suppuration of the shirt. This, however, is not remarked in adults. The malady is rather mental than bodily, the mind of the patient being racked by a keen sense of indignity and a feeling of unworthiness. The only treatment is immediate isolation, with a careful stitching of the affected part.

In conclusion, it may be stated that at the first symptom of disease the patient should not hesitate to put himself in the hands of a professional tailor. In so brief a compass as the present article the discussion has of necessity been rather suggestive than exhaustive. Much yet remains to be done, and the subject opens wide to the inquiring eye. The writer will, however, feel amply satisfied if this brief outline may help to direct the attention of medical men to what is yet an unexplored field.

The Poet Answered

Dear Sir:

In answer to your repeated questions and requests which have appeared for some years past in the columns of the rural press, I beg to submit the following solutions of your chief difficulties:—

Topic I.—You frequently ask, where are the friends of your childhood, and urge that they shall be brought back to you. As far as I am able to learn, those of your friends who are not in jail are still right there in your native village. You point out that they were wont to share your gambols. If so, you are certainly entitled to have theirs now.

Topic II.—You have taken occasion to say:

"Give me not silk, nor rich attire.
Nor gold, nor jewels rare."

But, my dear fellow, this is preposterous. Why, these are the very things I had bought for you. If you won't take any of these, I shall have to give you factory cotton and cordwood.

Topic III.—You also ask, "How fares my love across the sea?" Intermediate, I presume. She would hardly travel steerage.

Topic IV.—"Why was I born? Why should I breathe?" Here I quite agree with you. I don't think you ought to breathe.

Topic V.—You demand that I shall show you the man whose soul is dead and then mark him. I am awfully sorry; the man was around here all day yesterday, and if I had only known I could easily have marked him so that we could pick him out again.

Topic VI.—I notice that you frequently say, "Oh, for the sky of your native land." Oh, for it, by all means, if you wish. But remember that you already owe for a great deal.

Topic VII.—On more than one occasion you wish to be informed, "What boots it, that you idly dream?" Nothing boots it at present—a fact, sir, which ought to afford you the highest gratification.

The Force of Statistics

THEY were sitting on a seat of the car, immediately in front of me. I was consequently able to hear all that they were saying. They were evidently strangers who had dropped into a conversation. They both had the air of men who considered themselves profoundly interesting as minds. It was plain that each laboured under the impression that he was a ripe thinker.

One had just been reading a book which lay in his lap.

"I've been reading some very interesting statistics," he was saying to the other thinker.

"Ah, statistics!" said the other; "wonderful things, sir, statistics; very fond of them myself."

"I find, for instance," the first man went on, "that a drop of water is filled with little... with little... I forget just what you call them... little—er—things, every cubic inch containing—er—containing... let me see..."

"Say a million," said the other thinker, encouragingly.

"Yes, a million, or possibly a billion... but at any rate, ever so many of them."

"Is it possible?" said the other. "But really, you know, there are wonderful things in the world. Now, coal... take coal...."

"Very good," said his friend, "let us take coal," settling back in his seat with the air of an intellect about to feed itself.

"Do you know that every ton of coal burnt in an engine will drag a train of cars as long as... I forget the exact length, but say a train of cars of such and such a length, and weighing, say so much... from... from... hum! for the moment the exact distance escapes me... drag it from..."

"From here to the moon," suggested the other.

"Ah, very likely; yes, from here to the moon. Wonderful, isn't it?"

"But the most stupendous calculation of all, sir, is in regard to the distance from the earth to the sun. Positively, sir, a cannon-ball—er—fired at the sun..."

"Fired at the sun," nodded the other, approvingly, as if he had often seen it done.

"And travelling at the rate of... of..."

"Of three cents a mile," hinted the listener.

"No, no, you misunderstand me—but travelling at a fearful rate, simply fearful, sir, would take a hundred million—no, a hundred billion—in short would take a scandalously long time in getting there——"

At this point I could stand no more. I interrupted—"Provided it were fired from Philadelphia," I said, and passed into the smoking-car.

Men Who Have Shaved Me

A BARBER is by nature and inclination a sport. He can tell you at what exact hour the ball game of the day is to begin, can foretell its issue without losing a stroke of the razor, and can explain the points of inferiority of all the players, as compared with better men that he has personally seen elsewhere, with the nicety of a professional. He can do all this, and then stuff the customer's mouth with a soap-brush, and leave him while he goes to the other end of the shop to make a side bet with one of the other barbers on the outcome of the Autumn Handicap. In the barbershops they knew the result of the Jeffries-Johnson prize fight long before it happened. It is on information of this kind that they make their living. The performance of shaving is only incidental to it. Their real vocation in life is imparting information. To the barber the outside world is made up of customers, who are to be thrown into chairs, strapped, manacled, gagged with soap, and then given such necessary information on the athletic events of the moment as will carry them through the business hours of the day without open disgrace.

As soon as the barber has properly filled up the customer with information of this sort, he rapidly removes his whiskers as a sign that the man is now fit to talk to, and lets him out of the chair.

The public has grown to understand the situation. Every reasonable business man is willing to sit and wait half an hour for a shave which he could give himself in three minutes, because he knows that if he goes down town without understanding exactly why Chicago lost two games straight he will appear an ignoramus.

At times, of course, the barber prefers to test his customer, with a question or two. He gets him pinned in the chair, with his head well back, covers the customer's face with soap, and then planting his knee on his chest and holding his hand firmly across the customer's mouth, to prevent all utterance and to force him to swallow the soap, he asks: "Well, what did you think of the Detroit-St. Louis game yesterday?" This is not really meant for a question at all. It is only equivalent to saying: "Now, you poor fool, I'll bet you don't know anything about the great events of your country at all." There is a gurgle in the customer's throat as if he were trying to answer, and his eyes are seen to move sideways, but the barber merely thrusts the soap-brush into each eye, and if any motion still persists, he breathes gin and peppermint over the face, till all sign of life is extinct. Then he talks the game over in detail with the barber at the next chair, each leaning across an inanimate thing extended under steaming towels that was once a man.

To know all these things barbers have to be highly educated. It is true that some of the greatest barbers that have ever lived have begun as uneducated, illiterate men, and by sheer energy and indomitable industry have forced their way to the front. But these are exceptions. To succeed nowadays it is practically necessary to be a college graduate. As the courses at Harvard and Yale have been found too superficial, there are now established regular Barbers' Colleges, where a bright young man can learn as much in three weeks as he would be likely to know after three years at Harvard. The courses at these colleges cover such things as (1) PHYSIOLOGY, including *Hair and its Destruction*, *The Origin and Growth of Whiskers*, *Soap in its Relation to Eyesight*; (2) CHEMISTRY, including lectures on Florida Water; and How to Make it out of Sardine Oil; (3) PRACTICAL ANATOMY, including *The Scalp and How to Lift it*, *The*

Ears and How to Remove them, and, as the Major Course for advanced students, The Veins of the Face and how to open and close them at will by the use of alum.

The education of the customer is, as I have said, the chief part of the barber's vocation. But it must be remembered that the incidental function of removing his whiskers in order to mark him as a well-informed man is also of importance, and demands long practice and great natural aptitude. In the barbers' shops of modern cities shaving has been brought to a high degree of perfection. A good barber is not content to remove the whiskers of his client directly and immediately. He prefers to cook him first. He does this by immersing the head in hot water and covering the victim's face with steaming towels until he has him boiled to a nice pink. From time to time the barber removes the towels and looks at the face to see if it is yet boiled pink enough for his satisfaction. If it is not, he replaces the towels again and jams them down firmly with his hand until the cooking is finished. The final result, however, amply justifies this trouble, and the well-boiled customer only needs the addition of a few vegetables on the side to present an extremely appetizing appearance.

During the process of the shave, it is customary for the barber to apply the particular kind of mental torture known as the third degree. This is done by terrorising the patient as to the very evident and proximate loss of all his hair and whiskers, which the barber is enabled by his experience to foretell. "Your hair," he says, very sadly and sympathetically, "is all falling out. Better let me give you a shampoo?" "No." "Let me singe your hair to close up the follicles?" "No." "Let me plug up the ends of your hair with sealing-wax, it's the only thing that will save it for you?" "No." "Let me rub an egg on your scalp?" "No." "Let me squirt a lemon on your eyebrows?" "No."

The barber sees that he is dealing with a man of determination, and he warms to his task. He bends low and whispers into the prostrate ear: "You've got a good many grey hairs coming in; better let me give you an application of Hairocene, only cost you half a dollar?" "No." "Your face," he whispers again, with a soft, caressing voice, "is all covered with wrinkles; better let me rub some of this Rejuvenator into the face."

This process is continued until one of two things happens. Either the customer is obdurate, and staggers to his feet at last and gropes his way out of the shop with the knowledge that he is a wrinkled, prematurely senile man, whose wicked life is stamped upon his face, and whose unstopped hair-ends and failing follicles menace him with the certainty of complete baldness within twenty-four hours—or else, as in nearly all instances, he succumbs. In the latter case, immediately on his saying "yes" there is a shout of exultation from the barber, a roar of steaming water, and within a moment two barbers have grabbed him by the feet and thrown him under the tap, and, in spite of his struggles, are giving him the Hydro-magnetic treatment. When he emerges from their hands, he steps out of the shop looking as if he had been varnished.

But even the application of the Hydro-magnetic and the Rejuvenator do not by any means exhaust the resources of the up-to-date barber. He prefers to perform on the customer a whole variety of subsidiary services not directly connected with shaving, but carried on during the process of the shave.

In a good, up-to-date shop, while one man is shaving the customer, others black his boots, brush his clothes, darn his socks, point his nails, enamel his teeth, polish his eyes, and alter the shape of any of his joints which they think unsightly. During this operation they often stand seven deep round a customer, fighting for a chance to get at him.

All of these remarks apply to barber-shops in the city, and not to country places. In the country there is only one barber and one customer at a time. The thing assumes the aspect of a straight-out, rough-and-tumble, catch-as-catch-can fight, with a few spectators sitting round the shop to see fair play. In the city they can shave a man without removing any of his clothes. But in the country, where the customer insists on getting the full value for his money, they remove the collar and necktie, the coat and the waistcoat, and, for a really good shave and hair-cut, the customer is stripped to the waist. The barber can then take a rush at him from the other side of the room, and drive the clippers up the full length of the spine, so as to come at the heavier hair on the back of the head with the impact of a lawn-mower driven into long grass.

Getting the Thread of It

HAVE you ever had a man try to explain to you what happened in a book as far as he has read? It is a most instructive thing. Sinclair, the man who shares my rooms with me, made such an attempt the other night. I had come in cold and tired from a walk and found him full of excitement, with a bulky magazine in one hand and a paper-cutter gripped in the other.

"Say, here's a grand story," he burst out as soon as I came in; "it's great! most fascinating thing I ever read. Wait till I read you some of it. I'll just tell you what has happened up to where I am—you'll easily catch the thread of it—and then we'll finish it together."

I wasn't feeling in a very responsive mood, but I saw no way to stop him, so I merely said, "All right, throw me your thread. I'll catch it."

"Well," Sinclair began with great animation, "this count gets this letter..."

"Hold on," I interrupted, "what count gets what letter?"

"Oh, the count it's about, you know. He gets this letter from this Porphirio..."

"From which Porphirio?"

"Why, Porphirio sent the letter, don't you see, he sent it," Sinclair exclaimed a little impatiently—"sent it through Demonio and told him to watch for him with him, and kill him when he got him."

"Oh, see here!" I broke in, "who is to meet who, and who is to get stabbed?"

"They're going to stab Demonio."

"And who brought the letter?"

"Demonio."

"Well, now, Demonio must be a clam! What did he bring it for?"

"Oh, but he don't know what's in it, that's just the slick part of it," and Sinclair began to snigger to himself at the thought of it. "You see, this Carlo Carlotti the Condottiere..."

"Stop right there," I said. "What's a Condottiere?"

"It's a sort of brigand. He, you understand, was in league with this Fra Fraliccolo..."

A suspicion flashed across my mind. "Look here," I said firmly, "if the scene of this story is laid in the Highlands, I refuse to listen to it. Call it off."

"No, no," Sinclair answered quickly, "that's all right. It's laid in Italy... time of Pius the something. He comes in—say, but he's great! so darned crafty. It's him, you know, that persuades this Franciscan..."

"Pause," I said, "what Franciscan?"

"Fra Fraliccolo, of course," Sinclair said snappishly. "You see, Pio tries to..."

"Whoa!" I said, "who is Pio?"

"Oh, hang it all, Pio is Italian, it's short for Pius. He tries to get Fra Fraliccolo and Carlo Carlotti the Condottiere to steal the document from... let me see, what was he called?... Oh, yes... from the Dog of Venice, so that... or... no, hang it, you put me out, that's all wrong. It's the other way round. Pio wasn't clever at all; he's a regular darned fool. It's the Dog that's crafty. By Jove, he's fine," Sinclair went on, warming up to enthusiasm again, "he just does anything he wants. He makes this Demonio (Demonio is one of those hirelings, you know, he's the tool of the Dog)... makes him steal the document off Porphirio, and..."

"But how does he get him to do that?" I asked.

"Oh, the Dog has Demonio pretty well under his thumb, so he makes Demonio scheme round till he gets old Pio—er—gets him under his thumb, and then, of course, Pio thinks that Porphirio—I mean he thinks that he has Porphirio—er—has him under his thumb."

"Half a minute, Sinclair," I said, "who did you say was under the Dog's thumb?"

"Demonio."

"Thanks. I was mixed in the thumbs. Go on."

"Well, just when things are like this..."

"Like what?"

"Like I said."

"All right."

"Who should turn up and thwart the whole scheme, but this Signorina Tarara in her domino..."

"Hully Gee!" I said, "you make my head ache. What the deuce does she come in her domino for?"

"Why, to thwart it."

"To thwart what?"

"Thwart the whole darned thing," Sinclair exclaimed emphatically.

"But can't she thwart it without her domino?"

"I should think not! You see, if it hadn't been for the domino, the Dog would have spotted her quick as a wink. Only when he sees her in the domino with this rose in her hair, he thinks she must be Lucia dell' Esterolla."

"Say, he fools himself, doesn't he? Who's this last girl?"

"Lucia? Oh, she's great!" Sinclair said. "She's one of those Southern natures, you know, full of—er—full of..."

"Full of fun," I suggested.

"Oh, hang it all, don't make fun of it! Well, anyhow, she's sister, you understand, to the Contessa Carantarata, and that's why Fra Fraliccolo, or... hold on, that's not it, no, no, she's not sister to anybody. She's cousin, that's it; or, anyway, she thinks she is cousin to Fra Fraliccolo himself, and that's why Pio tries to stab Fra Fraliccolo."

"Oh, yes," I assented, "naturally he would."

"Ah," Sinclair said hopefully, getting his paper-cutter ready to cut the next pages, "you begin to get the thread now, don't you?"

"Oh, fine!" I said. "The people in it are the Dog and Pio, and Carlo Carlotti the Condottiere, and those others that we spoke of."

"That's right," Sinclair said. "Of course, there are more still that I can tell you about if..."

"Oh, never mind," I said, "I'll work along with those, they're a pretty representative crowd. Then Porphirio is under Pio's thumb, and Pio is under Demonio's thumb, and the Dog is crafty, and Lucia is full of something all the time. Oh, I've got a mighty clear idea of it," I concluded bitterly.

"Oh, you've got it," Sinclair said, "I knew you'd like it. Now we'll go on. I'll just finish to the bottom of my page and then I'll go on aloud."

He ran his eyes rapidly over the lines till he came to the bottom of the page, then he cut the leaves and turned over. I saw his eye rest on the half-dozen lines that confronted him on the next page with an expression of utter consternation.

"Well, I will be cursed!" he said at length.

"What's the matter?" I said gently, with a great joy at my heart.

"This infernal thing's a serial," he gasped, as he pointed at the words *To be continued*, "and that's all there is in this number."

Telling His Faults

"OH, do, Mr. Sapling," said the beautiful girl at the summer hotel, "do let me read the palm of your hand! I can tell you all your faults."

Mr. Sapling gave an inarticulate gurgle and a roseate flush swept over his countenance as he surrendered his palm to the grasp of the fair enchantress.

"Oh, you're just full of faults, just full of them, Mr. Sapling!" she cried.

Mr. Sapling looked it.

"To begin with," said the beautiful girl, slowly and reflectingly, "you are dreadfully cynical: you hardly believe in anything at all, and you've utterly no faith in us poor women."

The feeble smile that had hitherto kindled the features of Mr. Sapling into a ray of chastened imbecility, was distorted in an effort at cynicism.

"Then your next fault is that you are too determined: much too determined. When once you have set your will on any object, you crush every obstacle under your feet."

Mr. Sapling looked meekly down at his tennis shoes, but began to feel calmer, more lifted up. Perhaps he had been all these things without knowing it.

"Then you are cold and sarcastic."

Mr. Sapling attempted to look cold and sarcastic. He succeeded in a rude leer.

"And you're horribly world-weary, you care for nothing. You have drained philosophy to the dregs, and scoff at everything."

Mr. Sapling's inner feeling was that from now on he would simply scoff and scoff and scoff.

"Your only redeeming quality is that you are generous. You have tried to kill even this, but cannot. Yes," concluded the beautiful girl, "those are your faults, generous still, but cold, cynical and relentless. Good night, Mr. Sapling."

And resisting all entreaties the beautiful girl passed from the verandah of the hotel and vanished.

And when later in the evening the brother of the beautiful girl borrowed Mr. Sapling's tennis racket, and his bicycle for a fortnight, and the father of the beautiful girl got Sapling to endorse his note for a couple of hundreds, and her uncle Zephas borrowed his bedroom candle and used his razor to cut up a plug of tobacco, Mr. Sapling felt proud to be acquainted with the family.

Winter Pastimes

It is in the depth of winter, when the intense cold renders it desirable to stay at home, that the really Pleasant Family is wont to serve invitations upon a few friends to spend a Quiet Evening.

It is at these gatherings that that gay thing, the indoor winter game, becomes rampant. It is there that the old euchre deck and the staring domino become fair and beautiful things; that the rattle of the Loto counter rejoices the heart, that the old riddle feels the sap stirring in its limbs again, and the amusing spilikin completes the mental ruin of the jaded guest. Then does the Jolly Maiden Aunt propound the query: What is the difference between an elephant and a silk hat? Or declare that her first is a vowel, her second a preposition, and her third an archipelago. It is to crown such a quiet evening, and to give the finishing stroke to those of the visitors who have not escaped early, with a fierce purpose of getting at the saloons before they have time to close, that the indoor game or family reservoir of fun is dragged from its long sleep. It is spread out upon the table. Its paper of directions is unfolded. Its cards, its counters, its pointers and its markers are distributed around the table, and the visitor forces a look of reckless pleasure upon his face. Then the "few simple directions" are read aloud by the Jolly Aunt, instructing each player to challenge the player holding the golden letter corresponding to the digit next in order, to name a dead author beginning with *X*, failing which the player must declare himself in fault, and pay the forfeit of handing over to the Jolly Aunt his gold watch and all his money, or having a hot plate put down his neck.

With a view to bringing some relief to the guests at entertainments of this kind, I have endeavoured to construct one or two little winter pastimes of a novel character. They are quite inexpensive, and as they need no background of higher arithmetic or ancient history, they are within reach of the humblest intellect. Here is one of them. It is called Indoor Football, or Football without a Ball.

In this game any number of players, from fifteen to thirty, seat themselves in a heap on any one player, usually the player next to the dealer. They then challenge him to get up, while one player stands with a stop-watch in his hand and counts forty seconds. Should the first player fail to rise before forty seconds are counted, the player with the watch declares him suffocated. This is called a "Down" and counts one. The player who was the Down is then leant against the wall; his wind is supposed to be squeezed out. The player called the referee then blows a whistle and the players select another player and score a down off him. While the player is supposed to be down, all the rest must remain seated as before, and not rise from him until the referee by counting forty and blowing his whistle announces that in his opinion the other player is stifled. He is then leant against the wall beside the first player. When the whistle again blows the player nearest the referee strikes him behind the right ear. This is a "Touch," and counts two.

It is impossible, of course, to give all the rules in detail. I might add, however, that while it counts *two* to strike the referee, to kick him counts *three*. To break his arm or leg counts *four*, and to kill him outright is called *Grand Slam* and counts one game.

Here is another little thing that I have worked out, which is superior to parlour games in that it combines their intense excitement with sound out-of-door exercise.

It is easily comprehended, and can be played by any number of players, old and young. It requires no other apparatus than a trolley car of the ordinary type, a mile or two of track, and a few thousand volts of electricity. It is called:

The Suburban Trolley Car
A Holiday Game for Old and Young

The chief part in the game is taken by two players who station themselves one at each end of the car, and who adopt some distinctive costumes to indicate that they are "it." The other players occupy the body of the car, or take up their position at intervals along the track.

The object of each player should be to enter the car as stealthily as possible in such a way as to escape the notice of the players in distinctive dress. Should he fail to do this he must pay the philopena or forfeit. Of these there are two: philopena No. 1, the payment of five cents, and philopena No. 2, being thrown off the car by the neck. Each player may elect which philopena he will pay. Any player who escapes paying the philopena scores one.

The players who are in the car may elect to adopt a standing attitude, or to seat themselves, but no player may seat himself in the lap of another without the second player's consent. The object of those who elect to remain standing is to place their feet upon the toes of those who sit; when they do this they score. The object of those who elect to sit is to elude the feet of the standing players. Much merriment is thus occasioned.

The player in distinctive costume at the front of the car controls a crank, by means of which he is enabled to bring the car to a sudden stop, or to cause it to plunge violently forward. His aim in so doing is to cause all the standing players to fall over backward. Every time he does this he scores. For this purpose he is generally in collusion with the other player in distinctive costume, whose business it is to let him know by a series of bells and signals when the players are not looking, and can be easily thrown down. A sharp fall of this sort gives rise to no end of banter and good-natured drollery, directed against the two players who are "it."

Should a player who is thus thrown backward save himself from falling by sitting down in the lap of a female player, he scores one. Any player who scores in this manner is entitled to remain seated while he may count six, after which he must remove himself or pay philopena No. 2.

Should the player who controls the crank perceive a player upon the street desirous of joining in the game by entering the car, his object should be: primo, to run over him and kill him; secundo, to kill him by any other means in his power; tertio, to let him into the car, but to exact the usual philopena.

Should a player, in thus attempting to get on the car from without, become entangled in the machinery, the player controlling the crank shouts "huff!" and the car is supposed to pass over him. All within the car score one.

A fine spice of the ludicrous may be added to the game by each player pretending that he has a destination or stopping-place, where he would wish to alight. It now becomes the aim of the two players who are "it" to carry him past his point. A player who is thus carried beyond his imaginary stopping-place must feign a violent passion, and imitate angry gesticulations. He may, in addition, feign a great age or a painful infirmity, which will be found to occasion the most convulsive fun for the other players in the game.

These are the main outlines of this most amusing pastime. Many other agreeable features may, of course, be readily introduced by persons of humour and imagination.

Number Fifty-Six

What I narrate was told me one winter's evening by my friend Ah-Yen in the little room behind his laundry. Ah-Yen is a quiet little celestial with a grave and thoughtful face, and that melancholy contemplative disposition so often noticed in his countrymen. Between myself and Ah-Yen there exists a friendship of some years' standing, and we spend many a long evening in the dimly lighted room behind his shop, smoking a dreamy pipe together and plunged in silent meditation. I am chiefly attracted to my friend by the highly imaginative cast of his mind, which is, I believe, a trait of the Eastern character and which enables him to forget to a great extent the sordid cares of his calling in an inner life of his own creation. Of the keen, analytical side of his mind, I was in entire ignorance until the evening of which I write.

The room where we sat was small and dingy, with but little furniture except our chairs and the little table at which we filled and arranged our pipes, and was lighted only by a tallow candle. There were a few pictures on the walls, for the most part rude prints cut from the columns of the daily press and pasted up to hide the bareness of the room. Only one picture was in any way noticeable, a portrait admirably executed in pen and ink. The face was that of a young man, a very beautiful face, but one of infinite sadness. I had long been aware, although I know not how, that Ah-Yen had met with a great sorrow, and had in some way connected the fact with this portrait. I had always refrained, however, from asking him about it, and it was not until the evening in question that I knew its history.

We had been smoking in silence for some time when Ah-Yen spoke. My friend is a man of culture and wide reading, and his English is consequently perfect in its construction; his speech is, of course, marked by the lingering liquid accent of his country which I will not attempt to reproduce.

"I see," he said, "that you have been examining the portrait of my unhappy friend, Fifty-Six. I have never yet told you of my bereavement, but as to-night is the anniversary of his death, I would fain speak of him for a while."

Ah-Yen paused; I lighted my pipe afresh, and nodded to him to show that I was listening.

"I do not know," he went on, "at what precise time Fifty-Six came into my life. I could indeed find it out by examining my books, but I have never troubled to do so. Naturally I took no more interest in him at first than in any other of my customers—less, perhaps, since he never in the course of our connection brought his clothes to me himself but always sent them by a boy. When I presently perceived that he was becoming one of my regular customers, I allotted to him his number, Fifty-Six, and began to speculate as to who and what he was. Before long I had reached several conclusions in regard to my unknown client. The quality of his linen showed me that, if not rich, he was at any rate fairly well off. I could see that he was a young man of regular Christian life, who went out into society to a certain extent; this I could tell from his sending the same number of articles to the laundry, from his washing always coming on Saturday night, and from the fact that he wore a dress shirt about once a week. In disposition he was a modest, unassuming fellow, for his collars were only two inches high."

I stared at Ah-Yen in some amazement, the recent publications of a favourite novelist had rendered me familiar with this process of analytical reasoning, but I was prepared for no such revelations from my Eastern friend.

"When I first knew him," Ah-Yen went on, "Fifty-Six was a student at the university. This, of course, I did not know for some time. I inferred it, however, in the course of time, from his absence from town during the four summer months, and from the fact that during the time of the university examinations the cuffs of his shirts came to me covered with dates, formulas, and propositions in geometry. I followed him with no little interest through his university career. During the four years which it lasted, I washed for him every week; my regular connection with him and the insight which my observation gave me into the lovable character of the man, deepened my first esteem into a profound affection and I became most anxious for his success. I helped him at each succeeding examination, as far as lay in my power, by starching his shirts half-way to the elbow, so as to leave him as much room as possible for annotations. My anxiety during the strain of his final examination I will not attempt to describe. That Fifty-Six was undergoing the great crisis of his academic career, I could infer from the state of his handkerchiefs which, in apparent unconsciousness, he used as pen-wipers during the final test. His conduct throughout the examination bore witness to the moral development which had taken place in his character during his career as an undergraduate; for the notes upon his cuffs which had been so copious at his earlier examinations were limited now to a few hints, and these upon topics so intricate as to defy an ordinary memory. It was with a thrill of joy that I at last received in his laundry bundle one Saturday early in June, a ruffled dress shirt, the bosom of which was thickly spattered with the spillings of the wine-cup, and realised that Fifty-Six had banqueted as a Bachelor of Arts.

"In the following winter the habit of wiping his pen upon his handkerchief, which I had remarked during his final examination, became chronic with him, and I knew that he had entered upon the study of law.

He worked hard during that year, and dress shirts almost disappeared from his weekly bundle. It was in the following winter, the second year of his legal studies, that the tragedy of his life began. I became aware that a change had come over his laundry; from one, or at most two a week, his dress shirts rose to four, and silk handkerchiefs began to replace his linen ones. It dawned upon me that Fifty-Six was abandoning the rigorous tenor of his student life and was going into society. I presently perceived something more; Fifty-Six was in love. It was soon impossible to doubt it. He was wearing seven shirts a week; linen handkerchiefs disappeared from his laundry; his collars rose from two inches to two and a quarter, and finally to two and a half. I have in my possession one of his laundry lists of that period; a glance at it will show the scrupulous care which he bestowed upon his person. Well do I remember the dawning hopes of those days, alternating with the gloomiest despair. Each Saturday I opened his bundle with a trembling eagerness to catch the first signs of a return of his love. I helped my friend in every way that I could. His shirts and collars were masterpieces of my art, though my hand often shook with agitation as I applied the starch. She was a brave noble girl, that I knew; her influence was elevating the whole nature of Fifty-Six; until now he had had in his possession a certain number of detached cuffs and false shirt-fronts. These he discarded now—at first the false shirt-fronts, scorning the very idea of fraud, and after a time, in his enthusiasm, abandoning even the cuffs. I cannot look back upon those bright happy days of courtship without a sigh.

"The happiness of Fifty-Six seemed to enter into and fill my whole life. I lived but from Saturday to Saturday. The appearance of false shirt-fronts would cast me to the lowest depths of despair; their absence raised me to a pinnacle of hope. It was not till winter softened into spring that Fifty-Six nerved himself to learn his fate. One Saturday he sent me a new white waistcoat, a garment which had hitherto been shunned by his modest nature, to prepare for his use. I bestowed upon it all the resources of my art; I read his purpose in it. On the Saturday following it was returned to me and, with tears of joy, I marked where a warm little hand had rested fondly on the right shoulder, and knew that Fifty-Six was the accepted lover of his sweetheart."

Ah-Yen paused and sat for some time silent; his pipe had sputtered out and lay cold in the hollow of his hand; his eye was fixed upon the wall where the light and shadows shifted in the dull flickering of the candle. At last he spoke again:

"I will not dwell upon the happy days that ensued—days of gaudy summer neckties and white waistcoats, of spotless shirts and lofty collars worn but a single day by the fastidious lover. Our happiness seemed complete and I asked no more from fate. Alas! it was not destined to continue! When the bright days of summer were fading into autumn, I was grieved to notice an occasional quarrel—only four shirts instead of seven, or the reappearance of the abandoned cuffs and shirt-fronts. Reconciliations followed, with tears of penitence upon the shoulder of the white waistcoat, and the seven shirts came back. But the quarrels grew more frequent and there came at times stormy scenes of passionate emotion that left a track of broken buttons down the waistcoat. The shirts went slowly down to three, then fell to two, and the collars of my unhappy friend subsided to an inch and three-quarters. In vain I lavished my utmost care upon Fifty-Six. It seemed to my tortured mind that the gloss upon his shirts and collars would have melted a heart of stone. Alas! my every effort at reconciliation seemed to fail. An awful month passed; the false fronts and detached cuffs were all back again; the unhappy lover seemed to glory in their perfidy. At last, one gloomy evening, I found on opening his bundle that he had bought a stock of celluloids, and my heart told me that she had abandoned him for ever. Of what my poor friend suffered at this time, I can give you no idea; suffice it to say that he passed from celluloid to a blue flannel shirt and from blue to grey. The sight of a red cotton handkerchief in his wash at length warned me that his disappointed love had unhinged his mind, and I feared the worst. Then came an agonising interval of three weeks during which he sent me nothing, and after that came the last parcel that I ever received from him—an enormous bundle that seemed to contain all his effects. In this, to my horror, I discovered one shirt the breast of which was stained a deep crimson with his blood, and pierced by a ragged hole that showed where a bullet had singed through into his heart.

"A fortnight before, I remembered having heard the street boys crying the news of an appalling suicide, and I know now that it must have been he. After the first shock of my grief had passed, I sought to keep him in my memory by drawing the portrait which hangs beside you. I have some skill in the art, and I feel assured that I have caught the expression of his face. The picture is, of course, an ideal one, for, as you know, I never saw Fifty-Six."

The bell on the door of the outer shop tinkled at the entrance of a customer. Ah-Yen rose with that air of quiet resignation that habitually marked his demeanour, and remained for some time in the shop. When he returned he seemed in no mood to continue speaking of his lost friend. I left him soon after and walked sorrowfully home to my lodgings. On my way I mused much upon my little Eastern friend and the sympathetic grasp of his imagination. But a burden lay heavy on my heart—something I would fain have told him but which I could not bear to mention. I could not find it in my heart to shatter the airy castle of his fancy. For my life has been secluded and lonely and I have known no love like that of my ideal friend. Yet I have a haunting recollection of a certain huge bundle of washing that I sent to him about a year ago. I had been absent from town for three weeks and my laundry was much larger than usual in consequence. And if I mistake not there was in the bundle a tattered shirt that had been grievously stained by the breaking of a bottle of red ink in my portmanteau, and burnt in one place where an ash fell from my cigar as I made up the bundle. Of all this I cannot feel absolutely certain, yet I know at least that until a year ago, when I transferred my custom to a more modern establishment, my laundry number with Ah-Yen was Fifty-Six.

Aristocratic Education

House of lords, Jan. 25, 1920—The House of Lords commenced to-day in Committee the consideration of Clause No. 52,000 of the Education Bill, dealing with the teaching of Geometry in schools.

The Leader of the Government in presenting the clause urged upon their Lordships the need of conciliation. The Bill, he said, had now been before their Lordships for sixteen years. The Government had made every concession. They had accepted all the amendments of their Lordships on the opposite side in regard to the original provisions of the Bill. They had consented also to insert in the Bill a detailed programme of studies of which the present clause, enunciating the fifth proposition of Euclid, was a part. He would therefore ask their Lordships to accept the clause drafted as follows:

"The angles at the base of an isosceles triangle are equal, and if the equal sides of the triangle are produced, the exterior angles will also be equal."

He would hasten to add that the Government had no intention of producing the sides. Contingencies might arise to render such a course necessary, but in that case their Lordships would receive an early intimation of the fact.

The Archbishop of Canterbury spoke against the clause. He

considered it, in its present form, too secular. He should wish to amend the clause so as to make it read:

"The angles at the base of an isosceles triangle are, in every Christian community, equal, and if the sides be produced by a member of a Christian congregation, the exterior angles will be equal."

He was aware, he continued, that the angles at the base of an isosceles triangle are extremely equal, but he must remind the Government that the Church had been aware of this for several years past. He was willing also to admit that the opposite sides and ends of a parallelogram are equal, but he thought that such an admission should be coupled with a distinct recognition of the existence of a Supreme Being.

The Leader of the Government accepted His Grace's amendment with pleasure. He considered it the brightest amendment His Grace had made that week. The Government, he said, was aware of the intimate relation in which His Grace stood to the bottom end of a parallelogram and was prepared to respect it.

Lord Halifax rose to offer a further amendment. He thought the present case was one in which the "four-fifths" clause ought to apply: he should wish it stated that the angles are equal for two days every week, except in the case of schools where four-fifths of the parents are conscientiously opposed to the use of the isosceles triangle.

The Leader of the Government thought the amendment was a singularly pleasing one. He accepted it and would like it understood that the words isosceles triangle were not meant in any offensive sense.

Lord Rosebery spoke at some length. He considered the clause unfair to Scotland where the high state of morality rendered education unnecessary. Unless an amendment in this sense was accepted, it might be necessary to reconsider the Act of Union of 1707.

The Leader of the Government said that Lord Rosebery's amendment was the best he had heard yet. The Government accepted it at once. They were willing to make every concession. They would, if need be, reconsider the Norman Conquest.

The Duke of Devonshire took exception to the part of the clause relating to the production of the sides. He did not think the country was prepared for it. It was unfair to the producer. He would like the clause altered to read, "if the sides be produced in the home market."

The Leader of the Government accepted with pleasure His Grace's amendment. He considered it quite sensible. He would now, as it was near the hour of rising, present the clause in its revised form. He hoped, however, that their Lordships would find time to think out some further amendments for the evening sitting.

The clause was then read.

His Grace of Canterbury then moved that the House, in all humility, adjourn for dinner.

The Conjurer's Revenge

"NOW, ladies and gentlemen," said the conjurer, "having shown you that the cloth is absolutely empty, I will proceed to take from it a bowl of goldfish. Presto!"

All around the hall people were saying, "Oh, how wonderful! How does he do it?"

But the Quick Man on the front seat said in a big whisper to the people near him, "He—had—it—up—his—sleeve."

Then the people nodded brightly at the Quick Man and said, "Oh, of course"; and everybody whispered round the hall, "He—had—it—up—his—sleeve."

"My next trick," said the conjurer, "is the famous Hindostanee rings. You will notice that the rings are apparently separate; at a blow they all join (clang, clang, clang)—Presto!"

There was a general buzz of stupefaction till the Quick Man was heard to whisper, "He—must—have—had—another—lot—up—his—sleeve."

Again everybody nodded and whispered, "The—rings—were—up—his—sleeve."

The brow of the conjurer was clouded with a gathering frown.

"I will now," he continued, "show you a most amusing trick by which

I am enabled to take any number of eggs from a hat. Will some gentleman kindly lend me his hat? Ah, thank you—Presto!"

He extracted seventeen eggs, and for thirty-five seconds the audience began to think that he was wonderful. Then the Quick Man whispered along the front bench, "He—has—a—hen—up—his—sleeve," and all the people whispered it on. "He—has—a—lot—of—hens—up—his—sleeve."

The egg trick was ruined.

It went on like that all through. It transpired from the whispers of the Quick Man that the conjurer must have concealed up his sleeve, in addition to the rings, hens, and fish, several packs of cards, a loaf of bread, a doll's cradle, a live guinea-pig, a fifty-cent piece, and a rocking-chair.

The reputation of the conjurer was rapidly sinking below zero. At the close of the evening he rallied for a final effort.

"Ladies and gentlemen," he said, "I will present to you, in conclusion, the famous Japanese trick recently invented by the natives of Tipperary. Will you, sir," he continued, turning toward the Quick Man, "will you kindly hand me your gold watch?"

It was passed to him.

"Have I your permission to put it into this mortar and pound it to pieces?" he asked savagely.

The Quick Man nodded and smiled.

The conjurer threw the watch into the mortar and grasped a sledge hammer from the table. There was a sound of violent smashing. "He's—slipped—it—up—his—sleeve," whispered the Quick Man.

"Now, sir," continued the conjurer, "will you allow me to take your handkerchief and punch holes in it? Thank you. You see, ladies and gentlemen, there is no deception, the holes are visible to the eye."

The face of the Quick Man beamed. This time the real mystery of the thing fascinated him.

"And now, sir, will you kindly pass me your silk hat and allow me to dance on it? Thank you."

The conjurer made a few rapid passes with his feet and exhibited the hat crushed beyond recognition.

"And will you now, sir, take off your celluloid collar and permit me to burn it in the candle? Thank you, sir. And will you allow me to smash your spectacles for you with my hammer? Thank you."

By this time the features of the Quick Man were assuming a puzzled expression. "This thing beats me," he whispered, "I don't see through it a bit."

There was a great hush upon the audience. Then the conjurer drew himself up to his full height and, with a withering look at the Quick Man, he concluded:

"Ladies and gentlemen, you will observe that I have, with this gentleman's permission, broken his watch, burnt his collar, smashed his spectacles, and danced on his hat. If he will give me the further permission to paint green stripes on his overcoat, or to tie his suspenders in a knot, I shall be delighted to entertain you. If not, the performance is at an end."

And amid a glorious burst of music from the orchestra the curtain fell, and the audience dispersed, convinced that there are some tricks, at any rate, that are not done up the conjurer's sleeve.

Hints to Travellers

THE following hints and observations have occurred to me during a recent trip across the continent: they are written in no spirit of complaint against existing railroad methods, but merely in the hope that they may prove useful to those who travel, like myself, in a spirit of meek, observant ignorance.

1. Sleeping in a Pullman car presents some difficulties to the novice. Care should be taken to allay all sense of danger. The frequent whistling of the engine during the night is apt to be a source of alarm. Find out, therefore, before travelling, the meaning of the various whistles. One means "station," two, "rail-road crossing," and so on. Five whistles, short and rapid, mean sudden danger. When you hear whistles in the night, sit up smartly in your bunk and count them. Should they reach five, draw on your trousers over your pyjamas and leave the train instantly. As a further precaution against accident, sleep with the feet towards the engine if you prefer to have the feet crushed, or with the head towards the engine, if you think it best to have the head crushed. In making this decision try to be as unselfish as possible. If indifferent, sleep crosswise with the head hanging over into the aisle.
2. I have devoted some thought to the proper method of changing

trains. The system which I have observed to be the most popular with travellers of my own class, is something as follows: Suppose that you have been told on leaving New York that you are to change at Kansas City. The evening before approaching Kansas City, stop the conductor in the aisle of the car (you can do this best by putting out your foot and tripping him), and say politely, "Do I change at Kansas City?" He says "Yes." Very good. Don't believe him. On going into the dining-car for supper, take a negro aside and put it to him as a personal matter between a white man and a black, whether he thinks you ought to change at Kansas City. Don't be satisfied with this. In the course of the evening pass through the entire train from time to time, and say to people casually, "Oh, can you tell me if I change at Kansas City?" Ask the conductor about it a few more times in the evening: a repetition of the question will ensure pleasant relations with him. Before falling asleep watch for his passage and ask him through the curtains of your berth, "Oh, by the way, did you say I changed at Kansas City?" If he refuses to stop, hook him by the neck with your walking-stick, and draw him gently to your bedside. In the morning when the train stops and a man calls, "Kansas City! All change!" approach the conductor and say, "Is this Kansas City?" Don't be discouraged at his answer. Pick yourself up and go to the other end of the car and say to the brakesman, "Do you know, sir, if this is Kansas City?" Don't be too easily convinced. Remember that both brakesman and conductor may be in collusion to deceive you. Look around, therefore, for the name of the station on the signboard. Having found it, alight and ask the first man you see if this is Kansas City. He will answer, "Why, where in blank are your blank eyes? Can't you see it there, plain as blank?" When you hear language of this sort, ask no more. You are now in Kansas and this is Kansas City.

3. I have observed that it is now the practice of the conductors to stick bits of paper in the hats of the passengers. They do this, I believe, to mark which ones they like best. The device is pretty, and adds much

to the scenic appearance of the car. But I notice with pain that the system is fraught with much trouble for the conductors. The task of crushing two or three passengers together, in order to reach over them and stick a ticket into the chinks of a silk skull cap is embarrassing for a conductor of refined feelings. It would be simpler if the conductor should carry a small hammer and a packet of shingle nails and nail the paid-up passenger to the back of the seat. Or better still, let the conductor carry a small pot of paint and a brush, and mark the passengers in such a way that he cannot easily mistake them. In the case of bald-headed passengers, the hats might be politely removed and red crosses painted on the craniums. This will indicate that they are bald. Through passengers might be distinguished by a complete coat of paint. In the hands of a man of taste, much might be effected by a little grouping of painted passengers and the leisure time of the conductor agreeably occupied.

4. I have observed in travelling in the West that the irregularity of railroad accidents is a fruitful cause of complaint. The frequent disappointment of the holders of accident policy tickets on western roads is leading to widespread protest. Certainly the conditions of travel in the West are altering rapidly and accidents can no longer be relied upon. This is deeply to be regretted, in so much as, apart from accidents, the tickets may be said to be practically valueless.

A Manual of Education

THE few selections below are offered as a specimen page of a little book which I have in course of preparation.

Every man has somewhere in the back of his head the wreck of a thing which he calls his education. My book is intended to embody in concise form these remnants of early instruction.

Educations are divided into splendid educations, thorough classical educations, and average educations. All very old men have splendid educations; all men who apparently know nothing else have thorough classical educations; nobody has an average education.

An education, when it is all written out on foolscap, covers nearly ten sheets. It takes about six years of severe college training to acquire it. Even then a man often finds that he somehow hasn't got his education just where he can put his thumb on it. When my little book of eight or ten pages has appeared, everybody may carry his education in his hip pocket.

Those who have not had the advantage of an early training will be enabled, by a few hours of conscientious application, to put themselves on an equal footing with the most scholarly.

The selections are chosen entirely at random.

I.—Remains of Astronomy

Astronomy teaches the correct use of the sun and the planets. These may be put on a frame of little sticks and turned round. This causes the tides. Those at the ends of the sticks are enormously far away. From time to time a diligent search of the sticks reveals new planets. The orbit of a planet is the distance the stick goes round in going round. Astronomy is intensely interesting: it should be done at night, in a high tower in Spitzbergen. This is to avoid the astronomy being interrupted. A really good astronomer can tell when a comet is coming too near him by the warning buzz of the revolving sticks.

II.—Remains of History

Aztecs: A fabulous race, half man, half horse, half mound-builder. They flourished at about the same time as the early Calithumpians. They have left some awfully stupendous monuments of themselves somewhere.

Life of Cæsar: A famous Roman general, the last who ever landed in Britain without being stopped at the custom house. On returning to his Sabine farm (to fetch something), he was stabbed by Brutus, and died with the words "Veni, vidi, tekel, upharsim" in his throat. The jury returned a verdict of strangulation.

Life of Voltaire: A Frenchman; very bitter.

Life of Schopenhauer: A German; very deep; but it was not really noticeable when he sat down.

Life of Dante: An Italian; the first to introduce the banana and the class of street organ known as "Dante's Inferno."

Peter the Great, Alfred the Great, Frederick the Great, John the Great, Tom the Great, Jim the Great, Jo the Great, etc., etc.	} It is impossible for a busy man to keep these apart. They sought a living as kings and apostles and pugilists and so on.

III.—Remains of Botany

Botany is the art of plants. Plants are divided into trees, flowers, and vegetables. The true botanist knows a tree as soon as he sees it. He learns to distinguish it from a vegetable by merely putting his ear to it.

IV.—Remains of Natural Science

Natural Science treats of motion and force. Many of its teachings remain as part of an educated man's permanent equipment in life.

Such are:

(*a*) The harder you shove a bicycle the faster it will go. This is because of natural science.

(*b*) If you fall from a high tower, you fall quicker and quicker and quicker; a judicious selection of a tower will ensure any rate of speed.

(*c*) If you put your thumb in between two cogs it will go on and on, until the wheels are arrested, by your suspenders. This is machinery.

(*d*) Electricity is of two kinds, positive and negative. The difference is, I presume, that one kind comes a little more expensive, but is more durable; the other is a cheaper thing, but the moths get into it.

Hoodoo McFiggin's Christmas

THIS Santa Claus business is played out. It's a sneaking, underhand method, and the sooner it's exposed the better.

For a parent to get up under cover of the darkness of night and palm off a ten-cent necktie on a boy who had been expecting a ten-dollar watch, and then say that an angel sent it to him, is low, undeniably low.

I had a good opportunity of observing how the thing worked this Christmas, in the case of young Hoodoo McFiggin, the son and heir of the McFiggins, at whose house I board.

Hoodoo McFiggin is a good boy—a religious boy. He had been given to understand that Santa Claus would bring nothing to his father and mother because grown-up people don't get presents from the angels. So he saved up all his pocket-money and bought a box of cigars for his father and a seventy-five-cent diamond brooch for his mother. His own fortunes he left in the hands of the angels. But he prayed. He prayed every night for weeks that Santa Claus would bring him a pair of skates and a puppy-dog and an air-gun and a bicycle and a Noah's ark and a sleigh and a drum—altogether about a hundred and fifty dollars' worth of stuff.

I went into Hoodoo's room quite early Christmas morning. I had an idea that the scene would be interesting. I woke him up and he sat up in bed, his eyes glistening with radiant expectation, and began hauling things out of his stocking.

The first parcel was bulky; it was done up quite loosely and had an odd look generally.

"Ha! ha!" Hoodoo cried gleefully, as he began undoing it. "I'll bet it's the puppy-dog, all wrapped up in paper!"

And was it the puppy-dog? No, by no means. It was a pair of nice, strong, number-four boots, laces and all, labelled, "Hoodoo, from Santa Claus," and underneath Santa Claus had written, "95 net."

The boy's jaw fell with delight. "It's boots," he said, and plunged in his hand again.

He began hauling away at another parcel with renewed hope on his face.

This time the thing seemed like a little round box. Hoodoo tore the paper off it with a feverish hand. He shook it; something rattled inside.

"It's a watch and chain! It's a watch and chain!" he shouted. Then he pulled the lid off.

And was it a watch and chain? No. It was a box of nice, brand-new celluloid collars, a dozen of them all alike and all his own size.

The boy was so pleased that you could see his face crack up with pleasure.

He waited a few minutes until his intense joy subsided. Then he tried again.

This time the packet was long and hard. It resisted the touch and had a sort of funnel shape.

"It's a toy pistol!" said the boy, trembling with excitement. "Gee! I hope there are lots of caps with it! I'll fire some off now and wake up father."

No, my poor child, you will not wake your father with that. It is a useful thing, but it needs not caps and it fires no bullets, and you cannot wake a sleeping man with a tooth-brush. Yes, it was a tooth-brush—a regular beauty, pure bone all through, and ticketed with a little paper, "Hoodoo, from Santa Claus."

Again the expression of intense joy passed over the boy's face, and the tears of gratitude started from his eyes. He wiped them away with his tooth-brush and passed on.

The next packet was much larger and evidently contained something soft and bulky. It had been too long to go into the stocking and was tied outside.

"I wonder what this is," Hoodoo mused, half afraid to open it. Then his heart gave a great leap, and he forgot all his other presents in the anticipation of this one. "It's the drum, all wrapped up!"

Drum nothing! It was pants—a pair of the nicest little short pants—yellowish-brown short pants—with dear little stripes of colour running across both ways, and here again Santa Claus had written, "Hoodoo, from Santa Claus, one fort net."

But there was something wrapped up in it. Oh, yes! There was a pair of braces wrapped up in it, braces with a little steel sliding thing so that you could slide your pants up to your neck, if you wanted to.

The boy gave a dry sob of satisfaction. Then he took out his last present. "It's a book," he said, as he unwrapped it. "I wonder if it is fairy stories or adventures. Oh, I hope it's adventures! I'll read it all morning."

No, Hoodoo, it was not precisely adventures. It was a small family Bible. Hoodoo had now seen all his presents, and he arose and dressed. But he still had the fun of playing with his toys. That is always the chief delight of Christmas morning.

First he played with his tooth-brush. He got a whole lot of water and brushed all his teeth with it. This was huge.

Then he played with his collars. He had no end of fun with them, taking them all out one by one and swearing at them, and then putting them back and swearing at the whole lot together.

The next toy was his pants. He had immense fun there, putting them on and taking them off again, and then trying to guess which side was which by merely looking at them.

After that he took his book and read some adventures called "Genesis" till breakfast-time.

Then he went downstairs and kissed his father and mother. His father was smoking a cigar, and his mother had her new brooch on. Hoodoo's face was thoughtful, and a light seemed to have broken in upon his mind. Indeed, I think it altogether likely that next Christmas he will hang on to his own money and take chances on what the angels bring.

The Life of John Smith

THE lives of great men occupy a large section of our literature. The great man is certainly a wonderful thing. He walks across his century and leaves the marks of his feet all over it, ripping out the dates on his goloshes as he passes. It is impossible to get up a revolution or a new religion, or a national awakening of any sort, without his turning up, putting himself at the head of it and collaring all the gate-receipts for himself. Even after his death he leaves a long trail of second-rate relations spattered over the front seats of fifty years of history.

Now the lives of great men are doubtless infinitely interesting. But at times I must confess to a sense of reaction and an idea that the ordinary common man is entitled to have his biography written too. It is to illustrate this view that I write the life of John Smith, a man neither good nor great, but just the usual, everyday homo like you and me and the rest of us.

From his earliest childhood John Smith was marked out from his comrades by nothing. The marvellous precocity of the boy did not astonish his preceptors. Books were not a passion for him from his youth, neither did any old man put his hand on Smith's head and say, mark his words, this boy would some day become a man. Nor yet was it his father's wont to gaze on him with a feeling amounting almost to awe. By no means! All his father did was to wonder whether Smith was a darn fool because he couldn't help it, or because he thought it smart. In other words, he was just like you and me and the rest of us.

In those athletic sports which were the ornament of the youth of his day, Smith did not, as great men do, excel his fellows. He couldn't ride worth a darn. He couldn't skate worth a darn. He couldn't swim worth a darn. He couldn't shoot worth a darn. He couldn't do anything worth a darn. He was just like us.

Nor did the bold cast of the boy's mind offset his physical defects, as it invariably does in the biographies. On the contrary. He was afraid of his father. He was afraid of his school-teacher. He was afraid of dogs. He was afraid of guns. He was afraid of lightning. He was afraid of hell. He was afraid of girls.

In the boy's choice of a profession there was not seen that keen longing for a life-work that we find in the celebrities. He didn't want to be a lawyer, because you have to know law. He didn't want to be a doctor, because you have to know medicine. He didn't want to be a businessman, because you have to know business; and he didn't want to be a school-teacher, because he had seen too many of them. As far as he had any choice, it lay between being Robinson Crusoe and being the Prince of Wales. His father refused him both and put him into a dry-goods establishment.

Such was the childhood of Smith. At its close there was nothing in his outward appearance to mark the man of genius. The casual observer could have seen no genius concealed behind the wide face, the massive mouth, the long slanting forehead, and the tall ear that swept up to the close-cropped head. Certainly he couldn't. There wasn't any concealed there.

It was shortly after his start in business life that Smith was stricken with the first of those distressing attacks, to which he afterwards became subject. It seized him late one night as he was returning home from a delightful evening of song and praise with a few old school chums. Its symptoms were a peculiar heaving of the sidewalk, a dancing of the street lights, and a crafty shifting to and fro of the houses, requiring a very nice discrimination in selecting his own. There was a strong desire not to drink water throughout the entire attack, which showed that the thing was evidently a form of hydrophobia. From this time on, these painful attacks became chronic with Smith. They were liable to come on at any time, but especially on Saturday nights, on the first of the month, and on Thanksgiving Day. He always had a very severe attack of hydrophobia on Christmas Eve, and after elections it was fearful.

There was one incident in Smith's career which he did, perhaps, share with regret. He had scarcely reached manhood when he met the most beautiful girl in the world. She was different from all other women. She had a deeper nature than other people. Smith realised it at once. She could feel and understand things that ordinary people couldn't. She could understand him. She had a great sense of humour and an exquisite appreciation of a joke. He told her the six that he knew one night and she thought them great. Her mere presence made Smith feel as if he had swallowed a sunset: the first time that his finger brushed against hers, he felt a thrill all through him. He presently found that if he took a firm hold of her hand with his, he could get a fine thrill, and if he sat beside her on a sofa, with his head against her ear and his arm about once and a half round her, he could get what you might call a first-class, A-1 thrill. Smith became filled with the idea that he would like to have her always near him. He suggested an arrangement to her, by which she should come and live in the same house with him and take personal charge of his clothes and his meals. She was to receive in return her board and washing, about seventy-five cents a week in ready money, and Smith was to be her slave.

After Smith had been this woman's slave for some time, baby fingers stole across his life, then another set of them, and then more and more till the house was full of them. The woman's mother began to steal across his life, too, and every time she came, Smith had hydrophobia frightfully. Strangely enough there was no little prattler that was taken from his life and became a saddened, hallowed memory to him. Oh, no! The little Smiths were not that kind of prattler. The whole nine grew up into tall, lank boys with massive mouths and great sweeping ears like their father's, and no talent for anything.

The life of Smith never seemed to bring him to any of those great turning-points that occurred in the lives of the great. True, the passing years brought some change of fortune. He was moved up in his dry-goods establishment from the ribbon counter to the collar counter, from the collar counter to the gents' panting counter, and from the gents' panting to the gents' fancy shirting. Then, as he grew aged and inefficient, they moved him down again from the gents' fancy shirting to the gents' panting, and so on to the ribbon counter. And when he grew quite old they dismissed him and got a boy with a four-inch mouth and sandy-coloured hair, who did all Smith could do for half the money. That was John Smith's mercantile career: it won't stand comparison with Mr. Gladstone's, but it's not unlike your own.

Smith lived for five years after this. His sons kept him. They didn't want to, but they had to. In his old age the brightness of his mind and his fund of anecdote were *not* the delight of all who dropped in to see him. He told seven stories and he knew six jokes. The stories were long things all about himself, and the jokes were about a commercial traveller and a Methodist minister. But nobody dropped in to see him, anyway, so it didn't matter.

At sixty-five Smith was taken ill, and, receiving proper treatment, he died. There was a tombstone put up over him, with a hand pointing north-northeast.

But I doubt if he ever got there. He was too like us.

On Collecting Things

LIKE most other men, I have from time to time been stricken with a desire to make collections of things.

It began with postage stamps. I had a letter from a friend of mine who had gone out to South Africa. The letter had a three-cornered stamp on it, and I thought as soon as I looked at it, "That's the thing! Stamp collecting! I'll devote my life to it."

I bought an album with accommodation for the stamps of all nations, and began collecting right off. For three days the collection made wonderful progress. It contained:

One Cape of Good Hope stamp.

One one-cent stamp, United States of America.

One two-cent stamp, United States of America.

One five-cent stamp, United States of America.

One ten-cent stamp, United States of America.

After that the collection came to a dead stop. For a while I used to talk about it rather airily and say I had one or two rather valuable South African stamps. But I presently grew tired even of lying about it.

Collecting coins is a thing that I attempt at intervals. Every time I am given an old half-penny or a Mexican quarter, I get an idea that if a fellow made a point of holding on to rarities of that sort, he'd soon have quite a valuable collection. The first time that I tried it I was full of enthusiasm, and before long my collection numbered quite a few articles of vertu. The items were as follows:

No. 1. Ancient Roman coin. Time of Caligula. This one of course was the gem of the whole lot; it was given me by a friend, and that was what started me collecting.

No. 2. Small copper coin. Value one cent. United States of America. Apparently modern.

No. 3. Small nickel coin. Circular. United States of America. Value five cents.

No. 4. Small silver coin. Value ten cents. United States of America.

No. 5. Silver coin. Circular. Value twenty-five cents. United States of America. Very beautiful.

No. 6. Large silver coin. Circular. Inscription, "One Dollar." United States of America. Very valuable.

No. 7. Ancient British copper coin. Probably time of Caractacus. Very dim. Inscription, "Victoria Dei gratia regina." Very valuable.

No. 8. Silver coin. Evidently French. Inscription, "Fünf Mark. Kaiser Wilhelm."

No. 9. Circular silver coin. Very much defaced. Part of inscription, "E Pluribus Unum." Probably a Russian rouble, but quite as likely to be a Japanese yen or a Shanghai rooster.

That's as far as that collection got. It lasted through most of the winter and I was getting quite proud of it, but I took the coins down town one evening to show to a friend and we spent No. 3, No. 4, No. 5, No. 6 and No. 7 in buying a little dinner for two. After dinner I bought a yen's worth of cigars and traded the relic of Caligula for as many hot Scotches as they cared to advance on it. After that I felt reckless and put No. 2 and No. 8 into a Children's Hospital poor box.

I tried fossils next. I got two in ten years. Then I quit.

A friend of mine once showed me a very fine collection of ancient and curious weapons, and for a time I was full of that idea. I gathered several interesting specimens, such as:

No. 1. Old flint-lock musket, used by my grandfather. (He used it on the farm for years as a crowbar.)

No. 2. Old raw-hide strap, used by my father.

No. 3. Ancient Indian arrowhead, found by myself the very day after I began collecting. It resembles a three-cornered stone.

No. 4. Ancient Indian bow, found by myself behind a sawmill on the second day of my collecting. It resembles a straight stick of elm or oak. It is interesting to think that this very weapon may have figured in some fierce scene of savage warfare.

No. 5. Cannibal poniard or straight-handled dagger of the South Sea Islands. It will give the reader almost a thrill of horror to learn that this atrocious weapon, which I bought myself on the third day of collecting, was actually exposed in a second-hand store as a family carving-knife. In gazing at it one cannot refrain from conjuring up the awful scenes it must have witnessed.

I kept this collection for quite a long while until, in a moment of infatuation, I presented it to a young lady as a betrothal present. The gift proved too ostentatious and our relations subsequently ceased to be cordial.

On the whole I am inclined to recommend the beginner to confine himself to collecting coins. At present I am myself making a collection of American bills (time of Taft preferred), a pursuit I find most absorbing.

Society Chit-Chat

As It Should Be Written

I NOTICE that it is customary for the daily papers to publish a column or so of society gossip. They generally head it "Chit-Chat," or "On Dit," or "Le Boudoir," or something of the sort, and they keep it pretty full of French terms to give it the proper sort of swing. These columns may be very interesting in their way, but it always seems to me that they don't get hold of quite the right things to tell us about. They are very fond, for instance, of giving an account of the delightful dance at Mrs. De Smythe's—at which Mrs. De Smythe looked charming in a gown of old tulle with a stomacher of passementerie—or of the dinner-party at Mr. Alonzo Robinson's residence, or the smart pink tea given by Miss Carlotta Jones. No, that's all right, but it's not the kind of thing we want to get at; those are not the events which happen in our neighbours' houses that we really want to hear about. It is the quiet little family scenes, the little traits of home-life that—well, for example, take the case of that delightful party at the De Smythes. I am certain that all those who were present would much prefer a little paragraph like the following, which would give them some idea of the home-life of the De Smythes on the morning after the party.

Dejeuner de luxe at the de Smythe Residence

On Wednesday morning last at 7.15 a.m. a charming little breakfast was served at the home of Mr. De Smythe. The *déjeuner* was given in honour of Mr. De Smythe and his two sons, Master Adolphus and Master Blinks De Smythe, who were about to leave for their daily *travail* at their wholesale *Bureau de Flour et de Feed.* All the gentlemen were very quietly dressed in their *habits de work.* Miss Melinda De Smythe poured out tea, the *domestique* having *refusé* to get up so early after the *partie* of the night before. The menu was very handsome, consisting of eggs and bacon, *demi-froid,* and ice-cream. The conversation was sustained and lively. Mr. De Smythe sustained it and made it lively for his daughter and his *garçons.* In the course of the talk Mr. De Smythe stated that the next time he allowed the young people to turn his *maison* topsy-turvy he would see them in *enfer.* He wished to know if they were aware that some ass of the evening before had broken a pane of coloured glass in the hall that would cost him four dollars. Did they think he was made of *argent.* If so, they never made a bigger mistake in their *vie.* The meal closed with general expressions of good-feeling. A little bird has whispered to us that there will be no more parties at the De Smythes' *pour long-temps.*

Here is another little paragraph that would be of general interest in society.

Diner de fameel at the Boarding-house de McFiggin

Yesterday evening at half after six a pleasant little *diner* was given by Madame McFiggin of Rock Street, to her boarders. The *salle à manger* was very prettily decorated with texts, and the furniture upholstered with *cheveux de horse, Louis Quinze.* The boarders were all very quietly dressed: Mrs. McFiggin was daintily attired in some old clinging stuff with a *corsage de Whalebone* underneath. The ample board groaned under the bill of fare. The boarders groaned also. Their groaning was very noticeable. The *pièce de résistance* was a *hunko de bœuf boilé,* flanked with some old clinging stuff. The *entrées* were *pâté de pumpkin,* followed by *fromage McFiggin,* served under glass. Towards the end of the first course, speeches became the order of the day. Mrs. McFiggin was the first speaker. In commencing, she expressed her surprise that so few of the gentlemen seemed to care for the *hunko de bœuf;* her own mind, she said, had hesitated between *hunko de bœuf boilé* and a pair of roast chickens (sensation). She had finally decided in favour of the *hunko de bœuf* (no sensation). She referred at some length to the late Mr. McFiggin, who had always shown a marked preference for *hunko de bœuf.* Several other speakers followed. All spoke forcibly and to the point. The last to speak was the Reverend Mr. Whiner. The reverend gentleman, in rising, said that he confided himself and his fellow-boarders to the special interference of Providence. For what they had eaten, he said, he hoped that Providence would make them truly thankful. At the close of the *Repas* several of the boarders expressed their *intention* of going down the street to a *restourong* to get *quelque chose à manger.*

Here is another example. How interesting it would be to get a detailed account of that little affair at the Robinsons', of which the neighbours only heard indirectly! Thus:

Delightful Evening at the Residence of Mr. Alonzo Robinson

Yesterday the family of Mr. Alonzo Robinson spent a very lively evening at their home on ——th Avenue. The occasion was the seventeenth birthday of Master Alonzo Robinson, junior. It was the original intention of Master Alonzo Robinson to celebrate the day at home and invite a few of *les garçons.* Mr. Robinson, senior, however, having declared that he would be *damné* first, Master Alonzo spent the evening in visiting the salons of the town, which he painted *rouge.* Mr. Robinson, senior, spent the evening at home in quiet expectation of his son's return. He was very becomingly dressed in a *pantalon quatre vingt treize,* and had his *whippe de chien* laid across his knee. Madame Robinson and the Mademoiselles Robinson wore black. The guest of the evening arrived at a late hour. He wore his *habits de spri,* and had about *six pouces* of *eau de vie* in him. He was evidently full up to his *cou.* For some time after his arrival a very lively time was spent. Mr. Robinson having at length broken the *whippe de chien,* the family parted for the night with expressions of cordial goodwill.

Insurance up to Date

A MAN called on me the other day with the idea of insuring my life. Now, I detest life-insurance agents; they always argue that I shall some day die, which is not so. I have been insured a great many times, for about a month at a time, but have had no luck with it at all.

So I made up my mind that I would outwit this man at his own game. I let him talk straight ahead and encouraged him all I could, until he finally left me with a sheet of questions which I was to answer as an applicant. Now this was what I was waiting for; I had decided that, if the company wanted information about me, they should have it, and have the very best quality I could supply. So I spread the sheet of questions before me, and drew up a set of answers for them, which, I hoped, would settle for ever all doubts to my eligibility for insurance.

Question.—What is your age?

Answer.—I can't think.

Q.—What is your chest measurement?

A.—Nineteen inches.

Q.—What is your chest expansion?

A.—Half an inch.

Q.—What is your height?

A.—Six feet five, if erect, but less when I walk on all fours.

Q.—Is your grandfather dead?

A.—Practically.

Q.—Cause of death, if dead?

A.—Dipsomania, if dead.

Q.—Is your father dead?

A.—To the world.

Q.—Cause of death?

A.—Hydrophobia.

Q.—Place of father's residence?

A.—Kentucky.

Q.—What illnesses have you had?

A.—As a child, consumption, leprosy, and water on the knee. As a man, whooping-cough, stomach-ache, and water on the brain.

Q.—Have you any brothers?

A.—Thirteen; all nearly dead.

Q.—Are you aware of any habits or tendencies which might be expected to shorten your life?

A.—I am aware. I drink, I smoke, I take morphine and vaseline. I swallow grape seeds and I hate exercise.

I thought when I had come to the end of that list that I had made a dead sure thing of it, and I posted the paper with a cheque for three months' payment, feeling pretty confident of having the cheque sent back to me. I was a good deal surprised a few days later to receive the following letter from the company:

"DEAR SIR,—We beg to acknowledge your letter of application and cheque for fifteen dollars. After a careful comparison of your case with the average modern standard, we are pleased to accept you as a first-class risk."

Borrowing a Match

YOU might think that borrowing a match upon the street is a simple thing. But any man who has ever tried it will assure you that it is not, and will be prepared to swear on oath to the truth of my experience of the other evening.

I was standing on the corner of the street with a cigar that I wanted to light. I had no match. I waited till a decent, ordinary man came along. Then I said:

"Excuse me, sir, but could you oblige me with the loan of a match?"

"A match?" he said, "why, certainly." Then he unbuttoned his overcoat and put his hand in the pocket of his waistcoat. "I know I have one," he went on, "and I'd almost swear it's in the bottom pocket—or, hold on, though, I guess it may be in the top—just wait till I put these parcels down on the sidewalk."

"Oh, don't trouble," I said, "It's really of no consequence."

"Oh, it's no trouble, I'll have it in a minute; I know there must be one in here somewhere"—he was digging his fingers into his pockets as he spoke—"but you see this isn't the waistcoat I generally..."

I saw that the man was getting excited about it. "Well, never mind," I protested; "if that isn't the waistcoat that you generally—why, it doesn't matter."

"Hold on, now, hold on!" the man said, "I've got one of the cursed things in here somewhere. I guess it must be in with my watch. No, it's not there either. Wait till I try my coat. If that confounded tailor only knew enough to make a pocket so that a man could get at it!"

He was getting pretty well worked up now. He had thrown down his walking-stick and was plunging at his pockets with his teeth set. "It's that cursed young boy of mine," he hissed; "this comes of his fooling in my pockets. By Gad! perhaps I won't warm him up when I get home. Say, I'll bet that it's in my hip-pocket. You just hold up the tail of my overcoat a second till I..."

"No, no," I protested again, "please don't take all this trouble, it really doesn't matter. I'm sure you needn't take off your overcoat, and oh, pray don't throw away your letters and things in the snow like that, and tear out your packets by the roots! Please, please don't trample over your overcoat and put your feet through the parcels. I do hate to hear you swearing, at your little boy, with that peculiar whine in your voice. Don't—please don't tear your clothes so savagely."

Suddenly the man gave a grunt of exultation, and drew his hand up from inside the lining of his coat.

"I've got it," he cried. "Here you are!" Then he brought it out under the light.

It was a toothpick.

Yielding to the impulse of the moment I pushed him under the wheels of a trolley-car and ran.

A Lesson in Fiction

SUPPOSE that in the opening pages of the modern melodramatic novel you find some such situation as the following, in which is depicted the terrific combat between Gaspard de Vaux, the boy lieutenant, and Hairy Hank, the chief of the Italian banditti:

"The inequality of the contest was apparent. With a mingled yell of rage and contempt, his sword brandished above his head and his dirk between his teeth, the enormous bandit rushed upon his intrepid opponent. De Vaux seemed scarce more than a stripling, but he stood his ground and faced his hitherto invincible assailant. 'Mong Dieu,' cried De Smythe, 'he is lost!'"

Question.—On which of the parties to the above contest do you honestly feel inclined to put your money?

Answer.—On De Vaux. He'll win. Hairy Hank will force him down to one knee and with a brutal cry of "Har! har!" will be about to dirk him, when De Vaux will make a sudden lunge (one he had learnt at home out of a book of lunges) and——

Very good. You have answered correctly. Now, suppose you find, a little later in the book, that the killing of Hairy Hank has compelled De Vaux to flee from his native land to the East. Are you not fearful for his safety in the desert?

Answer.—Frankly, I am not. De Vaux is all right. His name is on the title page, and you can't kill him.

Question.—Listen to this, then: "The sun of Ethiopia beat fiercely upon the desert as De Vaux, mounted upon his faithful elephant, pursued his lonely way. Seated in his lofty hoo-doo, his eye scoured the waste. Suddenly a solitary horseman appeared on the horizon, then another, and another, and then six. In a few moments a whole crowd of solitary horsemen swooped down upon him. There was a fierce shout of 'Allah!' a rattle of firearms. De Vaux sank from his hoo-doo on to the sands, while the affrighted elephant dashed off in all directions. The bullet had struck him in the heart."

There now, what do you think of that? Isn't De Vaux killed now?

Answer.—I am sorry. De Vaux is not dead. True, the ball had hit him, oh yes, it had hit him, but it had glanced off against a family Bible, which he carried in his waistcoat in case of illness, struck some hymns that he had in his hip-pocket, and, glancing off again, had flattened itself against De Vaux's diary of his life in the desert, which was in his knapsack.

Question.—But even if this doesn't kill him, you must admit that he is near death when he is bitten in the jungle by the deadly dongola?

Answer.—That's all right. A kindly Arab will take De Vaux to the Sheik's tent.

Question.—What will De Vaux remind the Sheik of?

Answer.—Too easy. Of his long-lost son who disappeared years ago.

Question.—Was this son Hairy Hank?

Answer.—Of course he was. Anyone could see that but the Sheik never suspects it, and heals De Vaux. He heals him with an herb, a thing called a simple, an amazingly simple, known only to the Sheik. Since using this herb, the Sheik has used no other.

Question.—The Sheik will recognise an overcoat that De Vaux is wearing, and complications will arise in the matter of Hairy Hank deceased. Will this result in the death of the boy lieutenant?

Answer.—No. By this time De Vaux has realised that the reader knows he won't die, and resolves to quit the desert. The thought of his mother keeps recurring to him, and of his father, too, the grey, stooping old man—does he stoop still or has he stopped stooping? At times, too, there comes the thought of another, a fairer than his father; she whose—but enough, De Vaux returns to the old homestead in Piccadilly.

Question.—When De Vaux returns to England, what will happen?

Answer.—This will happen: "He who left England ten years before a raw boy, has returned a sunburnt soldierly man. But who is this that advances smilingly to meet him? Can the mere girl, the bright child that shared his hours of play, can she have grown into this peerless, graceful girl, at whose feet half the noble suitors of England are kneeling? 'Can this be her?' he asks himself in amazement."

Question.—Is it her?

Answer.—Oh, it's her all right. It is her, and it is him, and it is them. That girl hasn't waited fifty pages for nothing.

Question.—You evidently guess that a love affair will ensue between the boy lieutenant and the peerless girl with the broad feet. Do you imagine, however, that its course will run smoothly and leave nothing to record?

Answer.—Not at all. I feel certain that the scene of the novel having edged itself around to London, the writer will not feel satisfied unless he introduces the following famous scene:

"Stunned by the cruel revelation which he had received, unconscious of whither his steps were taking him, Gaspard de Vaux wandered on in the darkness from street to street until he found himself upon London Bridge. He leaned over the parapet and looked down upon the whirling stream below. There was something in the still, swift rush of it that seemed to beckon, to allure him. After all, why not? What was life now that he should prize it? For a moment De Vaux paused irresolute."

Question.—Will he throw himself in?

Answer.—Well, say you don't know Gaspard. He will pause irresolute up to the limit, then, with a fierce struggle, will recall his courage and hasten from the Bridge.

Question.—This struggle not to throw oneself in must be dreadfully difficult?

Answer.—Oh! dreadfully! Most of us are so frail we should jump in at once. But Gaspard has the knack of it. Besides he still has some of the Sheik's herb; he chews it.

Question.—What has happened to De Vaux anyway? Is it anything he has eaten?

Answer.—No, it is nothing that he has eaten. It's about her. The blow has come. She has no use for sunburn, doesn't care for tan; she is going to marry a duke and the boy lieutenant is no longer in it. The real trouble is that the modern novelist has got beyond the happy-marriage mode of ending. He wants tragedy and a blighted life to wind up with.

Question.—How will the book conclude?

Answer.—Oh, De Vaux will go back to the desert, fall upon the Sheik's neck, and swear to be a second Hairy Hank to him. There will be a final panorama of the desert, the Sheik and his newly found son at the door of the tent, the sun setting behind a pyramid, and De Vaux's faithful elephant crouched at his feet and gazing up at him with dumb affection.

Helping the Armenians

THE financial affairs of the parish church up at Doogalville have been getting rather into a tangle in the last six months. The people of the church were specially anxious to do something toward the general public subscription of the town on behalf of the unhappy Armenians, and to that purpose they determined to devote the collections taken up at a series of special evening services. To give the right sort of swing to the services and to stimulate generous giving, they put a new pipe organ into the church. In order to make a preliminary payment on the organ, it was decided to raise a mortgage on the parsonage.

To pay the interest on the mortgage, the choir of the church got up a sacred concert in the town hall.

To pay for the town hall, the Willing Workers' Guild held a social in the Sunday school. To pay the expenses of the social, the rector delivered a public lecture on "Italy and Her Past," illustrated by a magic lantern. To pay for the magic lantern, the curate and the ladies of the church got up some amateur theatricals.

Finally, to pay for the costumes for the theatricals, the rector felt it his duty to dispense with the curate.

So that is where the church stands just at present. What they chiefly want to do, is to raise enough money to buy a suitable gold watch as a testimonial to the curate. After that they hope to be able to do something for the Armenians. Meantime, of course, the Armenians, the ones right there in the town, are getting very troublesome. To begin with, there is the Armenian who rented the costumes for the theatricals: he has to be squared. Then there is the Armenian organ dealer, and the Armenian who owned the magic lantern. They want relief badly.

The most urgent case is that of the Armenian who holds the mortgage on the parsonage; indeed it is generally felt in the congregation, when the rector makes his impassioned appeals at the special services on behalf of the suffering cause, that it is to this man that he has special reference.

In the meanwhile, the general public subscription is not getting along very fast; but the proprietor of the big saloon further down the street and the man with the short cigar that runs the Doogalville Midway Plaisance have been most liberal in their contributions.

A Study in Still Life—The Country Hotel

THE country hotel stands on the sunny side of Main Street. It has three entrances.

There is one in front which leads into the Bar. There is one at the side called the Ladies' Entrance which leads into the Bar from the side. There is also the Main Entrance which leads into the Bar through the Rotunda.

The Rotunda is the space between the door of the bar-room and the cigar-case.

In it is a desk and a book. In the book are written down the names of the guests, together with marks indicating the direction of the wind and the height of the barometer. It is here that the newly arrived guest waits until he has time to open the door leading to the Bar.

The bar-room forms the largest part of the hotel. It constitutes the hotel proper. To it are attached a series of bedrooms on the floor above, many of which contain beds.

The walls of the bar-room are perforated in all directions with trap-doors. Through one of these, drinks are passed into the back sitting-room. Through others drinks are passed into the passages. Drinks are also passed through the floor and through the ceiling. Drinks once passed never return. The Proprietor stands in the doorway of the Bar. He weighs two hundred pounds. His face is immovable as putty. He is drunk. He has been drunk for twelve years. It makes no difference to him. Behind the Bar stands the Bar-tender. He wears wicker-sleeves, his hair is curled in a hook, and his name is Charlie.

Attached to the Bar is a pneumatic beer-pump, by means of which the Bar-tender can flood the Bar with beer. Afterwards he wipes up the beer with a rag. By this means he polishes the Bar. Some of the beer that is pumped up spills into glasses and has to be sold.

Behind the Bar-tender is a mechanism called a cash-register, which, on being struck a powerful blow, rings a bell, sticks up a card marked NO SALE, and opens a till from which the Bar-tender distributes money.

There is printed a tariff of drinks and prices on the wall.

It reads thus:

Beer ....5 cents.
Whisky ....5 cents.
Whisky and Soda ....5 cents.
Beer and Soda ....5 cents.
Whisky and Beer and Soda ....5 cents.
Whisky and Eggs ....5 cents.
Beer and Eggs ....5 cents.
Champagne ....5 cents.
Cigars ....5 cents.
Cigars, extra fine ....5 cents.

All calculations are made on this basis and are worked out to three places of decimals. Every seventh drink is on the house and is not followed by a distribution of money.

The bar-room closes at midnight, provided there are enough people in it. If there is not a quorum the Proprietor waits for a better chance. A careful closing of the Bar will often catch as many as twenty-five people. The Bar is not opened again till seven o'clock in the morning; after that the people may go home. There are also, nowadays, Local Option Hotels. These contain only one entrance, leading directly into the Bar.

An Experiment with Policeman Hogan

MR. SCALPER sits writing in the reporters' room of *The Daily Eclipse.* The paper has gone to press and he is alone; a wayward talented gentleman, this Mr. Scalper, and employed by *The Eclipse* as a delineator of character from handwriting. Any subscriber who forwards a specimen of his handwriting is treated to a prompt analysis of his character from Mr. Scalper's facile pen. The literary genius has a little pile of correspondence beside him, and is engaged in the practice of his art. Outside the night is dark and rainy. The clock on the City Hall marks the hour of two. In front of the newspaper office Policeman Hogan walks drearily up and down his beat. The damp misery of Hogan is intense. A belated gentleman in clerical attire, returning home from a bed of sickness, gives him a side-look of timid pity and shivers past. Hogan follows the retreating figure with his eye; then draws forth a notebook and sits down on the steps of *The Eclipse* building to write in the light of the gas lamp. Gentlemen of nocturnal habits have often wondered what it is that Policeman Hogan and his brethren write in their little books. Here are the words that are fashioned by the big fist of the policeman.

"Two o'clock. All is well. There is a light in Mr. Scalper's room above. The night is very wet and I am unhappy and cannot sleep—my fourth night of insomnia. Suspicious-looking individual just passed.

Alas, how melancholy is my life! Will the dawn never break! Oh, moist, moist stone."

Mr. Scalper up above is writing too, writing with the careless fluency of a man who draws his pay by the column. He is delineating with skill and rapidity. The reporters' room is gloomy and desolate. Mr. Scalper is a man of sensitive temperament and the dreariness of his surroundings depresses him. He opens the letter of a correspondent, examines the handwriting narrowly, casts his eye around the room for inspiration, and proceeds to delineate:

"G.H. You have an unhappy, despondent nature: your circumstances oppress you, and your life is filled with an infinite sadness. You feel that you are without hope——"

Mr. Scalper pauses, takes another look around the room, and finally lets his eye rest for some time upon a tall black bottle that stands on the shelf of an open cupboard. Then he goes on:

"—and you have lost all belief in Christianity and a future world and human virtue. You are very weak against temptation, but there is an ugly vein of determination in your character, when you make up your mind that you are going to have a thing——"

Here Mr. Scalper stops abruptly, pushes back his chair, and dashes across the room to the cupboard. He takes the black bottle from the shelf, applies it to his lips, and remains for some time motionless. He then returns to finish the delineation of G.H. with the hurried words:

"On the whole I recommend you to persevere; you are doing very well." Mr. Scalper's next proceeding is peculiar. He takes from the cupboard a roll of twine, about fifty feet in length, and attaches one end of it to the neck of the bottle. Going then to one of the windows, he opens it, leans out, and whistles softly. The alert ear of Policeman Hogan on the pavement below catches the sound, and he returns it. The bottle is lowered to the end of the string, the guardian of the peace applies it to his gullet, and for some time the policeman and the man of letters remain attached by a cord of sympathy. Gentlemen who lead the variegated life of Mr. Scalper find it well to propitiate the arm of the law, and attachments of this sort are not uncommon. Mr. Scalper hauls up the bottle, closes the window, and returns to his task; the policeman resumes his walk with a glow of internal satisfaction. A glance at the City Hall clock causes him to enter another note in his book.

"Half-past two. All is better. The weather is milder with a feeling of young summer in the air. Two lights in Mr. Scalper's room. Nothing has occurred which need be brought to the notice of the roundsman."

Things are going better upstairs too. The delineator opens a second envelope, surveys the writing of the correspondent with a critical yet charitable eye, and writes with more complacency.

"William H. Your writing shows a disposition which, though naturally melancholy, is capable of a temporary cheerfulness. You have known misfortune but have made up your mind to look on the bright side of things. If you will allow me to say so, you indulge in liquor but are quite moderate in your use of it. Be assured that no harm ever comes of this moderate use. It enlivens the intellect, brightens the faculties, and stimulates the dormant fancy into a pleasurable activity. It is only when carried to excess——"

At this point the feelings of Mr. Scalper, who had been writing very rapidly, evidently become too much for him. He starts up from his chair, rushes two or three times around the room, and finally returns to finish the delineation thus: "it is only when carried to excess that this moderation becomes pernicious."

Mr. Scalper succumbs to the train of thought suggested and gives an illustration of how moderation to excess may be avoided, after which he lowers the bottle to Policeman Hogan with a cheery exchange of greetings.

The half-hours pass on. The delineator is writing busily and feels that he is writing well. The characters of his correspondents lie bare to his keen eye and flow from his facile pen. From time to time he pauses and appeals to the source of his inspiration; his humanity prompts him to extend the inspiration to Policeman Hogan. The minion of the law walks his beat with a feeling of more than tranquillity. A solitary Chinaman, returning home late from his midnight laundry, scuttles past. The literary instinct has risen strong in Hogan from his connection with the man of genius above him, and the passage of the lone Chinee gives him occasion to write in his book.

"Four-thirty. Everything is simply great. There are four lights in Mr. Scalper's room. Mild, balmy weather with prospects of an earthquake, which may be held in check by walking with extreme caution. Two Chinamen have just passed—mandarins, I presume. Their walk was unsteady, but their faces so benign as to disarm suspicion."

Up in the office Mr. Scalper has reached the letter of a correspondent which appears to give him particular pleasure, for he delineates the character with a beaming smile of satisfaction. To the unpractised eye the writing resembles the prim, angular hand of an elderly spinster. Mr. Scalper, however, seems to think otherwise, for he writes:

"Aunt Dorothea. You have a merry, rollicking nature. At times you are seized with a wild tumultuous hilarity to which you give ample vent in shouting and song. You are much addicted to profanity, and you rightly feel that this is part of your nature and you must not check it. The world is a very bright place to you, Aunt Dorothea. Write to me again soon. Our minds seem cast in the same mould."

Mr. Scalper seems to think that he has not done full justice to the subject he is treating, for he proceeds to write a long private letter to Aunt Dorothea in addition to the printed delineation. As he finishes the City Hall clock points to five, and Policeman Hogan makes the last entry in his chronicle. Hogan has seated himself upon the steps of *The Eclipse* building for greater comfort and writes with a slow, leisurely fist:

"The other hand of the clock points north and the second longest points south-east by south. I infer that it is five o'clock. The electric lights in Mr. Scalper's room defy the eye. The roundsman has passed and examined my notes of the night's occurrences. They are entirely satisfactory, and he is pleased with their literary form. The earthquake which I apprehended was reduced to a few minor oscillations which cannot reach me where I sit——"

The lowering of the bottle interrupts Policeman Hogan. The long letter to Aunt Dorothea has cooled the ardour of Mr. Scalper. The generous blush has passed from his mind and he has been trying in vain to restore it. To afford Hogan a similar opportunity, he decides not to haul the bottle up immediately, but to leave it in his custody while he delineates a character. The writing of this correspondent would seem to the inexperienced eye to be that of a timid little maiden in her teens. Mr. Scalper is not to be deceived by appearances. He shakes his head mournfully at the letter and writes:

"Little Emily. You have known great happiness, but it has passed. Despondency has driven you to seek forgetfulness in drink. Your writing shows the worst phase of the liquor habit. I apprehend that you will shortly have delirium tremens. Poor little Emily! Do not try to break off; it is too late."

Mr. Scalper is visibly affected by his correspondent's unhappy condition. His eye becomes moist, and he decides to haul up the bottle while there is still time to save Policeman Hogan from acquiring a taste for liquor. He is surprised and alarmed to find the attempt to haul it up ineffectual. The minion of the law has fallen into a leaden slumber, and the bottle remains tight in his grasp. The baffled delineator lets fall the string and returns to finish his task. Only a few lines are now required to fill the column, but Mr. Scalper finds on examining the correspondence that he has exhausted the subjects. This, however, is quite a common occurrence and occasions no dilemma in the mind of the talented gentleman. It is his custom in such cases to fill up the space with an imaginary character or two, the analysis of which is a task most congenial to his mind. He bows his head in thought for a few moments, and then writes as follows:

"Policeman H. Your hand shows great firmness; when once set upon a thing you are not easily moved. But you have a mean, grasping disposition and a tendency to want more than your share. You have formed an attachment which you hope will be continued throughout life, but your selfishness threatens to sever the bond."

Having written which, Mr. Scalper arranges his manuscript for the printer next day, dons his hat and coat, and wends his way home in the morning twilight, feeling that his pay is earned.

The Passing of the Poet

STUDIES in what may be termed collective psychology are essentially in keeping with the spirit of the present century. The examination of the mental tendencies, the intellectual habits which we display not as individuals, but as members of a race, community, or crowd, is offering a fruitful field of speculation as yet but little exploited. One may, therefore, not without profit, pass in review the relation of the poetic instinct to the intellectual development of the present era.

Not the least noticeable feature in the psychological evolution of our time is the rapid disappearance of poetry. The art of writing poetry, or perhaps more fairly, the habit of writing poetry, is passing from us. The poet is destined to become extinct.

To a reader of trained intellect the initial difficulty at once suggests itself as to what is meant by poetry. But it is needless to quibble at a definition of the term. It may be designated, simply and fairly, as the art of expressing a simple truth in a concealed form of words, any number of which, at intervals greater or less, may or may not rhyme.

The poet, it must be said, is as old as civilisation. The Greeks had him with them, stamping out his iambics with the sole of his foot. The Romans, too, knew him—endlessly juggling his syllables together, long and short, short and long, to make hexameters. This can now be done by electricity, but the Romans did not know it.

But it is not my present purpose to speak of the poets of an earlier and ruder time. For the subject before us it is enough to set our age in comparison with the era that preceded it. We have but to contrast ourselves with our early Victorian grandfathers to realise the profound revolution that has taken place in public feeling. It is only with an effort that the practical common sense of the twentieth century can realise the excessive sentimentality of the earlier generation.

In those days poetry stood in high and universal esteem. Parents read poetry to their children. Children recited poetry to their parents. And he was a dullard, indeed, who did not at least profess, in his hours of idleness, to pour spontaneous rhythm from his flowing quill.

Should one gather statistics of the enormous production of poetry some sixty or seventy years ago, they would scarcely appear credible. Journals and magazines teemed with it. Editors openly countenanced it. Even the daily press affected it. Love sighed in home-made stanzas. Patriotism rhapsodised on the hustings, or cited rolling hexameters to an enraptured legislature. Even melancholy death courted his everlasting sleep in elegant elegiacs.

In that era, indeed, I know not how, polite society was haunted by the obstinate fiction that it was the duty of a man of parts to express himself from time to time in verse. Any special occasion of expansion or exuberance, of depression, torsion, or introspection, was sufficient to call it forth. So we have poems of dejection, of reflection, of deglutition, of indigestion.

Any particular psychological disturbance was enough to provoke an excess of poetry. The character and manner of the verse might vary with the predisposing cause. A gentleman who had dined too freely might disexpand himself in a short fit of lyric doggerel in which "bowl" and "soul" were freely rhymed. The morning's indigestion inspired a long-drawn elegiac, with "bier" and "tear," "mortal" and "portal" linked in sonorous sadness. The man of politics, from time to time, grateful to an appreciative country, sang back to it, "Ho, Albion, rising from the brine!" in verse whose intention at least was meritorious.

And yet it was but a fiction, a purely fictitious obligation, self-imposed by a sentimental society. In plain truth, poetry came no more easily or naturally to the early Victorian than to you or me. The lover twanged his obdurate harp in vain for hours for the rhymes that would not come, and the man of politics hammered at his heavy hexameter long indeed before his Albion was finally "hoed" into shape; while the beer-besotted convivialist cudgelled his poor wits cold sober in rhyming the light little bottle-ditty that should have sprung like Aphrodite from the froth of the champagne.

I have before me a pathetic witness of this fact. It is the note-book once used for the random jottings of a gentleman of the period. In it I read: "Fair Lydia, if my earthly harp." This is crossed out, and below it appears, "Fair Lydia, COULD my earthly harp." This again is erased, and under it appears, "FAIR LYDIA, should my earthly harp." This again is struck out with a despairing stroke, and amended to read: "Fair Lydia, DID my earthly harp." So that finally, when the lines appeared in the *Gentleman's Magazine* (1845) in their ultimate shape—"Fair Edith, when with fluent pen," etc., etc.—one can realise from what a desperate congelation the fluent pen had been so perseveringly rescued.

There can be little doubt of the deleterious effect occasioned both to public and private morals by this deliberate exaltation of mental susceptibility on the part of the early Victorian. In many cases we can detect the evidences of incipient paresis. The undue access of emotion frequently assumed a pathological character. The sight of a daisy, of a withered leaf or an upturned sod, seemed to disturb the poet's mental equipoise. Spring unnerved him. The lambs distressed him. The flowers made him cry. The daffodils made him laugh. Day dazzled him. Night frightened him.

This exalted mood, combined with the man's culpable ignorance of the plainest principles of physical science, made him see something out of the ordinary in the flight of a waterfowl or the song of a skylark. He complained that he could *hear* it, but not *see* it—a phenomenon too familiar to the scientific observer to occasion any comment.

In such a state of mind the most inconsequential inferences were drawn. One said that the brightness of the dawn—a fact easily explained by the diurnal motion of the globe—showed him that his soul was immortal. He asserted further that he had, at an earlier period of his life, trailed bright clouds behind him. This was absurd.

With the disturbance thus set up in the nervous system were coupled, in many instances, mental aberrations, particularly in regard to pecuniary matters. "Give me not silk, nor rich attire," pleaded one poet of the period to the British public, "nor gold nor jewels rare." Here was an evident hallucination that the writer was to become the recipient of an enormous secret subscription. Indeed, the earnest desire NOT to be given gold was a recurrent characteristic of the poetic temperament. The repugnance to accept even a handful of gold was generally accompanied by a desire for a draught of pure water or a night's rest.

It is pleasing to turn from this excessive sentimentality of thought and speech to the practical and concise diction of our time. We have learned to express ourselves with equal force, but greater simplicity. To illustrate this I have gathered from the poets of the earlier generation and from the prose writers of today parallel passages that may be fairly set in contrast. Here, for example, is a passage from the poet Grey, still familiar to scholars:

"Can storied urn or animated bust
Back to its mansion call the fleeting breath?
Can honour's voice invoke the silent dust
Or flattery soothe the dull cold ear of death?"

Precisely similar in thought, though different in form, is the more modern presentation found in Huxley's *Physiology*:

"Whether after the moment of death the ventricles of the heart can be again set in movement by the artificial stimulus of oxygen, is a question to which we must impose a decided negative."

How much simpler, and yet how far superior to Grey's elaborate phraseology! Huxley has here seized the central point of the poet's thought, and expressed it with the dignity and precision of exact science.

I cannot refrain, even at the risk of needless iteration, from quoting a further example. It is taken from the poet Burns. The original dialect, being written in inverted hiccoughs, is rather difficult to reproduce. It describes the scene attendant upon the return of a cottage labourer to his home on Saturday night:

"The cheerfu' supper done, wi' serious face
They round the ingle form in a circle wide;
The sire turns o'er, wi' patriarchal grace,
The big ha' Bible, ance his father's pride:
His bonnet rev'rently is laid aside,
His lyart haffets wearing thin an' bare:
Those strains that once did sweet in Zion glide,
He wales a portion wi' judeecious care."

Now I find almost the same scene described in more apt phraseology in the police news of the *Dumfries Chronicle* (October 3, 1909), thus: "It appears that the prisoner had returned to his domicile at the usual hour, and, after partaking of a hearty meal, had seated himself on his oaken settle, for the ostensible purpose of reading the Bible. It was while so occupied that his arrest was effected." With the trifling exception that Burns omits all mention of the arrest, for which, however, the whole tenor of the poem gives ample warrant, the two accounts are almost identical.

In all that I have thus said I do not wish to be misunderstood. Believing, as I firmly do, that the poet is destined to become extinct, I am not one of those who would accelerate his extinction. The time has not yet come for remedial legislation, or the application of the criminal law. Even in obstinate cases where pronounced delusions in reference to plants, animals, and natural phenomena are seen to exist, it is better that we should do nothing that might occasion a mistaken remorse. The inevitable natural evolution which is thus shaping the mould of human thought may safely be left to its own course.

Self-Made Men

THEY were both what we commonly call successful business-men—men with well-fed faces, heavy signet rings on fingers like sausages, and broad, comfortable waistcoats, a yard and a half round the equator. They were seated opposite each other at a table of a first-class restaurant, and had fallen into conversation while waiting to give their order to the waiter. Their talk had drifted back to their early days and how each had made his start in life when he first struck New York.

"I tell you what, Jones," one of them was saying, "I shall never forget my first few years in this town. By George, it was pretty uphill work! Do you know, sir, when I first struck this place, I hadn't more than fifteen cents to my name, hadn't a rag except what I stood up in, and all the place I had to sleep in—you won't believe it, but it's a gospel fact just the same—was an empty tar barrel. No, sir," he went on, leaning back and closing up his eyes into an expression of infinite experience, "no, sir, a fellow accustomed to luxury like you has simply no idea what sleeping out in a tar barrel and all that kind of thing is like."

"My dear Robinson," the other man rejoined briskly, "if you imagine I've had no experience of hardship of that sort, you never made a bigger mistake in your life. Why, when I first walked into this town I hadn't a cent, sir, not a cent, and as for lodging, all the place I had for months and months was an old piano box up a lane, behind a factory. Talk about hardship, I guess I had it pretty rough! You take a fellow that's used to a good warm tar barrel and put him into a piano box for a night or two, and you'll see mighty soon——"

"My dear fellow," Robinson broke in with some irritation, "you merely show that you don't know what a tar barrel's like. Why, on winter nights, when you'd be shut in there in your piano box just as snug as you please, I used to lie awake shivering, with the draught fairly running in at the bunghole at the back."

"Draught!" sneered the other man, with a provoking laugh, "draught! Don't talk to me about draughts. This box I speak of had a whole darned plank right off it, right on the north side too. I used to sit there studying in the evenings, and the snow would blow in a foot deep. And yet, sir," he continued more quietly, "though I know you'll not believe it, I don't mind admitting that some of the happiest days of my life were spent in that same old box. Ah, those were good old times! Bright, innocent days, I can tell you. I'd wake up there in the mornings and fairly shout with high spirits. Of course, you may not be able to stand that kind of life——"

"Not stand it!" cried Robinson fiercely; "me not stand it! By gad! I'm made for it. I just wish I had a taste of the old life again for a while. And as for innocence! Well, I'll bet you you weren't one-tenth as innocent as I was; no, nor one-fifth, nor one-third! What a grand old life it was! You'll swear this is a darned lie and refuse to believe it—but I can remember evenings when I'd have two or three fellows in, and we'd sit round and play pedro by a candle half the night."

"Two or three!" laughed Jones; "why, my dear fellow, I've known half a dozen of us to sit down to supper in my piano box, and have a game of pedro afterwards; yes, and charades and forfeits, and every other darned thing. Mighty good suppers they were too! By Jove, Robinson, you fellows round this town who have ruined your digestions with high living, have no notion of the zest with which a man can sit down to a few potato peelings, or a bit of broken pie crust, or——"

"Talk about hard food," interrupted the other, "I guess I know all about that. Many's the time I've breakfasted off a little cold porridge that somebody was going to throw away from a back-door, or that I've gone round to a livery stable and begged a little bran mash that they intended for the pigs. I'll venture to say I've eaten more hog's food——"

"Hog's food!" shouted Robinson, striking his fist savagely on the table, "I tell you hog's food suits me better than——"

He stopped speaking with a sudden grunt of surprise as the waiter appeared with the question:

"What may I bring you for dinner, gentlemen?"

"Dinner!" said Jones, after a moment of silence, "dinner! Oh, anything, nothing—I never care what I eat—give me a little cold porridge, if you've got it, or a chunk of salt pork—anything you like, it's all the same to me."

The waiter turned with an impassive face to Robinson.

"You can bring me some of that cold porridge too," he said, with a defiant look at Jones; "yesterday's, if you have it, and a few potato peelings and a glass of skim milk."

There was a pause. Jones sat back in his chair and looked hard across at Robinson. For some moments the two men gazed into each other's eyes with a stern, defiant intensity. Then Robinson turned slowly round in his seat and beckoned to the waiter, who was moving off with the muttered order on his lips.

"Here, waiter," he said with a savage scowl, "I guess I'll change that order a little. Instead of that cold porridge I'll take—um, yes—a little hot partridge. And you might as well bring me an oyster or two on the half shell, and a mouthful of soup (mock-turtle, consommé, anything), and perhaps you might fetch along a dab of fish, and a little peck of Stilton, and a grape, or a walnut."

The waiter turned to Jones.

"I guess I'll take the same," he said simply, and added, "and you might bring a quart of champagne at the same time."

And nowadays, when Jones and Robinson meet, the memory of the tar barrel and the piano box is buried as far out of sight as a home for the blind under a landslide.

A Model Dialogue

In which is shown how the drawing-room juggler may be permanently cured of his card trick.

The drawing-room juggler, having slyly got hold of the pack of cards at the end of the game of whist, says:

"Ever see any card tricks? Here's rather a good one; pick a card."

"Thank you, I don't want a card."

"No, but just pick one, any one you like, and I'll tell which one you pick."

"You'll tell who?"

"No, no; I mean, I'll know which it is, don't you see? Go on now, pick a card."

"Any one I like?"

"Yes."

"Any colour at all?"

"Yes, yes."

"Any suit?"

"Oh, yes; do go on."

"Well, let me see, I'll—pick—the—ace—of—spades."

"Great Cæsar! I mean you are to pull a card out of the pack."

"Oh, to pull it out of the pack! Now I understand. Hand me the pack. All right—I've got it."

"Have you picked one?"

"Yes, it's the three of hearts. Did you know it?"

"Hang it! Don't tell me like that. You spoil the thing. Here, try again. Pick a card."

"All right, I've got it."

"Put it back in the pack. Thanks. (Shuffle, shuffle, shuffle—flip)—There, is that it?" (triumphantly).

"I don't know. I lost sight of it."

"Lost sight of it! Confound it, you have to look at it and see what it is."

"Oh, you want me to look at the front of it!"

"Why, of course! Now then, pick a card."

"All right. I've picked it. Go ahead." (Shuffle, shuffle, shuffle—flip.)

"Say, confound you, did you put that card back in the pack?"

"Why, no. I kept it."

"Holy Moses! Listen. Pick—a—card—just one—look at it—see what it is—then put it back—do you understand?"

"Oh, perfectly. Only I don't see how you are ever going to do it. You must be awfully clever."

(Shuffle, shuffle, shuffle—flip.)

"There you are; that's your card, now, isn't it?" (This is the supreme moment.)

"NO. THAT IS NOT MY CARD." (This is a flat lie, but Heaven will pardon you for it.)

"Not that card ! ! ! ! Say—just hold on a second. Here, now, watch what you're at this time. I can do this cursed thing, mind you, every time. I've done it on father, on mother, and on every one that's ever come round our place. Pick a card. (Shuffle, shuffle, shuffle—flip, bang.) There, that's your card."

"NO. I AM SORRY. THAT IS NOT MY CARD. But won't you try it

again? Please do. Perhaps you are a little excited—I'm afraid I was rather stupid. Won't you go and sit quietly by yourself on the back verandah for half an hour and then try? You have to go home? Oh. I'm so sorry. It must be such an awfully clever little trick. Good night!"

Back to the Bush

I HAVE a friend called Billy who has the Bush Mania. By trade he is a doctor, but I do not think that he needs to sleep out of doors. In ordinary things his mind appears sound. Over the tops of his gold-rimmed spectacles, as he bends forward to speak to you, there gleams nothing but amiability and kindliness. Like all the rest of us he is, or was until he forgot it all, an extremely well-educated man.

I am aware of no criminal strain in his blood. Yet Billy is in reality hopelessly unbalanced. He has the Mania of the Open Woods.

Worse than that, he is haunted with the desire to drag his friends with him into the depths of the Bush.

Whenever we meet he starts to talk about it.

Not long ago I met him in the club.

"I wish," he said, "You'd let me take you clear away up the Gatineau."

"Yes, I wish I would, I don't think," I murmured to myself, but I humoured him and said:

"How do we go, Billy, in a motor-car or by train?"

"No, we paddle."

"And is it up-stream all the way?"

"Oh, yes," Billy said enthusiastically.

"And how many days do we paddle all day to get up?"

"Six."

"Couldn't we do it in less?"

"Yes," Billy answered, feeling that I was entering into the spirit of the thing, "if we start each morning just before daylight and paddle hard till moonlight, we could do it in five days and a half."

"Glorious! and are there portages?"

"Lots of them."

"And at each of these do I carry two hundred pounds of stuff up a hill on my back?"

"Yes."

"And will there be a guide, a genuine, dirty-looking Indian guide?"

"Yes."

"And can I sleep next to him?"

"Oh, yes, if you want to."

"And when we get to the top, what is there?"

"Well, we go over the height of land."

"Oh, we do, do we? And is the height of land all rock and about three hundred yards up-hill? And do I carry a barrel of flour up it? And does it roll down and crush me on the other side? Look here, Billy, this trip is a great thing, but it is too luxurious for me. If you will have me paddled up the river in a large iron canoe with an awning, carried over the portages in a sedan-chair, taken across the height of land in a palanquin or a howdah, and lowered down the other side in a derrick, I'll go. Short of that, the thing would be too fattening."

Billy was discouraged and left me. But he has since returned repeatedly to the attack.

He offers to take me to the head-waters of the Batiscan. I am content at the foot.

He wants us to go to the sources of the Attahwapiscat. I don't.

He says I ought to see the grand chutes of the Kewakasis. Why should I?

I have made Billy a counter-proposition that he strike through the Adirondacks (in the train) to New York, from there portage to Atlantic

City, then to Washington, carrying our own grub (in the dining-car), camp there a few days (at the Willard), and then back, I to return by train and Billy on foot with the outfit.

The thing is still unsettled.

Billy, of course, is only one of thousands that have got this mania. And the autumn is the time when it rages at its worst.

Every day there move northward trains, packed full of lawyers, bankers, and brokers, headed for the bush. They are dressed up to look like pirates. They wear slouch hats, flannel shirts, and leather breeches with belts. They could afford much better clothes than these, but they won't use them. I don't know where they get these clothes. I think the railroad lends them out. They have guns between their knees and big knives at their hips. They smoke the worst tobacco they can find, and they carry ten gallons of alcohol per man in the baggage car.

In the intervals of telling lies to one another they read the railroad pamphlets about hunting. This kind of literature is deliberately and fiendishly contrived to infuriate their mania. I know all about these pamphlets because I write them. I once, for instance, wrote up, from imagination, a little place called Dog Lake at the end of a branch line. The place had failed as a settlement, and the railroad had decided to turn it into a hunting resort. I did the turning. I think I did it rather well, rechristening the lake and stocking the place with suitable varieties of game. The pamphlet ran like this.

"The limpid waters of Lake Owatawetness (the name, according to the old Indian legends of the place, signifies, The Mirror of the Almighty) abound with every known variety of fish. Near to its surface, so close that the angler may reach out his hand and stroke them, schools of pike, pickerel, mackerel, doggerel, and chickerel jostle one another in the water. They rise instantaneously to the bait and swim gratefully ashore holding it in their mouths. In the middle depth of the waters of the lake, the sardine, the lobster, the kippered herring, the anchovy and other tinned varieties of fish disport themselves with evident gratification, while even lower in the pellucid depths the dog-fish, the hog-fish, the log-fish, and the sword-fish whirl about in never-ending circles.

"Nor is Lake Owatawetness merely an Angler's Paradise. Vast forests of primeval pine slope to the very shores of the lake, to which descend great droves of bears—brown, green, and bear-coloured—while as the shades of evening fall, the air is loud with the lowing of moose, cariboo, antelope, cantelope, musk-oxes, musk-rats, and other graminivorous mammalia of the forest. These enormous quadrumana generally move off about 10.30 p.m., from which hour until 11.45 p.m. the whole shore is reserved for bison and buffalo.

"After midnight hunters who so desire it can be chased through the woods, for any distance and at any speed they select, by jaguars, panthers, cougars, tigers, and jackals whose ferocity is reputed to be such that they will tear the breeches off a man with their teeth in their eagerness to sink their fangs in his palpitating flesh. Hunters, attention! Do not miss such attractions as these!"

I have seen men—quiet, reputable, well-shaved men—reading that pamphlet of mine in the rotundas of hotels, with their eyes blazing with excitement. I think it is the jaguar attraction that hits them the hardest, because I notice them rub themselves sympathetically with their hands while they read.

Of course, you can imagine the effect of this sort of literature on the brains of men fresh from their offices, and dressed out as pirates.

They just go crazy and stay crazy.

Just watch them when they get into the bush.

Notice that well-to-do stockbroker crawling about on his stomach in the underbrush, with his spectacles shining like gig lamps. What is he doing? He is after a cariboo that isn't there. He is "stalking" it. With his stomach. Of course, away down in his heart he knows that the cariboo isn't there and never was; but that man read my pamphlet and went crazy. He can't help it: he's *got* to stalk something. Mark him as he crawls along; see him crawl through a thimbleberry bush (very quietly so that the cariboo won't hear the noise of the prickles going into him), then through a bee's nest, gently and slowly, so that the cariboo will not take fright when the bees are stinging him. Sheer woodcraft! Yes, mark him. Mark him in any way you like. Go up behind him and paint a blue cross on the seat of his pants as he crawls. He'll never notice. He thinks he's a hunting-dog. Yet this is the man who laughs at his little son of ten for crawling round under the dining-room table with a mat over his shoulders, and pretending to be a bear.

Now see these other men in camp.

Someone has told them—I think I first started the idea in my pamphlet—that the thing is to sleep on a pile of hemlock branches. I think I told them to listen to the wind sowing (you know the word I mean), sowing and crooning in the giant pines. So there they are upside down, doubled up on a couch of green spikes that would have killed St. Sebastian. They stare up at the sky with blood-shot, restless eyes, waiting for the crooning to begin. And there isn't a sow in sight.

Here is another man, ragged and with a six days' growth of beard, frying a piece of bacon on a stick over a little fire. Now what does he think he is? The *chef* of the Waldorf Astoria? Yes, he does, and what's more he thinks that that miserable bit of bacon, cut with a tobacco knife from a chunk of meat that lay six days in the rain, is fit to eat. What's more, he'll eat it. So will the rest. They're all crazy together.

There's another man, the Lord help him, who thinks he has the "knack" of being a carpenter. He is hammering up shelves to a tree. Till the shelves fall down he thinks he is a wizard. Yet this is the same man who swore at his wife for asking him to put up a shelf in the back kitchen. "How the blazes," he asked, "could he nail the damn thing up? Did she think he was a plumber?"

After all, never mind.

Provided they are happy up there, let them stay.

Personally, I wouldn't mind if they didn't come back and lie about it. They get back to the city dead fagged for want of sleep, sogged with alcohol, bitten brown by the bush-flies, trampled on by the moose, and chased through the brush by bears and skunks—and they have the nerve to say that they like it.

Sometimes I think they do.

Men are only animals anyway. They like to get out into the woods and growl round at night and feel something bite them.

Only why haven't they the imagination to be able to do the same thing with less fuss? Why not take their coats and collars off in the office and crawl round on the floor and growl at one another. It would be just as good.

Reflections on Riding

THE writing of this paper has been inspired by a debate recently held at the literary society of my native town on the question, "Resolved: that the bicycle is a nobler animal than the horse." In order to speak for the negative with proper authority, I have spent some weeks in completely addicting myself to the use of the horse. I find that the difference between the horse and the bicycle is greater than I had supposed.

The horse is entirely covered with hair; the bicycle is not entirely covered with hair, except the '89 model they are using in Idaho.

In riding a horse the performer finds that the pedals in which he puts his feet will not allow of a good circular stroke. He will observe, however, that there is a saddle in which—especially while the horse is trotting—he is expected to seat himself from time to time. But it is simpler to ride standing up, with the feet in the pedals.

There are no handles to a horse, but the 1910 model has a string to each side of its face for turning its head when there is anything you want it to see.

Coasting on a good horse is superb, but should be under control. I have known a horse to suddenly begin to coast with me about two miles from home, coast down the main street of my native town at a terrific rate, and finally coast through a platoon of the Salvation Army into its livery stable.

I cannot honestly deny that it takes a good deal of physical courage to ride a horse. This, however, I have. I get it at about forty cents a flask, and take it as required.

I find that in riding a horse up the long street of a country town, it is not well to proceed at a trot. It excites unkindly comment. It is better to let the horse walk the whole distance. This may be made to seem natural by turning half round in the saddle with the hand on the horse's back, and gazing intently about two miles up the road. It then appears that you are the first in of about fourteen men.

Since learning to ride, I have taken to noticing the things that people do on horse-back in books. Some of these I can manage, but most of them are entirely beyond me. Here, for instance, is a form of equestrian performance that every reader will recognise and for which I have only a despairing admiration:

"With a hasty gesture of farewell, the rider set spurs to his horse and disappeared in a cloud of dust."

With a little practice in the matter of adjustment, I think I could set spurs to any size of horse, but I could never disappear in a cloud of dust—at least, not with any guarantee of remaining disappeared when the dust cleared away.

Here, however, is one that I certainly can do:

"The bridle-rein dropped from Lord Everard's listless hand, and, with his head bowed upon his bosom, he suffered his horse to move at a foot's pace up the sombre avenue. Deep in thought, he heeded not the movement of the steed which bore him."

That is, he looked as if he didn't; but in my case, Lord Everard has his eye on the steed pretty closely, just the same.

This next I am doubtful about:

"To horse! to horse!" cried the knight, and leaped into the saddle.

I think I could manage it if it read:

"To horse!" cried the knight, and, snatching a stepladder from the hands of his trusty attendant, he rushed into the saddle.

As a concluding remark, I may mention that my experience of riding has thrown a very interesting sidelight upon a rather puzzling point in history. It is recorded of the famous Henry the Second that he was "almost constantly in the saddle, and of so restless a disposition that he never sat down, even at meals." I had hitherto been unable to understand Henry's idea about his meals, but I think I can appreciate it now.

Saloonio

A Study in Shakespearean Criticism

THEY say that young men fresh from college are pretty positive about what they know. But from my own experience of life, I should say that if you take a comfortable, elderly man who hasn't been near a college for about twenty years, who has been pretty liberally fed and dined ever since, who measures about fifty inches around the circumference, and has a complexion like a cranberry by candlelight, you will find that there is a degree of absolute certainty about what he thinks he knows that will put any young man to shame. I am specially convinced of this from the case of my friend Colonel Hogshead, a portly, choleric gentleman who made a fortune in the cattle-trade out in Wyoming, and who, in his later days, has acquired a chronic idea that the plays of Shakespeare are the one subject upon which he is most qualified to speak personally.

He came across me the other evening as I was sitting by the fire in the club sitting-room looking over the leaves of *The Merchant of Venice*, and began to hold forth to me about the book.

"*Merchant of Venice*, eh? There's a play for you, sir! There's genius! Wonderful, sir, wonderful! You take the characters in that play and where will you find anything like them? You take Antonio, take Sherlock, take Saloonio——"

"Saloonio, Colonel?" I interposed mildly, "aren't you making a mistake? There's a Bassanio and a Salanio in the play, but I don't think there's any Saloonio, is there?"

For a moment Colonel Hogshead's eye became misty with doubt, but he was not the man to admit himself in error:

"Tut, tut! young man," he said with a frown, "don't skim through your books in that way. No Saloonio? Why, of course there's a Saloonio!"

"But I tell you, Colonel," I rejoined, "I've just been reading the play and studying it, and I know there's no such character——"

"Nonsense, sir, nonsense!" said the Colonel, "why he comes in all through; don't tell me, young man, I've read that play myself. Yes, and seen it played, too, out in Wyoming, before you were born, by fellers, sir, that could act. No Saloonio, indeed! why, who is it that is Antonio's friend all through and won't leave him when Bassoonio turns against him? Who rescues Clarissa from Sherlock, and steals the casket of flesh from the Prince of Aragon? Who shouts at the Prince of Morocco, 'Out, out, you damned candlestick'? Who loads up the jury in the trial scene and fixes the doge? No Saloonio! By gad! in my opinion, he's the most important character in the play——"

"Colonel Hogshead," I said very firmly, "there isn't any Saloonio and you know it."

But the old man had got fairly started on whatever dim recollection had given birth to Saloonio; the character seemed to grow more and more luminous in the Colonel's mind, and he continued with increasing animation:

"I'll just tell you what Saloonio is: he's a type. Shakespeare means him to embody the type of the perfect Italian gentleman. He's an idea, that's what he is, he's a symbol, he's a unit——"

Meanwhile I had been searching among the leaves of the play. "Look here," I said, "here's the list of the Dramatis Personæ. There's no Saloonio there."

But this didn't dismay the Colonel one atom. "Why, of course there isn't," he said. "You don't suppose you'd find Saloonio there! That's the whole art of it! That's Shakespeare! That's the whole gist of it! He's kept clean out of the Personæ—gives him scope, gives him a free hand, makes him more of a type than ever. Oh, it's a subtle thing, sir, the dramatic art!" continued the Colonel, subsiding into quiet reflection; "it takes a feller quite a time to get right into Shakespeare's mind and see what he's at all the time."

I began to see that there was no use in arguing any further with the old man. I left him with the idea that the lapse of a little time would soften his views on Saloonio. But I had not reckoned on the way in which old men hang on to a thing. Colonel Hogshead quite took up Saloonio. From that time on Saloonio became the theme of his constant conversation. He was never tired of discussing the character of Saloonio, the wonderful art of the dramatist in creating him, Saloonio's relation to modern life, Saloonio's attitude toward women, the ethical significance of Saloonio, Saloonio as compared with Hamlet, Hamlet as compared with Saloonio—and so on, endlessly. And the more he looked into Saloonio, the more he saw in him.

Saloonio seemed inexhaustible. There were new sides to him—new phases at every turn. The Colonel even read over the play, and finding no mention of Saloonio's name in it, he swore that the books were not the same books they had had out in Wyoming; that the whole part had been cut clean out to suit the book to the infernal public schools, Saloonio's language being—at any rate, as the Colonel quoted it—undoubtedly a trifle free. Then the Colonel took to annotating his book at the side with such remarks as, "Enter Saloonio," or "A tucket sounds; enter Saloonio, on the arm of the Prince of Morocco." When there was no reasonable excuse for bringing Saloonio on the stage the Colonel swore that he was concealed behind the arras, or feasting within with the doge.

But he got satisfaction at last. He had found that there was nobody in our part of the country who knew how to put a play of Shakespeare on the stage, and took a trip to New York to see Sir Henry Irving and Miss Terry do the play. The Colonel sat and listened all through with his face just beaming with satisfaction, and when the curtain fell at the close of Irving's grand presentation of the play, he stood up in his seat and cheered and yelled to his friends: "That's it! That's him! Didn't you see that man that came on the stage all the time and sort of put the whole play through, though you couldn't understand a word he said? Well, that's him! That's Saloonio!"

Half-Hours with the Poets

I. Mr. Wordsworth and the Little Cottage Girl

"I met a little cottage girl.
  She was eight years old she said
Her hair was thick with many a curl
  That clustered round her head."

THIS is what really happened.

Over the dreary downs of his native Cumberland the aged laureate was wandering with bowed head and countenance of sorrow.

Times were bad with the old man.

In the south pocket of his trousers, as he set his face to the north, jingled but a few odd coins and a cheque for St. Leon water. Apparently his cup of bitterness was full.

In the distance a child moved—a child in form, yet the deep lines upon her face bespoke a countenance prematurely old.

The poet espied, pursued and overtook the infant. He observed that apparently she drew her breath lightly and felt her life in every limb, and that presumably her acquaintance with death was of the most superficial character.

"I must sit awhile and ponder on that child," murmured the poet. So he knocked her down with his walking stick and seating himself upon her, he pondered.

Long he sat thus in thought. "His heart is heavy," sighed the child.

At length he drew forth a note-book and pencil and prepared to write upon his knee.

"Now then, my dear young friend," he said, addressing the elfin creature, "I want those lines upon your face. Are you seven?"

"Yes, we are seven," said the girl sadly, and added, "I know what you want. You are going to question me about my afflicted family. You are Mr. Wordsworth, and you are collecting mortuary statistics for the Cottagers' Edition of the Penny Encyclopædia."

"You are eight years old?" asked the bard.

"I suppose so," answered she. "I have been eight years old for years and years."

"And you know nothing of death, of course?" said the poet cheerfully.

"How can I?" answered the child.

"Now then," resumed the venerable William, "let us get to business. Name your brothers and sisters."

"Let me see," began the child wearily; "there was Rube and Ike, two I can't think of, and John and Jane."

"You must not count John and Jane," interrupted the bard reprovingly; "they're dead, you know, so that doesn't make seven."

"I wasn't counting them, but perhaps I added up wrongly," said the child; "and will you please move your overshoe off my neck?"

"Pardon," said the old man. "A nervous trick, I have been absorbed; indeed, the exigency of the metre almost demands my doubling up my feet. To continue, however; which died first?"

"The first to go was little Jane," said the child.

"She lay moaning in bed, I presume?"

"In bed she moaning lay."

"What killed her?"

"Insomnia," answered the girl. "The gaiety of our cottage life, previous to the departure of our elder brothers for Conway, and the constant field-sports in which she indulged with John, proved too much for a frame never too robust."

"You express yourself well," said the poet. "Now, in regard to your unfortunate brother, what was the effect upon him in the following winter of the ground being white with snow and your being able to run and slide?"

"My brother John was forced to go," answered she. "We have been at a loss to understand the cause of his death. We fear that the dazzling glare of the newly fallen snow, acting upon a restless brain, may have led him to a fatal attempt to emulate my own feats upon the ice. And, oh, sir," the child went on, "speak gently of poor Jane. You may rub it into John all you like; we always let him slide."

"Very well," said the bard, "and allow me, in conclusion, one rather delicate question: Do you ever take your little porringer?"

"Oh, yes," answered the child frankly—

"'Quite often after sunset,
When all is light and fair,
I take my little porringer'—

I can't quite remember what I do after that, but I know that I like it."

"That is immaterial," said Wordsworth. "I can say that you take your little porringer neat, or with bitters, or in water after every meal. As long as I can state that you take a little porringer regularly, but never to excess, the public is satisfied. And now," rising from his seat, "I will not detain you any longer. Here is sixpence—or stay," he added hastily, "here is a cheque for St. Leon water. Your information has been most valuable, and I shall work it, for all I am Wordsworth." With these words the aged poet bowed deferentially to the child and sauntered off in the direction of the Duke of Cumberland's Arms, with his eyes on the ground, as if looking for the meanest flower that blows itself.

II. How Tennyson Killed the May Queen

"If you're waking call me early, call me early, mother dear."

Part I

As soon as the child's malady had declared itself the afflicted parents of the May Queen telegraphed to Tennyson, "Our child gone crazy on subject of early rising, could you come and write some poetry about her?"

Alfred, always prompt to fill orders in writing from the country, came down on the evening train. The old cottager greeted the poet warmly, and began at once to speak of the state of his unfortunate daughter.

"She was took queer in May," he said, "along of a sort of bee that the young folks had; she ain't been just right since, happen you might do summat."

With these words he opened the door of an inner room.

The girl lay in feverish slumber. Beside her bed was an alarm-clock set for half-past three. Connected with the clock was an ingenious arrangement of a falling brick with a string attached to the child's toe.

At the entrance of the visitor she started up in bed. "Whoop," she yelled, "I am to be Queen of the May, mother, ye-e!"

Then perceiving Tennyson in the doorway, "If that's a caller," she said, "tell him to call me early."

The shock caused the brick to fall. In the subsequent confusion Alfred modestly withdrew to the sitting-room.

"At this rate," he chuckled, "I shall not have long to wait. A few weeks of that strain will finish her."

Part II

Six months had passed.

It was now mid-winter.

And still the girl lived. Her vitality appeared inexhaustible.

She got up earlier and earlier. She now rose yesterday afternoon.

At intervals she seemed almost sane, and spoke in a most pathetic manner of her grave and the probability of the sun shining on it early in the morning, and her mother walking on it later in the day. At other times her malady would seize her, and she would snatch the brick off the string and throw it fiercely at Tennyson. Once, in an uncontrollable fit of madness, she gave her sister Effie a half-share in her garden tools and an interest in a box of mignonette.

The poet stayed doggedly on. In the chill of the morning twilight he broke the ice in his water-basin and cursed the girl. But he felt that he had broken the ice and he stayed.

On the whole, life at the cottage, though rugged, was not cheerless. In the long winter evenings they would gather around a smoking fire of peat, while Tennyson read aloud the *Idylls of the King* to the rude old cottager. Not to show his rudeness, the old man kept awake by sitting on a tin-tack. This also kept his mind on the right tack. The two found that they had much in common, especially the old cottager. They called each other "Alfred" and "Hezekiah" now.

Part III

Time moved on and spring came.

Still the girl baffled the poet.

"I thought to pass away before," she would say with a mocking grin, "but yet alive I am, Alfred, alive I am."

Tennyson was fast losing hope.

Worn out with early rising, they engaged a retired Pullman-car porter to take up his quarters, and being a negro his presence added a touch of colour to their life.

The poet also engaged a neighbouring divine at fifty cents an evening to read to the child the best hundred books, with explanations. The May Queen tolerated him, and used to like to play with his silver hair, but protested that he was prosy.

At the end of his resources the poet resolved upon desperate measures.

He chose an evening when the cottager and his wife were out at a dinner-party.

At nightfall Tennyson and his accomplices entered the girl's room.

She defended herself savagely with her brick, but was overpowered.

The negro seated himself upon her chest, while the clergyman hastily read a few verses about the comfort of early rising at the last day.

As he concluded, the poet drove his pen into her eye.

"Last call!" cried the negro porter triumphantly.

III. Old Mr. Longfellow on Board the *Hesperus*

"It was the schooner *Hesperus* that sailed the wintry sea,
And the skipper had taken his little daughter to bear him company."

There were but three people in the cabin party of the *Hesperus*: old Mr. Longfellow, the skipper, and the skipper's daughter.

The skipper was much attached to the child, owing to the singular whiteness of her skin and the exceptionally limpid blue of her eyes; she had hitherto remained on shore to fill lucrative engagements as albino lady in a circus.

This time, however, her father had taken her with him for company. The girl was an endless source of amusement to the skipper and the crew. She constantly got up games of puss-in-the-corner, forfeits, and Dumb Crambo with her father and Mr. Longfellow, and made Scripture puzzles and geographical acrostics for the men.

Old Mr. Longfellow was taking the voyage to restore his shattered nerves. From the first the captain disliked Henry. He was utterly unused to the sea and was nervous and fidgety in the extreme. He complained that at sea his genius had not a sufficient degree of latitude. Which was unparalleled presumption.

On the evening of the storm there had been a little jar between Longfellow and the captain at dinner. The captain had emptied it several times, and was consequently in a reckless, quarrelsome humour.

"I confess I feel somewhat apprehensive," said old Henry nervously, "of the state of the weather. I have had some conversation about it with an old gentleman on deck who professed to have sailed the Spanish main. He says you ought to put into yonder port."

"I have," hiccoughed the skipper, eyeing the bottle, and added with a brutal laugh that he "could weather the roughest gale that ever wind did blow." A whole Gaelic society, he said, wouldn't fizz on him.

Draining a final glass of grog, he rose from his chair, said grace, and staggered on deck.

All the time the wind blew colder and louder.

The billows frothed like yeast. It was a yeast wind.

The evening wore on.

Old Henry shuffled about the cabin in nervous misery.

The skipper's daughter sat quietly at the table selecting verses from a Biblical clock to amuse the ship's bosun, who was suffering from toothache.

At about ten Longfellow went to his bunk, requesting the girl to remain up in his cabin.

For half an hour all was quiet, save the roaring of the winter wind.

Then the girl heard the old gentleman start up in bed.

"What's that bell, what's that bell?" he gasped.

A minute later he emerged from his cabin wearing a cork jacket and trousers over his pyjamas.

"Sissy," he said, "go up and ask your pop who rang that bell."

The obedient child returned.

"Please, Mr. Longfellow," she said, "pa says there weren't no bell."

The old man sank into a chair and remained with his head buried in his hands.

"Say," he exclaimed presently, "someone's firing guns and there's a glimmering light somewhere. You'd better go upstairs again."

Again the child returned.

"The crew are guessing at an acrostic, and occasionally they get a glimmering of it."

Meantime the fury of the storm increased.

The skipper had the hatches battered down.

Presently Longfellow put his head out of a porthole and called out, "Look here, you may not care, but the cruel rocks are goring the sides of this boat like the horns of an angry bull."

The brutal skipper heaved the log at him. A knot in it struck a plank and it glanced off.

Too frightened to remain below, the poet raised one of the hatches by picking out the cotton batting and made his way on deck. He crawled to the wheelhouse.

The skipper stood lashed to the helm all stiff and stark. He bowed stiffly to the poet. The lantern gleamed through the gleaming snow on his fixed and glassy eyes. The man was hopelessly intoxicated.

All the crew had disappeared. When the missile thrown by the captain had glanced off into the sea, they glanced after it and were lost.

At this moment the final crash came.

Something hit something. There was an awful click followed by a peculiar grating sound, and in less time than it takes to write it (unfortunately), the whole wreck was over.

As the vessel sank, Longfellow's senses left him. When he reopened his eyes he was in his own bed at home, and the editor of his local paper was bending over him.

"You have made a first-rate poem of it, Mr. Longfellow," he was saying, unbending somewhat as he spoke, "and I am very happy to give you our cheque for a dollar and a quarter for it."

"Your kindness checks my utterance," murmured Henry feebly, very feebly.

A, B, and C

The Human Element in Mathematics

THE student of arithmetic who has mastered the four rules of his art, and successfully striven with money sums and fractions, finds himself confronted by an unbroken expanse of questions known as problems. These are short stories of adventure and industry with the end omitted, and though betraying a strong family resemblance, are not without a certain element of romance.

The characters in the plot of a problem are three people called A, B, and C. The form of the question is generally of this sort:

"A, B, and C do a certain piece of work. A can do as much work in one hour as B in two, or C in four. Find how long they work at it."

Or thus:

"A, B, and C are employed to dig a ditch. A can dig as much in one hour as B can dig in two, and B can dig twice as fast as C. Find how long, etc., etc."

Or after this wise:

"A lays a wager that he can walk faster than B or C. A can walk half as fast again as B, and C is only an indifferent walker. Find how far, and so forth."

The occupations of A, B, and C are many and varied. In the older arithmetics they contented themselves with doing "a certain piece of work." This statement of the case, however, was found too sly and mysterious, or possibly lacking in romantic charm. It became the fashion to define the job more clearly and to set them at walking-matches, ditch-digging, regattas, and piling cord wood. At times they became commercial and entered into partnership, having with their old mystery a "certain" capital. Above all they revel in motion. When they tire of walking-matches—A rides on horseback, or borrows a bicycle and competes with his weaker-minded associates on foot. Now they race on locomotives; now they row; or again they become historical and engage stagecoaches; or at times they are aquatic and swim. If their occupation is actual work they prefer to pump water into cisterns, two of which leak through holes in the bottom and one of which is water-tight. A, of course, has the good one; he also takes the bicycle, and the best locomotive, and the right of swimming with the current. Whatever they do they put money on it, being all three sports. A always wins.

In the early chapters of the arithmetic, their identity is concealed under the names John, William, and Henry, and they wrangle over the division of marbles. In algebra they are often called X, Y, and Z. But these are only their Christian names, and they are really the same people.

Now to one who has followed the history of these men through countless pages of problems, watched them in their leisure hours dallying with cord wood, and seen their panting sides heave in the full frenzy of filling a cistern with a leak in it, they become something more than mere symbols. They appear as creatures of flesh and blood, living men with their own passions, ambitions, and aspirations like the rest of us. Let us view them in turn. A is a full-blooded blustering fellow, of energetic temperament, hot-headed and strong-willed. It is he who proposes everything, challenges B to work, makes the bets, and bends the others to his will. He is a man of great physical strength and phenomenal endurance. He has been known to walk forty-eight hours at a stretch, and to pump ninety-six. His life is arduous and full of peril. A mistake in the working of a sum may keep him digging a fortnight without sleep. A repeating decimal in the answer might kill him.

B is a quiet, easy-going fellow, afraid of A and bullied by him, but very gentle and brotherly to little C, the weakling. He is quite in A's power, having lost all his money in bets.

Poor C is an undersized, frail man, with a plaintive face. Constant walking, digging, and pumping has broken his health and ruined his nervous system. His joyless life has driven him to drink and smoke more than is good for him, and his hand often shakes as he digs ditches. He has not the strength to work as the others can, in fact, as Hamlin Smith has said, "A can do more work in one hour than C in four."

The first time that ever I saw these men was one evening after a regatta. They had all been rowing in it, and it had transpired that A could row as much in one hour as B in two, or C in four. B and C had come in dead fagged and C was coughing badly. "Never mind, old fellow," I heard B say. "I'll fix you up on the sofa and get you some hot tea." Just then A came blustering in and shouted, "I say, you fellows, Hamlin Smith has shown me three cisterns in his garden and he says we can pump them until tomorrow night. I bet I can beat you both. Come on. You can pump in your rowing things, you know. Your cistern leaks a little, I think, C." I heard B growl that it was a dirty shame and that C was used up now, but they went, and presently I could tell from the sound of the water that A was pumping four times as fast as C.

For years after that I used to see them constantly about town and always busy. I never heard of any of them eating or sleeping. Then owing to a long absence from home, I lost sight of them. On my return I was surprised to no longer find A, B, and C at their accustomed tasks; on inquiry I heard that work in this line was now done by N, M, and O, and that some people were employing for algebraical jobs four foreigners called Alpha, Beta, Gamma, and Delta.

Now it chanced one day that I stumbled upon old D, in the little garden in front of his cottage, hoeing in the sun. D is an aged labouring man who used occasionally to be called in to help A, B, and C. "Did I know 'em, sir?" he answered. "Why, I knowed 'em ever since they was little fellows in brackets. Master A, he were a fine lad, sir, though I always said, give me Master B for kind-heartedness-like. Many's the job as we've been on together, sir, though I never did no racing nor aught of that, but just the plain labour, as you might say. I'm getting a bit too old and stiff for it nowadays, sir—just scratch about in the garden here and grow a bit of a logarithm, or raise a common denominator or two. But Mr. Euclid he use me still for them propositions, he do."

From the garrulous old man I learned the melancholy end of my former acquaintances. Soon after I left town, he told me, C had been taken ill. It seems that A and B had been rowing on the river for a wager, and C had been running on the bank and then sat in a draught. Of course the bank had refused the draught and C was taken ill. A and B came home and found C lying helpless in bed. A shook him roughly and said, "Get up, C, we're going to pile wood." C looked so worn and pitiful that B said, "Look here, A, I won't stand this, he isn't fit to pile wood to-night." C smiled feebly and said, "Perhaps I might pile a little if I sat up in bed." Then B, thoroughly alarmed, said, "See here, A, I'm going to fetch a doctor; he's dying." A flared up and answered, "You've no money to fetch a doctor." "I'll reduce him to his lowest terms," B said firmly, "that'll fetch him." C's life might even then have been saved but they made a mistake about the medicine. It stood at the head of the bed on a bracket, and the nurse accidentally removed it from the bracket without changing the sign. After the fatal blunder C seems to have sunk rapidly. On the evening of the next day, as the shadows deepened in the little room, it was clear to all that the end was near. I think that even A was affected at the last as he stood with bowed head, aimlessly offering to bet with the doctor on C's laboured breathing. "A," whispered C, "I think I'm going fast." "How fast do you think you'll go, old man?" murmured A. "I don't know," said C, "but I'm going at any rate."—The end came soon after that. C rallied for a moment and asked for a certain piece of work that he had left downstairs. A put it in his arms and he expired. As his soul sped heavenward A watched its flight with melancholy admiration. B burst into a passionate flood of tears and sobbed, "Put away his little cistern and the rowing clothes he used to wear. I feel as if I could hardly ever dig again."—The funeral was plain and unostentatious. It differed in nothing from the ordinary, except that out of deference to sporting men and mathematicians, A engaged two hearses. Both vehicles started at the same time, B driving the one which bore the sable parallelepiped containing the last remains of his ill-fated friend. A on the box of the empty hearse generously consented to a handicap of a hundred yards, but arrived first at the cemetery by driving four times as fast as B. (Find the distance to the cemetery.) As the sarcophagus was lowered, the grave was surrounded by the broken figures of the first book of Euclid.—It was noticed that after the death of C, A became a changed man. He lost interest in racing with B, and dug but languidly. He finally gave up his work and settled down to live on the interest of his bets.—B never recovered from the shock of C's death; his grief preyed upon his intellect and it became deranged. He grew moody and spoke only in monosyllables. His disease became rapidly aggravated, and he presently spoke only in words whose spelling was regular and which presented no difficulty to the beginner. Realising his precarious condition he voluntarily submitted to be incarcerated in an asylum, where he abjured mathematics and devoted himself to writing the History of the Swiss Family Robinson in words of one syllable.

Sunshine Sketches of a Little Town

Contents

Preface

I KNOW NO way in which a writer may more fittingly introduce his work to the public than by giving a brief account of who and what he is. By this means some of the blame for what he has done is very properly shifted to the extenuating circumstances of his life.

I was born at Swanmoor, Hants, England, on December 30, 1869. I am not aware that there was any particular conjunction of the planets at the time, but should think it extremely likely. My parents migrated to Canada in 1876, and I decided to go with them. My father took up a farm near Lake Simcoe, in Ontario. This was during the hard times of Canadian farming, and my father was just able by great diligence to pay the hired men and, in years of plenty, to raise enough grain to have seed for the next year's crop without buying any. By this process my brothers and I were inevitably driven off the land, and have become professors, business men, and engineers, instead of being able to grow up as farm labourers. Yet I saw enough of farming to speak exuberantly in political addresses of the joy of early rising and the deep sleep, both of body and intellect, that is induced by honest manual toil.

I was educated at Upper Canada College, Toronto, of which I was head boy in 1887. From there I went to the University of Toronto, where I graduated in 1891. At the University I spent my entire time in the acquisition of languages, living, dead, and half-dead, and knew nothing of the outside world. In this diligent pursuit of words I spent about sixteen hours of each day. Very soon after graduation I had forgotten the languages, and found myself intellectually bankrupt. In other words I was what is called a distinguished graduate, and, as such, I took to school teaching as the only trade I could find that need neither experience nor intellect. I spent my time from 1891 to 1899 on the staff of Upper Canada College, an experience which has left me with a profound sympathy for the many gifted and brilliant men who are compelled to spend their lives in the most dreary, the most thankless, and the worst paid profession in the world. I have noted that of my pupils, those who seemed the laziest and the least enamoured of books are now rising to eminence at the bar, in business, and in public life; the really promising boys who took all the prizes are now able with difficulty to earn the wages of a clerk in a summer hotel or a deck hand on a canal boat.

In 1899 I gave up school teaching in disgust, borrowing enough money to live upon for a few months, and went to the University of Chicago to study economics and political science. I was soon appointed to a Fellowship in political economy, and by means of this and some temporary employment by McGill University, I survived until I took the degree of Doctor of Philosophy in 1903. The meaning of this degree is that the recipient of instruction is examined for the last time in his life, and is pronounced completely full. After this, no new ideas can be imparted to him.

From this time, and since my marriage, which had occurred at this period, I have belonged to the staff of McGill University, first as lecturer in Political Science, and later as head of the department of Economics and Political Science. As this position is one of the prizes of my profession, I am able to regard myself as singularly fortunate. The emolument is so high as to place me distinctly above the policemen, postmen, streetcar conductors, and other salaried officials of the neighbourhood, while I am able to mix with the poorer of the business men of the city on terms of something like equality. In point of leisure, I enjoy more in the four corners of a single year than a business man knows in his whole life. I thus have what the business man can never enjoy, an ability to think, and, what is still better, to stop thinking altogether for months at a time.

I have written a number of things in connection with my college life—a book on Political Science, and many essays, magazine articles, and so on. I belong to the Political Science Association of America, to the Royal Colonial Institute, and to the Church of England. These things, surely, are a proof of respectability. I have had some small connection with politics and public life. A few years ago I went all round the British Empire delivering addresses on Imperial organization. When I state that these lectures were followed almost immediately by the Union of South Africa, the Banana Riots in Trinidad, and the Turco-Italian war, I think the reader can form some idea of their importance. In Canada I belong to the Conservative party, but as yet I have failed entirely in Canadian politics, never having received a contract to build a bridge, or make a wharf, nor to construct even the smallest section of the Transcontinental Railway. This, however, is a form of national ingratitude to which one becomes accustomed in this Dominion.

Apart from my college work, I have written two books, one called "Literary Lapses" and the other "Nonsense Novels." Each of these is published by John Lane (London and New York), and either of them can be obtained, absurd though it sounds, for the mere sum of three shillings and sixpence. Any reader of this preface, for example, ridiculous though it appears, could walk into a bookstore and buy both of these books for seven shillings. Yet these works are of so humorous a character that for many years it was found impossible to print them. The compositors fell back from their task suffocated with laughter and gasping for air. Nothing but the intervention of the linotype machine—or rather, of the kind of men who operate it—made it possible to print these books. Even now people have to be very careful in circulating them, and the books should never be put into the hands of persons not in robust health.

Many of my friends are under the impression that I write these humorous nothings in idle moments when the wearied brain is unable to perform the serious labours of the economist. My own experience is exactly the other way. The writing of solid, instructive stuff fortified by facts and figures is easy enough. There is no trouble in writing a scientific treatise on the folk-lore of Central China, or a statistical enquiry into the declining population of Prince Edward Island. But to write something out of one's own mind, worth reading for its own sake, is an arduous contrivance only to be achieved in fortunate moments, few and far between. Personally, I would sooner have written "Alice in Wonderland" than the whole Encyclopaedia Britannica.

In regard to the present work I must disclaim at once all intentions of trying to do anything so ridiculously easy as writing about a real place and real people. Mariposa is not a real town. On the contrary, it is about seventy or eighty of them. You may find them all the way from Lake Superior to the sea, with the same square streets and the same maple trees and the same churches and hotels, and everywhere the sunshine of the land of hope.

Similarly, the Reverend Mr. Drone is not one person, but about eight or ten. To make him I clapped the gaiters of one ecclesiastic round the legs of another, added the sermons of a third and the character of a fourth, and so let him start on his way in the book to pick up such individual attributes as he might find for himself. Mullins and Bagshaw and Judge Pepperleigh and the rest are, it is true, personal friends of mine. But I have known them in such a variety of forms, with such alternations of tall and short, dark and fair, that, individually, I should have much ado to know them. Mr. Pupkin is found whenever a Canadian bank opens a branch in a county town and needs a teller. As for Mr. Smith, with his two hundred and eighty pounds, his hoarse voice, his loud check suit, his diamonds, the roughness of his address and the goodness of his heart,—all of this is known by everybody to be a necessary and universal adjunct of the hotel business.

The inspiration of the book,—a land of hope and sunshine where little towns spread their square streets and their trim maple trees beside placid lakes almost within echo of the primeval forest,—is large enough. If it fails in its portrayal of the scenes and the country that it depicts the fault lies rather with an art that is deficient than in an affection that is wanting.

Stephen Leacock.
McGill University,
June, 1912.

ONE

The Hostelry of Mr. Smith

I DON'T KNOW whether you know Mariposa. If not, it is of no consequence, for if you know Canada at all, you are probably well acquainted with a dozen towns just like it.

There it lies in the sunlight, sloping up from the little lake that spreads out at the foot of the hillside on which the town is built. There is a wharf beside the lake, and lying alongside of it a steamer that is tied to the wharf with two ropes of about the same size as they use on the Lusitania. The steamer goes nowhere in particular, for the lake is landlocked and there is no navigation for the Mariposa Belle except to "run trips" on the first of July and the Queen's Birthday, and to take excursions of the Knights of Pythias and the Sons of Temperance to and from the Local Option Townships.

In point of geography the lake is called Lake Wissanotti and the river running out of it the Ossawippi, just as the main street of Mariposa is called Missinaba Street and the county Missinaba County. But these names do not really matter. Nobody uses them. People simply speak of the "lake" and the "river" and the "main street," much in the same way as they always call the Continental Hotel, "Pete Robinson's" and the Pharmaceutical Hall, "Eliot's Drug Store." But I suppose this is just the same in every one else's town as in mine, so I need lay no stress on it.

The town, I say, has one broad street that runs up from the lake, commonly called the Main Street. There is no doubt about its width. When Mariposa was laid out there was none of that shortsightedness which is seen in the cramped dimensions of Wall Street and Piccadilly. Missinaba Street is so wide that if you were to roll Jeff Thorpe's barber shop over on its face it wouldn't reach half way across. Up and down the Main Street are telegraph poles of cedar of colossal thickness, standing at a variety of angles and carrying rather more wires than are commonly seen at a transatlantic cable station.

On the Main Street itself are a number of buildings of extraordinary importance,—Smith's Hotel and the Continental and the Mariposa House, and the two banks (the Commercial and the Exchange), to say nothing of McCarthy's Block (erected in 1878), and Glover's Hardware Store with the Oddfellows' Hall above it. Then on the "cross" street that intersects Missinaba Street at the main corner there is the Post Office and the Fire Hall and the Young Men's Christian Association and the office of the Mariposa Newspacket,—in fact, to the eye of discernment a perfect jostle of public institutions comparable only to Threadneedle Street or Lower Broadway. On all the side streets there are maple trees and broad sidewalks, trim gardens with upright calla lilies, houses with verandahs, which are here and there being replaced by residences with piazzas.

To the careless eye the scene on the Main Street of a summer afternoon is one of deep and unbroken peace. The empty street sleeps in the sunshine. There is a horse and buggy tied to the hitching post in front of Glover's hardware store. There is, usually and commonly, the burly figure of Mr. Smith, proprietor of Smith's Hotel, standing in his chequered waistcoat on the steps of his hostelry, and perhaps, further up the street, Lawyer Macartney going for his afternoon mail, or the Rev. Mr. Drone, the Rural Dean of the Church of England Church, going home to get his fishing rod after a mothers' auxiliary meeting.

But this quiet is mere appearance. In reality, and to those who know it, the place is a perfect hive of activity. Why, at Netley's butcher shop (established in 1882) there are no less than four men working on the sausage machines in the basement; at the Newspacket office there are as many more job-printing; there is a long distance telephone with four distracting girls on high stools wearing steel caps and talking incessantly; in the offices in McCarthy's block are dentists and lawyers with their coats off, ready to work at any moment; and from the big planing factory down beside the lake where the railroad siding is, you may hear all through the hours of the summer afternoon the long-drawn music of the running saw.

Busy—well, I should think so! Ask any of its inhabitants if Mariposa isn't a busy, hustling, thriving town. Ask Mullins, the manager of the Exchange Bank, who comes hustling over to his office from the Mariposa House every day at 10.30 and has scarcely time all morning to go out and take a drink with the manager of the Commercial; or ask—well, for the matter of that, ask any of them if they ever knew a more rushing go-a-head town than Mariposa.

Of course if you come to the place fresh from New York, you are deceived. Your standard of vision is all astray. You do think the place is quiet. You do imagine that Mr. Smith is asleep merely because he closes his eyes as he stands. But live in Mariposa for six months or a year and then you will begin to understand it better; the buildings get higher and higher; the Mariposa House grows more and more luxurious; McCarthy's block towers to the sky; the 'buses roar and hum to the station; the trains shriek; the traffic multiplies; the people move faster and faster; a dense crowd swirls to and fro in the post-office and the five and ten cent store—and amusements! well, now! lacrosse, baseball, excursions, dances, the Fireman's Ball every winter and the Catholic picnic every summer; and music—the town band in the park every Wednesday evening, and the Oddfellows' brass band on the street every other Friday; the Mariposa Quartette, the Salvation Army—why, after a few months' residence you begin to realize that the place is a mere mad round of gaiety.

In point of population, if one must come down to figures, the Canadian census puts the numbers every time at something round five thousand. But it is very generally understood in Mariposa that the census is largely the outcome of malicious jealousy. It is usual that after the census the editor of the Mariposa Newspacket makes a careful re-estimate (based on the data of relative non-payment of subscriptions), and brings the population up to 6,000. After that the Mariposa Times-Herald makes an estimate that runs the figures up to 6,500. Then Mr. Gingham, the undertaker, who collects the vital statistics for the provincial government, makes an estimate from the number of what he calls the "demised" as compared with the less interesting persons who are still alive, and brings the population to 7,000. After that somebody else works it out that it's 7,500; then the man behind the bar of the Mariposa House offers to bet the whole room that there are 9,000 people in Mariposa. That settles it, and the population is well on the way to 10,000, when down swoops the federal census taker on his next round and the town has to begin all over again.

Still, it is a thriving town and there is no doubt of it. Even the transcontinental railways, as any townsman will tell you, run through Mariposa. It is true that the trains mostly go through at night and don't stop. But in the wakeful silence of the summer night you may hear the long whistle of the through train for the west as it tears through Mariposa, rattling over the switches and past the semaphores and ending in a long, sullen roar as it takes the trestle bridge over the Ossawippi. Or, better still, on a winter evening about eight o'clock you will see the long row of the Pullmans and diners of the night express going north to the mining country, the windows flashing with brilliant light, and within them a vista of cut glass and snow-white table linen, smiling negroes and millionaires with napkins at their chins whirling past in the driving snowstorm.

I can tell you the people of Mariposa are proud of the trains, even if they don't stop! The joy of being on the main line lifts the Mariposa people above the level of their neighbours in such places as Tecumseh and Nichols Corners into the cosmopolitan atmosphere of through traffic and the larger life. Of course, they have their own train, too—the Mariposa Local, made up right there in the station yard, and running south to the city a hundred miles away. That, of course, is a real train, with a box stove on end in the passenger car, fed with cordwood upside down, and with seventeen flat cars of pine lumber set between the passenger car and the locomotive so as to give the train its full impact when shunting.

Outside of Mariposa there are farms that begin well but get thinner and meaner as you go on, and end sooner or later in bush and swamp and the rock of the north country. And beyond that again, as the background of it all, though it's far away, you are somehow aware of the great pine woods of the lumber country reaching endlessly into the north.

Not that the little town is always gay or always bright in the sunshine. There never was such a place for changing its character with the season. Dark enough and dull it seems of a winter night, the wooden sidewalks creaking with the frost, and the lights burning dim behind the shop windows. In olden times the lights were coal oil lamps; now, of course, they are, or are supposed to be, electricity,—brought from the power house on the lower Ossawippi nineteen miles away. But, somehow, though it starts off as electricity from the Ossawippi rapids, by the time it gets to Mariposa and filters into the little bulbs behind the frosty windows of the shops, it has turned into coal oil again, as yellow and bleared as ever.

After the winter, the snow melts and the ice goes out of the lake, the sun shines high and the shanty-men come down from the lumber woods and lie round drunk on the sidewalk outside of Smith's Hotel—and that's spring time. Mariposa is then a fierce, dangerous lumber town, calculated to terrorize the soul of a newcomer who does not understand that this also is only an appearance and that presently the rough-looking shanty-men will change their clothes and turn back again into farmers.

Then the sun shines warmer and the maple trees come out and

Lawyer Macartney puts on his tennis trousers, and that's summer time. The little town changes to a sort of summer resort. There are visitors up from the city. Every one of the seven cottages along the lake is full. The Mariposa Belle churns the waters of the Wissanotti into foam as she sails out from the wharf, in a cloud of flags, the band playing and the daughters and sisters of the Knights of Pythias dancing gaily on the deck.

That changes too. The days shorten. The visitors disappear. The golden rod beside the meadow droops and withers on its stem. The maples blaze in glory and die. The evening closes dark and chill, and in the gloom of the main corner of Mariposa the Salvation Army around a naphtha lamp lift up the confession of their sins—and that is autumn. Thus the year runs its round, moving and changing in Mariposa, much as it does in other places.

If, then, you feel that you know the town well enough to be admitted into the inner life and movement of it, walk down this June afternoon half way down the Main Street—or, if you like, half way up from the wharf—to where Mr. Smith is standing at the door of his hostelry. You will feel as you draw near that it is no ordinary man that you approach. It is not alone the huge bulk of Mr. Smith (two hundred and eighty pounds as tested on Netley's scales). It is not merely his costume, though the chequered waistcoat of dark blue with a flowered pattern forms, with his shepherd's plaid trousers, his grey spats and patent-leather boots, a colour scheme of no mean order. Nor is it merely Mr. Smith's finely mottled face. The face, no doubt, is a notable one,—solemn, inexpressible, unreadable, the face of the heaven-born hotel keeper. It is more than that. It is the strange dominating personality of the man that somehow holds you captive. I know nothing in history to compare with the position of Mr. Smith among those who drink over his bar, except, though in a lesser degree, the relation of the Emperor Napoleon to the Imperial Guard.

When you meet Mr. Smith first you think he looks like an overdressed pirate. Then you begin to think him a character. You wonder at his enormous bulk. Then the utter hopelessness of knowing what Smith is thinking by merely looking at his features gets on your mind and makes the Mona Lisa seem an open book and the ordinary human countenance as superficial as a puddle in the sunlight. After you have had a drink in Mr. Smith's bar, and he has called you by your Christian name, you realize that you are dealing with one of the greatest minds in the hotel business.

Take, for instance, the big sign that sticks out into the street above Mr. Smith's head as he stands. What is on it? "JOS. SMITH, PROP." Nothing more, and yet the thing was a flash of genius. Other men who had had the hotel before Mr. Smith had called it by such feeble names as the Royal Hotel and the Queen's and the Alexandria. Every one of them failed. When Mr. Smith took over the hotel he simply put up the sign with "JOS. SMITH, PROP.," and then stood underneath in the sunshine as a living proof that a man who weighs nearly three hundred pounds is the natural king of the hotel business.

But on this particular afternoon, in spite of the sunshine and deep peace, there was something as near to profound concern and anxiety as the features of Mr. Smith were ever known to express.

The moment was indeed an anxious one. Mr. Smith was awaiting a telegram from his legal adviser who had that day journeyed to the county town to represent the proprietor's interest before the assembled License Commissioners. If you know anything of the hotel business at all, you will understand that as beside the decisions of the License Commissioners of Missinaba County, the opinions of the Lords of the Privy Council are mere trifles.

The matter in question was very grave. The Mariposa Court had just fined Mr. Smith for the second time for selling liquors after hours. The Commissioners, therefore, were entitled to cancel the license.

Mr. Smith knew his fault and acknowledged it. He had broken the law. How he had come to do so, it passed his imagination to recall. Crime always seems impossible in retrospect. By what sheer madness of the moment could he have shut up the bar on the night in question, and shut Judge Pepperleigh, the district judge in Missinaba County, outside of it? The more so inasmuch as the closing up of the bar under the rigid license law of the province was a matter that the proprietor never trusted to any hands but his own. Punctually every night at 11 o'clock Mr. Smith strolled from the desk of the "rotunda" to the door of the bar. If it seemed properly full of people and all was bright and cheerful, then he closed it. If not, he kept it open a few minutes longer till he had enough people inside to warrant closing. But never, never unless he was assured that Pepperleigh, the judge of the court, and Macartney, the prosecuting attorney, were both safely in the bar, or the bar parlour, did the proprietor venture to close up. Yet on this fatal night Pepperleigh and Macartney had been shut out—actually left on the street without a drink, and compelled to hammer and beat at the street door of the bar to gain admittance.

This was the kind of thing not to be tolerated. Either a hotel must be run decently or quit. An information was laid next day and Mr. Smith convicted in four minutes, his lawyers practically refusing to plead. The Mariposa court, when the presiding judge was cold sober, and it had the force of public opinion behind it, was a terrible engine of retributive justice.

So no wonder that Mr. Smith awaited with anxiety the message of his legal adviser.

He looked alternately up the street and down it again, hauled out his watch from the depths of his embroidered pocket, and examined the hour hand and the minute hand and the second hand with frowning scrutiny.

Then wearily, and as one mindful that a hotel man is ever the servant of the public, he turned back into the hotel.

"Billy," he said to the desk clerk, "if a wire comes bring it into the bar parlour."

The voice of Mr. Smith is of a deep guttural such as Plancon or Edouard de Reske might have obtained had they had the advantages of the hotel business. And with that, Mr. Smith, as was his custom in off moments, joined his guests in the back room. His appearance, to the untrained eye, was merely that of an extremely stout hotel-keeper walking from the rotunda to the back bar. In reality, Mr. Smith was on the eve of one of the most brilliant and daring strokes ever effected in the history of licensed liquor. When I say that it was out of the agitation of this situation that Smith's Ladies' and Gent's Café originated, anybody who knows Mariposa will understand the magnitude of the moment.

Mr. Smith, then, moved slowly from the doorway of the hotel through the "rotunda," or more simply the front room with the desk and the cigar case in it, and so to the bar and thence to the little room or back bar behind it. In this room, as I have said, the brightest minds of Mariposa might commonly be found in the quieter part of a summer afternoon.

To-day there was a group of four who looked up as Mr. Smith entered, somewhat sympathetically, and evidently aware of the perplexities of the moment.

Henry Mullins and George Duff, the two bank managers, were both present. Mullins is a rather short, rather round, smooth-shaven man of less than forty, wearing one of those round banking suits of pepper and salt, with a round banking hat of hard straw, and with the kind of gold tie-pin and heavy watch-chain and seals necessary to inspire confidence in matters of foreign exchange. Duff is just as round and just as short, and equally smoothly shaven, while his seals and straw hat are calculated to prove that the Commercial is just as sound a bank as the Exchange. From the technical point of view of the banking business, neither of them had any objection to being in Smith's Hotel or to taking a drink as long as the other was present. This, of course, was one of the cardinal principles of Mariposa banking.

Then there was Mr. Diston, the high school teacher, commonly known as the "one who drank." None of the other teachers ever entered a hotel unless accompanied by a lady or protected by a child. But as Mr. Diston was known to drink beer on occasions and to go in and out of the Mariposa House and Smith's Hotel, he was looked upon as a man whose life was a mere wreck. Whenever the School Board raised the salaries of the other teachers, fifty or sixty dollars per annum at one lift, it was well understood that public morality wouldn't permit of an increase for Mr. Diston.

Still more noticeable, perhaps, was the quiet, sallow looking man dressed in black, with black gloves and with black silk hat heavily craped and placed hollow-side-up on a chair. This was Mr. Golgotha Gingham, the undertaker of Mariposa, and his dress was due to the fact that he had just come from what he called an "interment." Mr. Gingham had the true spirit of his profession, and such words as "funeral" or "coffin" or "hearse" never passed his lips. He spoke always of "interments," of "caskets," and "coaches," using terms that were calculated rather to bring out the majesty and sublimity of death than to parade its horrors.

To be present at the hotel was in accord with Mr. Gingham's general conception of his business. No man had ever grasped the true principles of undertaking more thoroughly than Mr. Gingham. I have often heard him explain that to associate with the living, uninteresting though they appear, is the only way to secure the custom of the dead.

"Get to know people really well while they are alive," said Mr. Gingham; "be friends with them, close friends, and then when they die you don't need to worry. You'll get the order every time."

So, naturally, as the moment was one of sympathy, it was Mr. Gingham who spoke first.

"What'll you do, Josh," he said, "if the Commissioners go against you?"

"Boys," said Mr. Smith, "I don't rightly know. If I have to quit, the next move is to the city. But I don't reckon that I will have to quit. I've got an idee that I think's good every time."

"Could you run a hotel in the city?" asked Mullins.

"I could," said Mr. Smith. "I'll tell you. There's big things doin' in the hotel business right now, big chances if you go into it right. Hotels in the city is branching out. Why, you take the dining-room side of it," continued Mr. Smith, looking round at the group, "there's thousands in it. The old plan's all gone. Folks won't eat now in an ordinary dining-room with a high ceiling and windows. You have to get 'em down underground in a room with no windows and lots of sawdust round and waiters that can't speak English. I seen them places last time I was in the city. They call 'em Rats' Coolers. And for light meals they want a Caff, a real French Caff, and for folks that come in late another place that they call a Girl Room that don't shut up at all. If I go to the city that's the kind of place I mean to run. What's yours, Gol? It's on the house?"

And it was just at the moment when Mr. Smith said this that Billy, the desk-clerk, entered the room with the telegram in his hand.

But stop—it is impossible for you to understand the anxiety with which Mr. Smith and his associates awaited the news from the Commissioners, without first realizing the astounding progress of Mr. Smith in the three past years, and the pinnacle of public eminence to which he had attained.

Mr. Smith had come down from the lumber country of the Spanish River, where the divide is toward the Hudson Bay,—"back north" as they called it in Mariposa.

He had been, it was said, a cook in the lumber shanties. To this day Mr. Smith can fry an egg on both sides with a lightness of touch that is the despair of his own "help."

After that, he had run a river driver's boarding-house.

After that, he had taken a food contract for a gang of railroad navvies on the transcontinental.

After that, of course, the whole world was open to him.

He came down to Mariposa and bought out the "inside" of what had been the Royal Hotel.

Those who are educated understand that by the "inside" of a hotel is meant everything except the four outer walls of it—the fittings, the furniture, the bar, Billy the desk-clerk, the three dining-room girls, and above all the license granted by King Edward VII., and ratified further by King George, for the sale of intoxicating liquors.

Till then the Royal had been a mere nothing. As "Smith's Hotel" it broke into a blaze of effulgence.

From the first, Mr. Smith, as a proprietor, was a wild, rapturous success.

He had all the qualifications.

He weighed two hundred and eighty pounds.

He could haul two drunken men out of the bar each by the scruff of the neck without the faintest anger or excitement.

He carried money enough in his trousers pockets to start a bank, and spent it on anything, bet it on anything, and gave it away in handfuls.

He was never drunk, and, as a point of chivalry to his customers, never quite sober. Anybody was free of the hotel who cared to come in. Anybody who didn't like it could go out. Drinks of all kinds cost five cents, or six for a quarter. Meals and beds were practically free. Any persons foolish enough to go to the desk and pay for them, Mr. Smith charged according to the expression of their faces.

At first the loafers and the shanty men settled down on the place in a shower. But that was not the "trade" that Mr. Smith wanted. He knew how to get rid of them. An army of charwomen, turned into the hotel, scrubbed it from top to bottom. A vacuum cleaner, the first seen in Mariposa, hissed and screamed in the corridors. Forty brass beds were imported from the city, not, of course, for the guests to sleep in, but to keep them out. A bar-tender with a starched coat and wicker sleeves was put behind the bar.

The loafers were put out of business. The place had become too "high toned" for them.

To get the high class trade, Mr. Smith set himself to dress the part. He wore wide cut coats of filmy serge, light as gossamer; chequered waistcoats with a pattern for every day in the week; fedora hats light as autumn leaves; four-in-hand ties of saffron and myrtle green with a diamond pin the size of a hazel nut. On his fingers there were as many gems as would grace a native prince of India; across his waistcoat lay a gold watch-chain in huge square links and in his pocket a gold watch that weighed a pound and a half and marked minutes, seconds and quarter seconds. Just to look at Josh Smith's watch brought at least ten men to the bar every evening.

Every morning Mr. Smith was shaved by Jefferson Thorpe, across the way. All that art could do, all that Florida water could effect, was lavished on his person.

Mr. Smith became a local character. Mariposa was at his feet. All the reputable business-men drank at Mr. Smith's bar, and in the little parlour behind it you might find at any time a group of the brightest intellects in the town.

Not but what there was opposition at first. The clergy, for example, who accepted the Mariposa House and the Continental as a necessary and useful evil, looked askance at the blazing lights and the surging crowd of Mr. Smith's saloon. They preached against him. When the Rev. Dean Drone led off with a sermon on the text "Lord be merciful even unto this publican Matthew Six," it was generally understood as an invitation to strike Mr. Smith dead. In the same way the sermon at the Presbyterian church the week after was on the text "Lo what now doeth Abiram in the land of Melchisideck Kings Eight and Nine?" and it was perfectly plain that what was meant was, "Lo, what is Josh Smith doing in Mariposa?"

But this opposition had been countered by a wide and sagacious philanthropy. I think Mr. Smith first got the idea of that on the night when the steam merry-go-round came to Mariposa. Just below the hostelry, on an empty lot, it whirled and whistled, steaming forth its tunes on the summer evening while the children crowded round it in hundreds. Down the street strolled Mr. Smith, wearing a soft fedora to indicate that it was evening.

"What d'you charge for a ride, boss?" said Mr. Smith.

"Two for a nickel," said the man.

"Take that," said Mr. Smith, handing out a ten-dollar bill from a roll of money, "and ride the little folks free all evening."

That night the merry-go-round whirled madly till after midnight, freighted to capacity with Mariposa children, while up in Smith's Hotel, parents, friends and admirers, as the news spread, were standing four deep along the bar. They sold forty dollars' worth of lager alone that night, and Mr. Smith learned, if he had not already suspected it, the blessedness of giving.

The uses of philanthropy went further. Mr. Smith subscribed to everything, joined everything, gave to everything. He became an Oddfellow, a Forester, A Knight of Pythias and a Workman. He gave a hundred dollars to the Mariposa Hospital and a hundred dollars to the Young Men's Christian Association.

He subscribed to the Ball Club, the Lacrosse Club, the Curling Club, to anything, in fact, and especially to all those things which needed premises to meet in and grew thirsty in their discussions.

As a consequence the Oddfellows held their annual banquet at Smith's Hotel and the Oyster Supper of the Knights of Pythias was celebrated in Mr. Smith's dining-room.

Even more effective, perhaps, were Mr. Smith's secret benefactions, the kind of giving done by stealth of which not a soul in town knew anything, often, for a week after it was done. It was in this way that Mr. Smith put the new font in Dean Drone's church, and handed over a hundred dollars to Judge Pepperleigh for the unrestrained use of the Conservative party.

So it came about that, little by little, the antagonism had died down. Smith's Hotel became an accepted institution in Mariposa. Even the temperance people were proud of Mr. Smith as a sort of character who added distinction to the town. There were moments, in the earlier quiet of the morning, when Dean Drone would go so far as to step in to the "rotunda" and collect a subscription. As for the Salvation Army, they ran in and out all the time unreproved.

On only one point difficulty still remained. That was the closing of the bar. Mr. Smith could never bring his mind to it,—not as a matter of profit, but as a point of honour. It was too much for him to feel that

Judge Pepperleigh might be out on the sidewalk thirsty at midnight, that the night hands of the Times-Herald on Wednesday might be compelled to go home dry. On this point Mr. Smith's moral code was simplicity itself,—do what is right and take the consequences. So the bar stayed open.

Every town, I suppose, has its meaner spirits. In every genial bosom some snake is warmed,—or, as Mr. Smith put it to Golgotha Gingham—"there are some fellers even in this town skunks enough to inform."

At first the Mariposa court quashed all indictments. The presiding judge, with his spectacles on and a pile of books in front of him, threatened the informer with the penitentiary. The whole bar of Mariposa was with Mr. Smith. But by sheer iteration the informations had proved successful. Judge Pepperleigh learned that Mr. Smith had subscribed a hundred dollars for the Liberal party and at once fined him for keeping open after hours. That made one conviction. On the top of this had come the untoward incident just mentioned and that made two. Beyond that was the deluge. This then was the exact situation when Billy, the desk clerk, entered the back bar with the telegram in his hand.

"Here's your wire, sir," he said.

"What does it say?" said Mr. Smith.

He always dealt with written documents with a fine air of detachment. I don't suppose there were ten people in Mariposa who knew that Mr. Smith couldn't read.

Billy opened the message and read, "Commissioners give you three months to close down."

"Let me read it," said Mr. Smith, "that's right, three months to close down."

There was dead silence when the message was read. Everybody waited for Mr. Smith to speak. Mr. Gingham instinctively assumed the professional air of hopeless melancholy.

As it was afterwards recorded, Mr. Smith stood and "studied" with the tray in his hand for at least four minutes. Then he spoke.

"Boys," he said, "I'll be darned if I close down till I'm ready to close down. I've got an idee. You wait and I'll show you."

And beyond that, not another word did Mr. Smith say on the subject.

But within forty-eight hours the whole town knew that something was doing. The hotel swarmed with carpenters, bricklayers and painters. There was an architect up from the city with a bundle of blue prints in his hand. There was an engineer taking the street level with a theodolite, and a gang of navvies with shovels digging like fury as if to dig out the back foundations of the hotel.

"That'll fool 'em," said Mr. Smith.

Half the town was gathered round the hotel crazy with excitement. But not a word would the proprietor say.

Great dray loads of square timber, and two-by-eight pine joists kept arriving from the planing mill. There was a pile of matched spruce sixteen feet high lying by the sidewalk.

Then the excavation deepened and the dirt flew, and the beams went up and the joists across, and all the day from dawn till dusk the hammers of the carpenters clattered away, working overtime at time and a half.

"It don't matter what it costs," said Mr. Smith; "get it done."

Rapidly the structure took form. It extended down the side street, joining the hotel at a right angle. Spacious and graceful it looked as it reared its uprights into the air.

Already you could see the place where the row of windows was to come, a veritable palace of glass, it must be, so wide and commodious were they. Below it, you could see the basement shaping itself, with a low ceiling like a vault and big beams running across, dressed, smoothed, and ready for staining. Already in the street there were seven crates of red and white awning.

And even then nobody knew what it was, and it was not till the seventeenth day that Mr. Smith, in the privacy of the back bar, broke the silence and explained.

"I tell you, boys," he says, "it's a caff—like what they have in the city—a ladies' and gent's caff, and that underneath (what's yours, Mr. Mullins?) is a Rats' Cooler. And when I get her started, I'll hire a French Chief to do the cooking, and for the winter I will put in a 'girl room,' like what they have in the city hotels. And I'd like to see who's going to close her up then."

Within two more weeks the plan was in operation. Not only was the caff built but the very hotel was transformed. Awnings had broken out in a red and white cloud upon its face, its every window carried a box of hanging plants, and above in glory floated the Union Jack. The very stationery was changed. The place was now Smith's Summer Pavilion. It was advertised in the city as Smith's Tourists' Emporium, and Smith's Northern Health Resort. Mr. Smith got the editor of the Times-Herald to write up a circular all about ozone and the Mariposa pine woods, with illustrations of the maskinonge (piscis mariposis) of Lake Wissanotti.

The Saturday after that circular hit the city in July, there were men with fishing rods and landing nets pouring in on every train, almost too fast to register. And if, in the face of that, a few little drops of whiskey were sold over the bar, who thought of it?

But the caff! that, of course, was the crowning glory of the thing, that and the Rats' Cooler below.

Light and cool, with swinging windows open to the air, tables with marble tops, palms, waiters in white coats—it was the standing marvel of Mariposa. Not a soul in the town except Mr. Smith, who knew it by instinct, ever guessed that waiters and palms and marble tables can be rented over the long distance telephone.

Mr. Smith was as good as his word. He got a French Chief with an aristocratic saturnine countenance, and a moustache and imperial that recalled the late Napoleon III. No one knew where Mr. Smith got him. Some people in the town said he was a French marquis. Others said he was a count and explained the difference.

No one in Mariposa had ever seen anything like the caff. All down the side of it were the grill fires, with great pewter dish covers that went up and down on a chain, and you could walk along the row and actually pick out your own cutlet and then see the French marquis throw it on to the broiling iron; you could watch a buckwheat pancake whirled into existence under your eyes and see fowls' legs devilled, peppered, grilled, and tormented till they lost all semblance of the original Mariposa chicken.

Mr. Smith, of course, was in his glory.

"What have you got to-day, Alf?" he would say, as he strolled over to the marquis. The name of the Chief was, I believe Alphonse, but "Alf" was near enough for Mr. Smith.

The marquis would extend to the proprietor the menu, "Voilà, m'sieu, la carte du jour."

Mr. Smith, by the way, encouraged the use of the French language in the caff. He viewed it, of course, solely in its relation to the hotel business, and, I think, regarded it as a recent invention.

"It's comin' in all the time in the city," he said, "and y'aint expected to understand it."

Mr. Smith would take the carte between his finger and thumb and stare at it. It was all covered with such devices as Potage à la Mariposa—Filet Mignon à la proprietaire—Côtellete à la Smith, and so on.

But the greatest thing about the caff were the prices. Therein lay, as everybody saw at once, the hopeless simplicity of Mr. Smith.

The prices stood fast at 25 cents a meal. You could come in and eat all they had in the caff for a quarter.

"No, sir," Mr. Smith said stoutly, "I ain't going to try to raise no prices on the public. The hotel's always been a quarter and the caff's a quarter."

Full? Full of people?

Well, I should think so! From the time the caff opened at 11 till it closed at 8.30, you could hardly find a table. Tourists, visitors, travellers, and half the people of Mariposa crowded at the little tables; crockery rattling, glasses tinkling on trays, corks popping, the waiters in their white coats flying to and fro, Alphonse whirling the cutlets and pancakes into the air, and in and through it all, Mr. Smith, in a white flannel suit and a broad crimson sash about his waist. Crowded and gay from morning to night, and even noisy in its hilarity.

Noisy, yes; but if you wanted deep quiet and cool, if you wanted to step from the glare of a Canadian August to the deep shadow of an enchanted glade,—walk down below into the Rats' Cooler. There you had it; dark old beams (who could believe they were put there a month ago?), great casks set on end with legends such as Amontillado Fino done in gilt on a black ground, tall steins filled with German beer soft as moss, and a German waiter noiseless as moving foam. He who entered the Rats' Cooler at three of a summer afternoon was buried there for the day. Mr. Golgotha Gingham spent anything from four to seven hours there of every day. In his mind the place had all the quiet charm of an interment, with none of its sorrows.

But at night, when Mr. Smith and Billy, the desk clerk, opened up the cash register and figured out the combined losses of the caff and the Rats' Cooler, Mr. Smith would say:

"Billy, just wait till I get the license renood, and I'll close up this damn caff so tight they'll never know what hit her. What did that lamb cost? Fifty cents a pound, was it? I figure it, Billy, that every one of them hogs eats about a dollar's worth a grub for every twenty-five cents they pay on it. As for Alf—by gosh, I'm through with him."

But that, of course, was only a confidential matter as between Mr. Smith and Billy.

I don't know at what precise period it was that the idea of a petition to the License Commissioners first got about the town. No one seemed to know just who suggested it. But certain it was that public opinion began to swing strongly towards the support of Mr. Smith. I think it was perhaps on the day after the big fish dinner that Alphonse cooked for the Mariposa Canoe Club (at twenty cents a head) that the feeling began to find open expression. People said it was a shame that a man like Josh Smith should be run out of Mariposa by three license commissioners. Who were the license commissioners, anyway? Why, look at the license system they had in Sweden; yes, and in Finland and in South America. Or, for the matter of that, look at the French and Italians, who drink all day and all night. Aren't they all right? Aren't they a musical people? Take Napoleon, and Victor Hugo; drunk half the time, and yet look what they did.

I quote these arguments not for their own sake, but merely to indicate the changing temper of public opinion in Mariposa. Men would sit in the caff at lunch perhaps for an hour and a half and talk about the license question in general, and then go down into the Rats' Cooler and talk about it for two hours more.

It was amazing the way the light broke in in the case of particular individuals, often the most unlikely, and quelled their opposition.

Take, for example, the editor of the Newspacket. I suppose there wasn't a greater temperance advocate in town. Yet Alphonse queered him with an Omelette à la License in one meal.

Or take Pepperleigh himself, the judge of the Mariposa court. He was put to the bad with a game pie,—pâté normand aux fines herbes—the real thing, as good as a trip to Paris in itself. After eating it, Pepperleigh had the common sense to realize that it was sheer madness to destroy a hotel that could cook a thing like that.

In the same way, the secretary of the School Board was silenced with a stuffed duck à la Ossawippi.

Three members of the town council were converted with a Dindon farci à la Josh Smith.

And then, finally, Mr. Diston persuaded Dean Drone to come, and as soon as Mr. Smith and Alphonse saw him they landed him with a fried flounder that even the apostles would have appreciated.

After that, every one knew that the license question was practically settled. The petition was all over the town. It was printed in duplicate at the Newspacket and you could see it lying on the counter of every shop in Mariposa. Some of the people signed it twenty or thirty times.

It was the right kind of document too. It began—"Whereas in the bounty of providence the earth putteth forth her luscious fruits and her vineyards for the delight and enjoyment of mankind—" It made you thirsty just to read it. Any man who read that petition over was wild to get to the Rats' Cooler.

When it was all signed up they had nearly three thousand names on it.

Then Nivens, the lawyer, and Mr. Gingham (as a provincial official) took it down to the county town, and by three o'clock that afternoon the news had gone out from the long distance telephone office that Smith's license was renewed for three years.

Rejoicings! Well, I should think so! Everybody was down wanting to shake hands with Mr. Smith. They told him that he had done more to boom Mariposa than any ten men in town. Some of them said he ought to run for the town council, and others wanted to make him the Conservative candidate for the next Dominion election. The caff was a mere babel of voices, and even the Rats' Cooler was almost floated away from its moorings.

And in the middle of it all, Mr. Smith found time to say to Billy, the desk clerk: "Take the cash registers out of the caff and the Rats' Cooler and start counting up the books."

And Billy said: "Will I write the letters for the palms and the tables and the stuff to go back?"

And Mr. Smith said: "Get 'em written right away."

So all evening the laughter and the chatter and the congratulations went on, and it wasn't till long after midnight that Mr. Smith was able to join Billy in the private room behind the "rotunda." Even when he did, there was a quiet and a dignity about his manner that had never been there before. I think it must have been the new halo of the Conservative candidacy that already radiated from his brow. It was, I imagine, at this very moment that Mr. Smith first realised that the hotel business formed the natural and proper threshold of the national legislature.

"Here's the account of the cash registers," said Billy.

"Let me see it," said Mr. Smith. And he studied the figures without a word.

"And here's the letters about the palms, and here's Alphonse up to yesterday—"

And then an amazing thing happened.

"Billy," said Mr. Smith, "tear 'em up. I ain't going to do it. It ain't right and I won't do it. They got me the license for to keep the caff and I'm going to keep the caff. I don't need to close her. The bar's good for anything from forty to a hundred a day now, with the Rats' Cooler going good, and that caff will stay right here."

And stay it did.

There it stands, mind you, to this day. You've only to step round the corner of Smith's Hotel on the side street and read the sign: LADIES' AND GENT'S CAFÉ, just as large and as imposing as ever.

Mr. Smith said that he'd keep the caff, and when he said a thing he meant it!

Of course there were changes, small changes.

I don't say, mind you, that the fillet de beef that you get there now is perhaps quite up to the level of the filet de boeufs aux champignons of the days of glory.

No doubt the lamb chops in Smith's Caff are often very much the same, nowadays, as the lamb chops of the Mariposa House or the Continental.

Of course, things like Omelette aux Trufles practically died out when Alphonse went. And, naturally, the leaving of Alphonse was inevitable. No one knew just when he went, or why. But one morning he was gone. Mr. Smith said that "Alf had to go back to his folks in the old country."

So, too, when Alf left, the use of the French language, as such, fell off tremendously in the caff. Even now they use it to some extent. You can still get fillet de beef, and saucisson au juice, but Billy the desk clerk has considerable trouble with the spelling.

The Rats' Cooler, of course, closed down, or rather Mr. Smith closed it for repairs, and there is every likelihood that it will hardly open for three years. But the caff is there. They don't use the grills, because there's no need to, with the hotel kitchen so handy.

The "girl room," I may say, was never opened. Mr. Smith promised it, it is true, for the winter, and still talks of it. But somehow there's been a sort of feeling against it. Every one in town admits that every big hotel in the city has a "girl room" and that it must be all right. Still, there's a certain—well, you know how sensitive opinion is in a place like Mariposa.

TWO

The Speculations of Jefferson Thorpe

IT WAS NOT until the mining boom, at the time when everybody went simply crazy over the Cobalt and Porcupine mines of the new silver country near the Hudson Bay, that Jefferson Thorpe reached what you might call public importance in Mariposa.

Of course everybody knew Jeff and his little barber shop that stood just across the street from Smith's Hotel. Everybody knew him and everybody got shaved there. From early morning, when the commercial travellers off the 6.30 express got shaved into the resemblance of human beings, there were always people going in and out of the barber shop.

Mullins, the manager of the Exchange Bank, took his morning shave from Jeff as a form of resuscitation, with enough wet towels laid on his face to stew him and with Jeff moving about in the steam, razor in hand, as grave as an operating surgeon.

Then, as I think I said, Mr. Smith came in every morning and there was a tremendous outpouring of Florida water and rums, essences and revivers and renovators, regardless of expense. What with Jeff's white coat and Mr. Smith's flowered waistcoat and the red geranium in the window and the Florida water and the double extract of hyacinth, the little shop seemed multi-coloured and luxurious enough for the annex of a Sultan's harem.

But what I mean is that, till the mining boom, Jefferson Thorpe never occupied a position of real prominence in Mariposa. You couldn't, for example, have compared him with a man like Golgotha Gingham, who, as undertaker, stood in a direct relation to life and death, or to Trelawney, the postmaster, who drew money from the Federal Government of Canada, and was regarded as virtually a member of the Dominion Cabinet.

Everybody knew Jeff and liked him, but the odd thing was that till he made money nobody took any stock in his ideas at all. It was only after he made the "clean up" that they came to see what a splendid fellow he was. "Level-headed" I think was the term; indeed in the speech of Mariposa, the highest form of endowment was to have the head set on horizontally as with a theodolite.

As I say, it was when Jeff made money that they saw how gifted he was, and when he lost it,—but still, there's no need to go into that. I believe it's something the same in other places too.

The barber shop, you will remember, stands across the street from Smith's Hotel, and stares at it face to face.

It is one of those wooden structures—I don't know whether you know them—with a false front that sticks up above its real height and gives it an air at once rectangular and imposing. It is a form of architecture much used in Mariposa and understood to be in keeping with the pretentious and artificial character of modern business. There is a red, white and blue post in front of the shop and the shop itself has a large square window out of proportion to its little flat face.

Painted on the panes of the window is the remains of a legend that once spelt BARBER SHOP, executed with the flourishes that prevailed in the golden age of sign painting in Mariposa. Through the window you can see the geraniums in the window shelf and behind them Jeff Thorpe with his little black scull cap on and his spectacles drooped upon his nose as he bends forward in the absorption of shaving.

As you open the door, it sets in violent agitation a coiled spring up above and a bell that almost rings. Inside, there are two shaving chairs of the heavier, or electrocution pattern, with mirrors in front of them and pigeon holes with individual shaving mugs. There must be ever so many of them, fifteen or sixteen. It is the current supposition of each of Jeff's customers that everyone else but himself uses a separate mug. One corner of the shop is partitioned off and bears the sign: HOT AND COLD BATHS, 50 cents. There has been no bath inside the partition for twenty years—only old newspapers and a mop. Still, it lends distinction somehow, just as do the faded cardboard signs that hang against the mirror with the legends: TURKISH SHAMPOO, 75 cents, and ROMAN MASSAGE, $1.00.

They said commonly in Mariposa that Jeff made money out of the barber shop. He may have, and it may have been that that turned his mind to investment. But it's hard to see how he could. A shave cost five cents, and a hair-cut fifteen (or the two, if you liked, for a quarter), and at that it is hard to see how he could make money, even when he had both chairs going and shaved first in one and then in the other.

You see, in Mariposa, shaving isn't the hurried, perfunctory thing that it is in the city. A shave is looked upon as a form of physical pleasure and lasts anywhere from twenty-five minutes to three-quarters of an hour.

In the morning hours, perhaps, there was a semblance of haste about it, but in the long quiet of the afternoon, as Jeff leaned forward towards the customer and talked to him in a soft confidential monotone, like a portrait painter, the razor would go slower and slower, and pause and stop, move and pause again, till the shave died away into the mere drowse of conversation.

At such hours, the Mariposa barber shop would become a very Palace of Slumber, and as you waited your turn in one of the wooden armchairs beside the wall, what with the quiet of the hour, and the low drone of Jeff's conversation, the buzzing of the flies against the window pane and the measured tick of the clock above the mirror, your head sank dreaming on your breast, and the Mariposa Newspacket rustled unheeded on the floor. It makes one drowsy just to think of it!

The conversation, of course, was the real charm of the place. You see, Jefferson's forte, or specialty, was information. He could tell you more things within the compass of a half-hour's shave than you get in days of laborious research in an encyclopaedia. Where he got it all, I don't know, but I am inclined to think it came more or less out of the newspapers.

In the city, people never read the newspapers, not really, only little bits and scraps of them. But in Mariposa it's different. There they read the whole thing from cover to cover, and they build up on it, in the course of years, a range of acquirement that would put a college president to the blush. Anybody who has ever heard Henry Mullins and Peter Glover talk about the future of China will know just what I mean.

And, of course, the peculiarity of Jeff's conversation was that he could suit it to his man every time. He had a kind of divination about it. There was a certain kind of man that Jeff would size up sideways as he stropped the razor, and in whose ear he would whisper: "I see where Saint Louis has took four straight games off Chicago,"—and so hold him fascinated to the end.

In the same way he would say to Mr. Smith: "I see where it says that this 'Flying Squirl' run a dead heat for the King's Plate."

To a humble intellect like mine he would explain in full the relations of the Keesar to the German Rich Dog.

But first and foremost, Jeff's specialty in the way of conversation was finance and the money market, the huge fortunes that a man with the right kind of head could make.

I've known Jefferson to pause in his shaving with the razor suspended in the air as long as five minutes while he described, with his eye half closed, exactly the kind of a head a man needed in order to make a "haul" or a "clean up." It was evidently simply a matter of the head, and as far as one could judge, Jeff's own was the very type required.

I don't know just at what time or how Jefferson first began his speculative enterprises. It was probably in him from the start. There is no doubt that the very idea of such things as Traction Stock and

Amalgamated Asbestos went to his head: and whenever he spoke of Mr. Carnegie and Mr. Rockefeller, the yearning tone of his voice made it as soft as lathered soap.

I suppose the most rudimentary form of his speculation was the hens. That was years ago. He kept them out at the back of his house,—which itself stood up a grass plot behind and beyond the barber shop,—and in the old days Jeff would say, with a certain note of pride in his voice, that The Woman had sold as many as two dozen eggs in a day to the summer visitors.

But what with reading about Amalgamated Asbestos and Consolidated Copper and all that, the hens began to seem pretty small business, and, in any case, the idea of two dozen eggs at a cent apiece almost makes one blush. I suppose a good many of us have felt just as Jeff did about our poor little earnings. Anyway, I remember Jeff telling me one day that he could take the whole lot of the hens and sell them off and crack the money into Chicago wheat on margin and turn it over in twenty-four hours. He did it too. Only somehow when it was turned over it came upside down on top of the hens.

After that the hen house stood empty and The Woman had to throw away chicken feed every day, at a dead loss of perhaps a shave and a half. But it made no difference to Jeff, for his mind had floated away already on the possibilities of what he called "displacement" mining on the Yukon.

So you can understand that when the mining boom struck Mariposa, Jefferson Thorpe was in it right from the very start. Why, no wonder; it seemed like the finger of Providence. Here was this great silver country spread out to north of us, where people had thought there was only a wilderness. And right at our very doors! You could see, as I saw, the night express going north every evening; for all one knew Rockefeller or Carnegie or anyone might be on it! Here was the wealth of Calcutta, as the Mariposa Newspacket put it, poured out at our very feet.

So no wonder the town went wild! All day in the street you could hear men talking of veins, and smelters and dips and deposits and faults,—the town hummed with it like a geology class on examination day. And there were men about the hotels with mining outfits and theodolites and dunnage bags, and at Smith's bar they would hand chunks of rock up and down, some of which would run as high as ten drinks to the pound.

The fever just caught the town and ran through it! Within a fortnight they put a partition down Robertson's Coal and Wood Office and opened the Mariposa Mining Exchange, and just about every man on the Main Street started buying scrip. Then presently young Fizzlechip, who had been teller in Mullins's Bank and that everybody had thought a worthless jackass before, came back from the Cobalt country with a fortune, and loafed round in the Mariposa House in English khaki and a horizontal hat, drunk all the time, and everybody holding him up as an example of what it was possible to do if you tried.

They all went in. Jim Eliot mortgaged the inside of the drug store and jammed it into Twin Tamagami. Pete Glover at the hardware store bought Nippewa stock at thirteen cents and sold it to his brother at seventeen and bought it back in less than a week at nineteen. They didn't care! They took a chance. Judge Pepperleigh put the rest of his wife's money into Temiskaming Common, and Lawyer Macartney got the fever, too, and put every cent that his sister possessed into Tulip Preferred.

And even when young Fizzlechip shot himself in the back room of the Mariposa House, Mr. Gingham buried him in a casket with silver handles and it was felt that there was a Monte Carlo touch about the whole thing.

They all went in—or all except Mr. Smith. You see, Mr. Smith had come down from there, and he knew all about rocks and mining and canoes and the north country. He knew what it was to eat flour-baked dampers under the lee side of a canoe propped among the underbrush, and to drink the last drop of whiskey within fifty miles. Mr. Smith had mighty little use for the north. But what he did do, was to buy up enough early potatoes to send fifteen carload lots into Cobalt at a profit of five dollars a bag.

Mr. Smith, I say, hung back. But Jeff Thorpe was in the mining boom right from the start. He bought in on the Nippewa mine even before the interim prospectus was out. He took a "block" of 100 shares of Abbitibbi Development at fourteen cents, and he and Johnson, the livery stable-keeper next door, formed a syndicate and got a thousand shares of Metagami Lake at 3 ¼ cents and then "unloaded" them on one of the sausage men at Netley's butcher shop at a clear cent per cent advance.

Jeff would open the little drawer below the mirror in the barber shop and show you all kinds and sorts of Cobalt country mining certificates,—blue ones, pink ones, green ones, with outlandish and fascinating names on them that ran clear from the Mattawa to the Hudson Bay.

And right from the start he was confident of winning.

"There ain't no difficulty to it," he said, "there's lots of silver up there in that country and if you buy some here and some there you can't fail to come out somewhere. I don't say," he used to continue, with the scissors open and ready to cut, "that some of the greenhorns won't get bit. But if a feller knows the country and keeps his head level, he can't lose."

Jefferson had looked at so many prospectuses and so many pictures of mines and pine trees and smelters, that I think he'd forgotten that he'd never been in the country. Anyway, what's two hundred miles!

To an onlooker it certainly didn't seem so simple. I never knew the meanness, the trickery, of the mining business, the sheer obstinate determination of the bigger capitalists not to make money when they might, till I heard the accounts of Jeff's different mines. Take the case of Corona Jewel. There was a good mine, simply going to ruin for lack of common sense.

"She ain't been developed," Jeff would say. "There's silver enough in her so you could dig it out with a shovel. She's full of it. But they won't get at her and work her."

Then he'd take a look at the pink and blue certificates of the Corona Jewel and slam the drawer on them in disgust.

Worse than that was the Silent Pine,—a clear case of stupid incompetence! Utter lack of engineering skill was all that was keeping the Silent Pine from making a fortune for its holders.

"The only trouble with that mine," said Jeff, "is they won't go deep enough. They followed the vein down to where it kind o' thinned out and then they quit. If they'd just go right into her good, they'd get it again. She's down there all right."

But perhaps the meanest case of all was the Northern Star. That always seemed to me, every time I heard of it, a straight case for the criminal law. The thing was so evidently a conspiracy.

"I bought her," said Jeff, "at thirty-two, and she stayed right there tight, like she was stuck. Then a bunch of these fellers in the city started to drive her down and they got her pushed down to twenty-four, and I held on to her and they shoved her down to twenty-one. This morning they've got her down to sixteen, but I don't mean to let go. No, sir."

In another fortnight they shoved her, the same unscrupulous crowd, down to nine cents, and Jefferson still held on.

"They're working her down," he admitted, "but I'm holding her."

No conflict between vice and virtue was ever grimmer.

"She's at six," said Jeff, "but I've got her. They can't squeeze me."

A few days after that, the same criminal gang had her down further than ever.

"They've got her down to three cents," said Jeff, "but I'm with her. Yes, sir, they think they can shove her clean off the market, but they can't do it. I've boughten in Johnson's shares, and the whole of Netley's, and I'll stay with her till she breaks."

So they shoved and pushed and clawed her down—that unseen nefarious crowd in the city—and Jeff held on to her and they writhed and twisted at his grip, and then—

And then—well, that's just the queer thing about the mining business. Why, sudden as a flash of lightning, it seemed, the news came over the wire to the Mariposa Newspacket, that they had struck a vein of silver in the Northern Star as thick as a sidewalk, and that the stock had jumped to seventeen dollars a share, and even at that you couldn't get it! And Jeff stood there flushed and half-staggered against the mirror of the little shop, with a bunch of mining scrip in his hand that was worth forty thousand dollars!

Excitement! It was all over the town in a minutes. They ran off a news extra at the Mariposa Newspacket, and in less than no time there wasn't standing room in the barber shop, and over in Smith's Hotel they had three extra barkeepers working on the lager beer pumps.

They were selling mining shares on the Main Street in Mariposa that afternoon and people were just clutching for them. Then at night there was a big oyster supper in Smith's caff, with speeches, and the Mariposa band outside.

And the queer thing was that the very next afternoon was the funeral of young Fizzlechip, and Dean Drone had to change the whole text of his Sunday sermon at two days' notice for fear of offending public sentiment.

But I think what Jeff liked best of it all was the sort of public recognition that it meant. He'd stand there in the shop, hardly bothering to shave, and explain to the men in the arm-chairs how he held her, and they shoved her, and he clung to her, and what he'd said to himself—a perfect Iliad—while he was clinging to her.

The whole thing was in the city papers a few days after with a photograph of Jeff, taken specially at Ed Moore's studio (upstairs over Netley's). It showed Jeff sitting among palm trees, as all mining men do, with one hand on his knee, and a dog, one of those regular mining dogs, at his feet, and a look of piercing intelligence in his face that would easily account for forty thousand dollars.

I say that the recognition meant a lot to Jeff for its own sake. But no doubt the fortune meant quite a bit to him too on account of Myra.

Did I mention Myra, Jeff's daughter? Perhaps not. That's the trouble with the people in Mariposa; they're all so separate and so different—not a bit like the people in the cities—that unless you hear about them separately and one by one you can't for a moment understand what they're like.

Myra had golden hair and a Greek face and would come bursting through the barber shop in a hat at least six inches wider than what they wear in Paris. As you saw her swinging up the street to the Telephone Exchange in a suit that was straight out of the Delineator and brown American boots, there was style written all over her,—the kind of thing that Mariposa recognised and did homage to. And to see her in the Exchange,—she was one of the four girls that I spoke of,—on her high stool with a steel cap on,—jabbing the connecting plugs in and out as if electricity cost nothing—well, all I mean is that you could understand why it was that the commercial travellers would stand round in the Exchange calling up all sorts of impossible villages, and waiting about so pleasant and genial!—it made one realize how naturally good-tempered men are. And then when Myra would go off duty and Miss Cleghorn, who was sallow, would come on, the commercial men would be off again like autumn leaves.

It just shows the difference between people. There was Myra who treated lovers like dogs and would slap them across the face with a banana skin to show her utter independence. And there was Miss Cleghorn, who was sallow, and who bought a forty cent Ancient History to improve herself: and yet if she'd hit any man in Mariposa with a banana skin, he'd have had her arrested for assault.

Mind you, I don't mean that Myra was merely flippant and worthless. Not at all. She was a girl with any amount of talent. You should have heard her recite "The Raven," at the Methodist Social! Simply genius! And when she acted Portia in the Trial Scene of the Merchant of Venice at the High School concert, everybody in Mariposa admitted that you couldn't have told it from the original.

So, of course, as soon as Jeff made the fortune, Myra had her resignation in next morning and everybody knew that she was to go to a dramatic school for three months in the fall and become a leading actress.

But, as I said, the public recognition counted a lot for Jeff. The moment you begin to get that sort of thing it comes in quickly enough. Brains, you know, are recognized right away. That was why, of course, within a week from this Jeff received the first big packet of stuff from the Cuban Land Development Company, with coloured pictures of Cuba, and fields of bananas, and haciendas and insurrectos with machetes and Heaven knows what. They heard of him, somehow,—it wasn't for a modest man like Jefferson to say how. After all, the capitalists of the world are just one and the same crowd. If you're in it, you're in it, that's all! Jeff realized why it is that of course men like Carnegie or Rockefeller and Morgan all know one another. They have to.

For all I know, this Cuban stuff may have been sent from Morgan himself. Some of the people in Mariposa said yes, others said no. There was no certainty.

Anyway, they were fair and straight, this Cuban crowd that wrote to Jeff. They offered him to come right in and be one of themselves. If a man's got the brains, you may as well recognize it straight away. Just as well write him to be a director now as wait and hesitate till he forces his way into it.

Anyhow, they didn't hesitate, these Cuban people that wrote to Jeff from Cuba—or from a post-office box in New York—it's all the same thing, because Cuba being so near to New York the mail is all distributed from there. I suppose in some financial circles they might have been slower, wanted guarantees of some sort, and so on, but these Cubans, you know, have got a sort of Spanish warmth of heart that you don't see in business men in America, and that touches you. No, they asked no guarantee. Just send the money—whether by express order or by bank draft or cheque, they left that entirely to oneself, as a matter between Cuban gentlemen.

And they were quite frank about their enterprise—bananas and tobacco in the plantation district reclaimed from the insurrectos. You could see it all there in the pictures—tobacco plants and the insurrectos—everything. They made no rash promises, just admitted straight out that the enterprise might realise 400 per cent or might conceivably make less. There was no hint of more.

So within a month, everybody in Mariposa knew that Jeff Thorpe was "in Cuban lands" and would probably clean up half a million by New Year's. You couldn't have failed to know it. All round the little shop there were pictures of banana groves and the harbour of Habana, and Cubans in white suits and scarlet sashes, smoking cigarettes in the sun and too ignorant to know that you can make four hundred per cent by planting a banana tree.

I liked it about Jeff that he didn't stop shaving. He went on just the same. Even when Johnson, the livery stable man, came in with five hundred dollars and asked him to see if the Cuban Board of Directors would let him put it in, Jeff laid it in the drawer and then shaved him for five cents, in the same old way. Of course, he must have felt proud when, a few days later, he got a letter from the Cuban people, from New York, accepting the money straight off without a single question, and without knowing anything more of Johnson except that he was a friend of Jeff's. They wrote most handsomely. Any friends of Jeff's were friends of Cuba. All money they might send would be treated just as Jeff's would be treated.

One reason, perhaps, why Jeff didn't give up shaving was because it allowed him to talk about Cuba. You see, everybody knew in Mariposa that Jeff Thorpe had sold out of Cobalts and had gone into Cuban Renovated Lands—and that spread round him a kind of halo of wealth and mystery and outlandishness—oh, something Spanish. Perhaps you've felt it about people that you know. Anyhow, they asked him about the climate, and yellow fever and what the negroes were like and all that sort of thing.

"This Cubey, it appears is an island," Jeff would explain. Of course, everybody knows how easily islands lend themselves to making money,—"and for fruit, they say it comes up so fast you can't stop it." And then he would pass into details about the Hash-enders and the resurrectos and technical things like that till it was thought a wonder how he could know it. Still, it was realized that a man with money has got to know these things. Look at Morgan and Rockefeller and all the men that make a pile.

They know just as much as Jeff did about the countries where they make it. It stands to reason.

Did I say that Jeff shaved in the same old way? Not quite. There was something even dreamier about it now, and a sort of new element in the way Jeff fell out of his monotone into lapses of thought that I, for one, misunderstood. I thought that perhaps getting so much money,—well, you know the way it acts on people in the larger cities. It seemed to spoil one's idea of Jeff that copper and asbestos and banana lands should form the goal of his thought when, if he knew it, the little shop and the sunlight of Mariposa was so much better.

In fact, I had perhaps borne him a grudge for what seemed to me his perpetual interest in the great capitalists. He always had some item out of the paper about them.

"I see where this here Carnegie has give fifty thousand dollars for one of them observatories," he would say.

And another day he would pause in the course of shaving, and almost whisper: "Did you ever see this Rockefeller?"

It was only by a sort of accident that I came to know that there was another side to Jefferson's speculation that no one in Mariposa ever knew, or will ever know now.

I knew it because I went in to see Jeff in his house one night. The house,—I think I said it,—stood out behind the barber shop. You went out of the back door of the shop, and through a grass plot with petunias beside it, and the house stood at the end. You could see the light of the lamp behind the blind, and through the screen door as you came along. And it was here that Jefferson used to sit in the evenings when the shop got empty.

There was a round table that The Woman used to lay for supper, and after supper there used to be a chequered cloth on it and a lamp with a shade. And beside it Jeff would sit, with his spectacles on and the paper spread out, reading about Carnegie and Rockefeller. Near him, but away from the table, was The Woman doing needlework, and Myra, when she wasn't working in the Telephone Exchange, was there too with her elbows on the table reading Marie Corelli—only now, of course, after the fortune, she was reading the prospectuses of Dramatic Schools.

So this night,—I don't know just what it was in the paper that caused it,—Jeff laid down what he was reading and started to talk about Carnegie.

"This Carnegie, I bet you, would be worth," said Jeff, closing up his eyes in calculation, "as much as perhaps two million dollars, if you was to sell him up. And this Rockefeller and this Morgan, either of them, to sell them up clean, would be worth another couple of million—"

I may say in parentheses that it was a favourite method in Mariposa if you wanted to get at the real worth of a man, to imagine him clean sold up, put up for auction, as it were. It was the only way to test him.

"And now look at 'em," Jeff went on. "They make their money and what do they do with it? They give it away. And who do they give it to? Why, to those as don't want it, every time. They give it to these professors and to this research and that, and do the poor get any of it? Not a cent and never will."

"I tell you, boys," continued Jeff (there were no boys present, but in Mariposa all really important speeches are addressed to an imaginary audience of boys)—"I tell you, if I was to make a million out of this Cubey, I'd give it straight to the poor, yes, sir—divide it up into a hundred lots of a thousand dollars each and give it to the people that hadn't nothing."

So always after that I knew just what those bananas were being grown for.

Indeed, after that, though Jefferson never spoke of his intentions directly, he said a number of things that seemed to bear on them. He asked me, for instance, one day, how many blind people it would take to fill one of these blind homes and how a feller could get ahold of them. And at another time he asked whether if a feller advertised for some of these incurables a feller could get enough of them to make a showing.

I know for a fact that he got Nivens, the lawyer, to draw up a document that was to give an acre of banana land in Cuba to every idiot in Missinaba county.

But still,—what's the use of talking of what Jeff meant to do? Nobody knows or cares about it now.

The end of it was bound to come. Even in Mariposa some of the people must have thought so. Else how was it that Henry Mullins made such a fuss about selling a draft for forty thousand on New York? And why was it that Mr. Smith wouldn't pay Billy, the desk clerk, his back wages when he wanted to put it into Cuba?

Oh yes; some of them must have seen it. And yet when it came it seemed so quiet,—ever so quiet,—not a bit like the Northern Star mine and the oyster supper and the Mariposa band. It is strange how quiet these things look, the other way round.

You remember the Cuban Land frauds in New York—and Porforio Gomez shooting the detective, and him and Maximo Morez getting clear away with two hundred thousand? No, of course you don't; why, even in the city papers it only filled an inch or two of type, and anyway the names were hard to remember. That was Jeff's money—part of it. Mullins got the telegram, from a broker or someone, and he showed it to Jeff just as he was going up the street with an estate agent to look at a big empty lot on the hill behind the town—the very place for these incurables.

And Jeff went back to the shop so quiet—have you ever seen an animal that is stricken through, how quiet it seems to move?

Well, that's how he walked.

And since that, though it's quite a little while ago, the shop's open till eleven every night now, and Jeff is shaving away to pay back that five hundred that Johnson, the livery man, sent to the Cubans, and—

Pathetic? tut! tut! You don't know Mariposa. Jeff has to work pretty late, but that's nothing—nothing at all, if you've worked hard all your lifetime. And Myra is back at the Telephone Exchange—they were glad enough to get her, and she says now that if there's one thing she hates, it's the stage, and she can't see how the actresses put up with it.

Anyway, things are not so bad. You see it was just at this time that Mr. Smith's caff opened, and Mr. Smith came to Jeff's Woman and said he wanted seven dozen eggs a day, and wanted them handy, and so the hens are back, and more of them, and they exult so every morning over the eggs they lay that if you wanted to talk of Rockefeller in the barber shop you couldn't hear his name for the cackling.

THREE

The Marine Excursion of the Knights of Pythias

HALF-PAST SIX on a July morning! The Mariposa Belle is at the wharf, decked in flags, with steam up ready to start.

Excursion day!

Half-past six on a July morning, and Lake Wissanotti lying in the sun as calm as glass. The opal colours of the morning light are shot from the surface of the water.

Out on the lake the last thin threads of the mist are clearing away like flecks of cotton wool.

The long call of the loon echoes over the lake. The air is cool and fresh. There is in it all the new life of the land of the silent pine and the moving waters. Lake Wissanotti in the morning sunlight! Don't talk to me of the Italian lakes, or the Tyrol or the Swiss Alps. Take them away. Move them somewhere else. I don't want them.

Excursion Day, at half-past six of a summer morning! With the boat all decked in flags and all the people in Mariposa on the wharf, and the band in peaked caps with big cornets tied to their bodies ready to play at any minute! I say! Don't tell me about the Carnival of Venice and the Delhi Durbar. Don't! I wouldn't look at them. I'd shut my eyes! For light and colour give me every time an excursion out of Mariposa down the lake to the Indian's Island out of sight in the morning mist. Talk of your Papal Zouaves and your Buckingham Palace Guard! I want to see the Mariposa band in uniform and the Mariposa Knights of Pythias with their aprons and their insignia and their picnic baskets and their five-cent cigars!

Half-past six in the morning, and all the crowd on the wharf and the boat due to leave in half an hour. Notice it!—in half an hour. Already she's whistled twice (at six, and at six fifteen), and at any minute now, Christie Johnson will step into the pilot house and pull the string for the warning whistle that the boat will leave in half an hour. So keep ready. Don't think of running back to Smith's Hotel for the sandwiches. Don't be fool enough to try to go up to the Greek Store, next to Netley's, and buy fruit. You'll be left behind for sure if you do. Never mind the sandwiches and the fruit! Anyway, here comes Mr. Smith himself with a huge basket of provender that would feed a factory. There must be sandwiches in that. I think I can hear them clinking. And behind Mr. Smith is the German waiter from the caff with another basket—indubitably lager beer; and behind him, the bar-tender of the hotel, carrying nothing, as far as one can see. But of course if you know Mariposa you will understand that why he looks so nonchalant and empty-handed is because he has two bottles of rye whiskey under his linen duster. You know, I think, the peculiar walk of a man with two bottles of whiskey in the inside pockets of a linen coat. In Mariposa, you see, to bring beer to an excursion is quite in keeping with public opinion. But, whiskey,—well, one has to be a little careful.

Do I say that Mr. Smith is here? Why, everybody's here. There's Hussell the editor of the Newspacket, wearing a blue ribbon on his coat, for the Mariposa Knights of Pythias are, by their constitution, dedicated to temperance; and there's Henry Mullins, the manager of the Exchange Bank, also a Knight of Pythias, with a small flask of Pogram's Special in his hip pocket as a sort of amendment to the constitution. And there's Dean Drone, the Chaplain of the Order, with a fishing-rod (you never saw such green bass as lie among the rocks at Indian's Island), and with a trolling line in case of maskinonge, and a landing net in case of pickerel, and with his eldest daughter, Lilian Drone, in case of young men. There never was such a fisherman as the Rev. Rupert Drone.

~ ~ ~

Perhaps I ought to explain that when I speak of the excursion as being of the Knights of Pythias, the thing must not be understood in any narrow sense. In Mariposa practically everybody belongs to the Knights of Pythias just as they do to everything else. That's the great thing about the town and that's what makes it so different from the city. Everybody is in everything.

You should see them on the seventeenth of March, for example, when everybody wears a green ribbon and they're all laughing and glad,—you know what the Celtic nature is,—and talking about Home Rule.

On St. Andrew's Day every man in town wears a thistle and shakes hands with everybody else, and you see the fine old Scotch honesty beaming out of their eyes.

And on St. George's Day!—well, there's no heartiness like the good old English spirit, after all; why shouldn't a man feel glad that he's an Englishman?

Then on the Fourth of July there are stars and stripes flying over half the stores in town, and suddenly all the men are seen to smoke cigars, and to know all about Roosevelt and Bryan and the Philippine Islands. Then you learn for the first time that Jeff Thorpe's people came from Massachusetts and that his uncle fought at Bunker Hill (it must have been Bunker Hill,—anyway Jefferson will swear it was in Dakota all right enough); and you find that George Duff has a married sister in Rochester and that her husband is all right; in fact, George was down there as recently as eight years ago. Oh, it's the most American town imaginable is Mariposa,—on the fourth of July.

But wait, just wait, if you feel anxious about the solidity of the British connection, till the twelfth of the month, when everybody is wearing an orange streamer in his coat and the Orangemen (every man in town) walk in the big procession. Allegiance! Well, perhaps you remember the address they gave to the Prince of Wales on the platform of the Mariposa station as he went through on his tour to the west. I think that pretty well settled that question.

So you will easily understand that of course everybody belongs to the Knights of Pythias and the Masons and Oddfellows, just as they all belong to the Snow Shoe Club and the Girls' Friendly Society.

And meanwhile the whistle of the steamer has blown again for a quarter to seven:—loud and long this time, for any one not here now is late for certain; unless he should happen to come down in the last fifteen minutes.

What a crowd upon the wharf and how they pile on to the steamer! It's a wonder that the boat can hold them all. But that's just the marvellous thing about the Mariposa Belle.

I don't know,—I have never known,—where the steamers like the Mariposa Belle come from. Whether they are built by Harland and Wolff of Belfast, or whether, on the other hand, they are not built by Harland and Wolff of Belfast, is more than one would like to say offhand.

The Mariposa Belle always seems to me to have some of those strange properties that distinguish Mariposa itself. I mean, her size seems to vary so. If you see her there in the winter, frozen in the ice beside the wharf with a snowdrift against the windows of the pilot house, she looks a pathetic little thing the size of a butternut. But in the summer time, especially after you've been in Mariposa for a month or two, and have paddled alongside of her in a canoe, she gets larger and taller, and with a great sweep of black sides, till you see no difference between the Mariposa Belle and the Lusitania. Each one is a big steamer and that's all you can say.

Nor do her measurements help you much. She draws about eighteen inches forward, and more than that,—at least half an inch more, astern, and when she's loaded down with an excursion crowd she draws a good two inches more. And above the water,—why, look at all the decks on her! There's the deck you walk on to, from the wharf, all shut in, with windows along it, and the after cabin with the long table, and above that the deck with all the chairs piled upon it, and the deck in front where the band stand round in a circle, and the pilot house is higher than that, and above the pilot house is the board with the gold name and the flag pole and the steel ropes and the flags; and fixed in somewhere on the different levels is the lunch counter where they sell the sandwiches, and the engine room, and down below the deck level, beneath the water line, is the place where the crew sleep. What with steps and stairs and passages and piles of cordwood for the engine,—oh no, I guess Harland and Wolff didn't build her. They couldn't have.

Yet even with a huge boat like the Mariposa Belle, it would be impossible for her to carry all of the crowd that you see in the boat and on the wharf. In reality, the crowd is made up of two classes,—all of the people in Mariposa who are going on the excursion and all those who are not. Some come for the one reason and some for the other.

The two tellers of the Exchange Bank are both there standing side by side. But one of them,—the one with the cameo pin and the long face like a horse,—is going, and the other,—with the other cameo pin and the face like another horse,—is not. In the same way, Hussell of the Newspacket is going, but his brother, beside him, isn't. Lilian Drone is going, but her sister can't; and so on all through the crowd.

And to think that things should look like that on the morning of a steamboat accident.

How strange life is!

To think of all these people so eager and anxious to catch the steamer, and some of them running to catch it, and so fearful that they might miss it,—the morning of a steamboat accident. And the captain blowing his whistle, and warning them so severely that he would leave them behind,—leave them out of the accident! And everybody crowding so eagerly to be in the accident.

Perhaps life is like that all through.

Strangest of all to think, in a case like this, of the people who were left behind, or in some way or other prevented from going, and always afterwards told of how they had escaped being on board the Mariposa Belle that day!

Some of the instances were certainly extraordinary.

Nivens, the lawyer, escaped from being there merely by the fact that he was away in the city.

Towers, the tailor, only escaped owing to the fact that, not intending to go on the excursion he had stayed in bed till eight o'clock and so had not gone. He narrated afterwards that waking up that morning at half-past five, he had thought of the excursion and for some unaccountable reason had felt glad that he was not going.

The case of Yodel, the auctioneer, was even more inscrutable. He had been to the Oddfellows' excursion on the train the week before and to the Conservative picnic the week before that, and had decided not to go on this trip. In fact, he had not the least intention of going. He narrated afterwards how the night before someone had stopped him on the corner of Nippewa and Tecumseh Streets (he indicated the very spot) and asked: "Are you going to take in the excursion to-morrow?" and he had said, just as simply as he was talking when narrating it: "No." And ten minutes after that, at the corner of Dalhousie and Brock Streets (he offered to lead a party of verification to the precise place) somebody else had stopped him and asked: "Well, are you going on the steamer trip to-morrow?" Again he had answered: "No," apparently almost in the same tone as before.

He said afterwards that when he heard the rumour of the accident it seemed like the finger of Providence, and fell on his knees in thankfulness.

There was the similar case of Morison (I mean the one in Glover's hardware store that married one of the Thompsons). He said afterwards that he had read so much in the papers about accidents lately,—mining accidents, and aeroplanes and gasoline,—that he had grown nervous. The night before his wife had asked him at supper: "Are you going on the excursion?" He had answered: "No, I don't think I feel like it," and had added: "Perhaps your mother might like to go." And the next evening just at dusk, when the news ran through the town, he said the first thought that flashed through his head was: "Mrs. Thompson's on that boat."

He told this right as I say it—without the least doubt or confusion. He never for a moment imagined she was on the Lusitania or the Olympic or any other boat. He knew she was on this one. He said you could have knocked him down where he stood. But no one had. Not even when he got halfway down,—on his knees, and it would have been easier still to knock him down or kick him. People do miss a lot of chances.

Still, as I say, neither Yodel nor Morison nor anyone thought about there being an accident until just after sundown when they—

Well, have you ever heard the long booming whistle of a steamboat two miles out on the lake in the dusk, and while you listen and count and wonder, seen the crimson rockets going up against the sky and then heard the fire bell ringing right there beside you in the town, and seen the people running to the town wharf?

That's what the people of Mariposa saw and felt that summer evening as they watched the Mackinaw life-boat go plunging out into the lake with seven sweeps to a side and the foam clear to the gunwale with the lifting stroke of fourteen men!

But, dear me, I am afraid that this is no way to tell a story. I suppose the true art would have been to have said nothing about the accident till it happened. But when you write about Mariposa, or hear of it, if you know the place, it's all so vivid and real that a thing like the contrast between the excursion crowd in the morning and the scene at night leaps into your mind and you must think of it.

❧ ❧ ❧

But never mind about the accident,—let us turn back again to the morning.

The boat was due to leave at seven. There was no doubt about the hour,—not only seven, but seven sharp. The notice in the Newspacket said: "The boat will leave sharp at seven;" and the advertising posters on the telegraph poles on Missinaba Street that began "Ho, for Indian's Island!" ended up with the words: "Boat leaves at seven sharp." There was a big notice on the wharf that said: "Boat leaves sharp on time."

So at seven, right on the hour, the whistle blew loud and long, and then at seven fifteen three short peremptory blasts, and at seven thirty one quick angry call,—just one,—and very soon after that they cast off the last of the ropes and the Mariposa Belle sailed off in her cloud of flags, and the band of the Knights of Pythias, timing it to a nicety, broke into the "Maple Leaf for Ever!"

I suppose that all excursions when they start are much the same. Anyway, on the Mariposa Belle everybody went running up and down all over the boat with deck chairs and camp stools and baskets, and found places, splendid places to sit, and then got scared that there might be better ones and chased off again. People hunted for places out of the sun and when they got them swore that they weren't going to freeze to please anybody; and the people in the sun said that they hadn't paid fifty cents to be roasted. Others said that they hadn't paid fifty cents to get covered with cinders, and there were still others who hadn't paid fifty cents to get shaken to death with the propeller.

Still, it was all right presently. The people seemed to get sorted out into the places on the boat where they belonged. The women, the older ones, all gravitated into the cabin on the lower deck and by getting round the table with needlework, and with all the windows shut, they soon had it, as they said themselves, just like being at home.

All the young boys and the toughs and the men in the band got down on the lower deck forward, where the boat was dirtiest and where the anchor was and the coils of rope.

And upstairs on the after deck there were Lilian Drone and Miss Lawson, the high school teacher, with a book of German poetry,—Gothey I think it was,—and the bank teller and the younger men.

In the centre, standing beside the rail, were Dean Drone and Dr. Gallagher, looking through binocular glasses at the shore.

Up in front on the little deck forward of the pilot house was a group of the older men, Mullins and Duff and Mr. Smith in a deck chair, and beside him Mr. Golgotha Gingham, the undertaker of Mariposa, on a stool. It was part of Mr. Gingham's principles to take in an outing of this sort, a business matter, more or less,—for you never know what may happen at these water parties. At any rate, he was there in a neat suit of black, not, of course, his heavier or professional suit, but a soft clinging effect as of burnt paper that combined gaiety and decorum to a nicety.

~ ~ ~

"Yes," said Mr. Gingham, waving his black glove in a general way towards the shore, "I know the lake well, very well. I've been pretty much all over it in my time."

"Canoeing?" asked somebody.

"No," said Mr. Gingham, "not in a canoe." There seemed a peculiar and quiet meaning in his tone.

"Sailing, I suppose," said somebody else.

"No," said Mr. Gingham. "I don't understand it."

"I never knowed that you went on to the water at all, Gol," said Mr. Smith, breaking in.

"Ah, not now," explained Mr. Gingham; "it was years ago, the first summer I came to Mariposa. I was on the water practically all day. Nothing like it to give a man an appetite and keep him in shape."

"Was you camping?" asked Mr. Smith.

"We camped at night," assented the undertaker, "but we put in practically the whole day on the water. You see we were after a party that had come up here from the city on his vacation and gone out in a sailing canoe. We were dragging. We were up every morning at sunrise, lit a fire on the beach and cooked breakfast, and then we'd light our pipes and be off with the net for a whole day. It's a great life," concluded Mr. Gingham wistfully.

"Did you get him?" asked two or three together.

There was a pause before Mr. Gingham answered.

"We did," he said,—"down in the reeds past Horseshoe Point. But it was no use. He turned blue on me right away."

After which Mr. Gingham fell into such a deep reverie that the boat had steamed another half-mile down the lake before anybody broke the silence again.

Talk of this sort,—and after all what more suitable for a day on the water?—beguiled the way.

~ ~ ~

Down the lake, mile by mile over the calm water, steamed the Mariposa Belle. They passed Poplar Point where the high sand-banks are with all the swallows' nests in them, and Dean Drone and Dr. Gallagher looked at them alternately through the binocular glasses, and it was wonderful how plainly one could see the swallows and the banks and the shrubs,—just as plainly as with the naked eye.

And a little further down they passed the Shingle Beach, and Dr. Gallagher, who knew Canadian history, said to Dean Drone that it was strange to think that Champlain had landed there with his French explorers three hundred years ago; and Dean Drone, who didn't know

Canadian history, said it was stranger still to think that the hand of the Almighty had piled up the hills and rocks long before that; and Dr. Gallagher said it was wonderful how the French had found their way through such a pathless wilderness; and Dean Drone said that it was wonderful also to think that the Almighty had placed even the smallest shrub in its appointed place. Dr. Gallagher said it filled him with admiration. Dean Drone said it filled him with awe. Dr. Gallagher said he'd been full of it ever since he was a boy; and Dean Drone said so had he.

Then a little further, as the Mariposa Belle steamed on down the lake, they passed the Old Indian Portage where the great grey rocks are; and Dr. Gallagher drew Dean Drone's attention to the place where the narrow canoe track wound up from the shore to the woods, and Dean Drone said he could see it perfectly well without the glasses.

Dr. Gallagher said that it was just here that a party of five hundred French had made their way with all their baggage and accoutrements across the rocks of the divide and down to the Great Bay. And Dean Drone said that it reminded him of Xenophon leading his ten thousand Greeks over the hill passes of Armenia down to the sea. Dr. Gallagher said that he had often wished he could have seen and spoken to Champlain, and Dean Drone said how much he regretted to have never known Xenophon.

And then after that they fell to talking of relics and traces of the past, and Dr. Gallagher said that if Dean Drone would come round to his house some night he would show him some Indian arrow heads that he had dug up in his garden. And Dean Drone said that if Dr. Gallagher would come round to the rectory any afternoon he would show him a map of Xerxes' invasion of Greece. Only he must come some time between the Infant Class and the Mothers' Auxiliary.

So presently they both knew that they were blocked out of one another's houses for some time to come, and Dr. Gallagher walked forward and told Mr. Smith, who had never studied Greek, about Champlain crossing the rock divide.

Mr. Smith turned his head and looked at the divide for half a second and then said he had crossed a worse one up north back of the Wahnipitae and that the flies were Hades,—and then went on playing freezeout poker with the two juniors in Duff's bank.

So Dr. Gallagher realized that that's always the way when you try to tell people things, and that as far as gratitude and appreciation goes one might as well never read books or travel anywhere or do anything.

In fact, it was at this very moment that he made up his mind to give the arrows to the Mariposa Mechanics' Institute,—they afterwards became, as you know, the Gallagher Collection. But, for the time being, the doctor was sick of them and wandered off round the boat and watched Henry Mullins showing George Duff how to make a John Collins without lemons, and finally went and sat down among the Mariposa band and wished that he hadn't come.

So the boat steamed on and the sun rose higher and higher, and the freshness of the morning changed into the full glare of noon, and they went on to where the lake began to narrow in at its foot, just where the Indian's Island is,—all grass and trees and with a log wharf running into the water. Below it the Lower Ossawippi runs out of the lake, and quite near are the rapids, and you can see down among the trees the red brick of the power house and hear the roar of the leaping water.

The Indian's Island itself is all covered with trees and tangled vines, and the water about it is so still that it's all reflected double and looks the same either way up. Then when the steamer's whistle blows as it comes into the wharf, you hear it echo among the trees of the island, and reverberate back from the shores of the lake.

The scene is all so quiet and still and unbroken, that Miss Cleghorn,—the sallow girl in the telephone exchange, that I spoke of—said she'd like to be buried there. But all the people were so busy getting their baskets and gathering up their things that no one had time to attend to it.

I mustn't even try to describe the landing and the boat crunching against the wooden wharf and all the people running to the same side of the deck and Christie Johnson calling out to the crowd to keep to the starboard and nobody being able to find it. Everyone who has been on a Mariposa excursion knows all about that.

Nor can I describe the day itself and the picnic under the trees. There were speeches afterwards, and Judge Pepperleigh gave such offence by bringing in Conservative politics that a man called Patriotus Canadiensis wrote and asked for some of the invaluable space of the Mariposa Times-Herald and exposed it.

I should say that there were races too, on the grass on the open side of the island, graded mostly according to ages,—races for boys under thirteen and girls over nineteen and all that sort of thing. Sports are generally conducted on that plan in Mariposa. It is realized that a woman of sixty has an unfair advantage over a mere child.

Dean Drone managed the races and decided the ages and gave out the prizes; the Wesleyan minister helped, and he and the young student, who was relieving in the Presbyterian Church, held the string at the winning point.

They had to get mostly clergymen for the races because all the men had wandered off, somehow, to where they were drinking lager beer out of two kegs stuck on pine logs among the trees.

But if you've ever been on a Mariposa excursion you know all about these details anyway.

So the day wore on and presently the sun came through the trees on a slant and the steamer whistle blew with a great puff of white steam and all the people came straggling down to the wharf and pretty soon the Mariposa Belle had floated out on to the lake again and headed for the town, twenty miles away.

~ ~ ~

I suppose you have often noticed the contrast there is between an excursion on its way out in the morning and what it looks like on the way home.

In the morning everybody is so restless and animated and moves to and fro all over the boat and asks questions. But coming home, as the afternoon gets later and the sun sinks beyond the hills, all the people seem to get so still and quiet and drowsy.

So it was with the people on the Mariposa Belle. They sat there on the benches and the deck chairs in little clusters, and listened to the regular beat of the propeller and almost dozed off asleep as they sat. Then when the sun set and the dusk drew on, it grew almost dark on the deck and so still that you could hardly tell there was anyone on board.

And if you had looked at the steamer from the shore or from one of the islands, you'd have seen the row of lights from the cabin windows shining on the water and the red glare of the burning hemlock from the funnel, and you'd have heard the soft thud of the propeller miles away over the lake.

Now and then, too, you could have heard them singing on the steamer,—the voices of the girls and the men blended into unison by the distance, rising and falling in long-drawn melody: "*O—Can-a-da—O—Can-a-da.*"

You may talk as you will about the intoning choirs of your European cathedrals, but the sound of "O Can-a-da," borne across the waters of a silent lake at evening is good enough for those of us who know Mariposa.

I think that it was just as they were singing like this: "*O—Can-a-da,*" that word went round that the boat was sinking.

If you have ever been in any sudden emergency on the water, you will understand the strange psychology of it,—the way in which what is happening seems to become known all in a moment without a word being said. The news is transmitted from one to the other by some mysterious process.

At any rate, on the Mariposa Belle first one and then the other heard that the steamer was sinking. As far as I could ever learn the first of it was that George Duff, the bank manager, came very quietly to Dr. Gallagher and asked him if he thought that the boat was sinking. The doctor said no, that he had thought so earlier in the day but that he didn't now think that she was.

After that Duff, according to his own account, had said to Macartney, the lawyer, that the boat was sinking, and Macartney said that he doubted it very much.

Then somebody came to Judge Pepperleigh and woke him up and said that there was six inches of water in the steamer and that she was sinking. And Pepperleigh said it was perfect scandal and passed the news on to his wife and she said that they had no business to allow it and that if the steamer sank that was the last excursion she'd go on.

So the news went all round the boat and everywhere the people gathered in groups and talked about it in the angry and excited way that people have when a steamer is sinking on one of the lakes like Lake Wissanotti.

Dean Drone, of course, and some others were quieter about it, and said that one must make allowances and that naturally there were two sides to everything. But most of them wouldn't listen to reason at all. I think, perhaps, that some of them were frightened. You see the last time but one that the steamer had sunk, there had been a man drowned and it made them nervous.

What? Hadn't I explained about the depth of Lake Wissanotti? I had taken it for granted that you knew; and in any case parts of it are deep enough, though I don't suppose in this stretch of it from the big reed beds up to within a mile of the town wharf, you could find six feet of water in it if you tried. Oh, pshaw! I was not talking about a steamer sinking in the ocean and carrying down its screaming crowds of people into the hideous depths of green water. Oh, dear me no! That kind of thing never happens on Lake Wissanotti.

But what does happen is that the Mariposa Belle sinks every now and then, and sticks there on the bottom till they get things straightened up.

On the lakes round Mariposa, if a person arrives late anywhere and explains that the steamer sank, everybody understands the situation.

You see when Harland and Wolff built the Mariposa Belle, they left some cracks in between the timbers that you fill up with cotton waste every Sunday. If this is not attended to, the boat sinks. In fact, it is part of the law of the province that all the steamers like the Mariposa Belle must be properly corked,—I think that is the word,—every season. There are inspectors who visit all the hotels in the province to see that it is done.

So you can imagine now that I've explained it a little straighter, the indignation of the people when they knew that the boat had come uncorked and that they might be stuck out there on a shoal or a mud-bank half the night.

I don't say either that there wasn't any danger; anyway, it doesn't feel very safe when you realize that the boat is settling down with every hundred yards that she goes, and you look over the side and see only the black water in the gathering night.

Safe! I'm not sure now that I come to think of it that it isn't worse than sinking in the Atlantic. After all, in the Atlantic there is wireless telegraphy, and a lot of trained sailors and stewards. But out on Lake Wissanotti,—far out, so that you can only just see the lights of the town away off to the south,—when the propeller comes to a stop,—and you can hear the hiss of steam as they start to rake out the engine fires to prevent an explosion,—and when you turn from the red glare that comes from the furnace doors as they open them, to the black dark that is gathering over the lake,—and there's a night wind beginning to run among the rushes,—and you see the men going forward to the roof of the pilot house to send up the rockets to rouse the town,—safe? Safe yourself, if you like; as for me, let me once get back into Mariposa again, under the night shadow of the maple trees, and this shall be the last, last time I'll go on Lake Wissanotti.

Safe! Oh yes! Isn't it strange how safe other people's adventures seem after they happen? But you'd have been scared, too, if you'd been there just before the steamer sank, and seen them bringing up all the women on to the top deck.

I don't see how some of the people took it so calmly; how Mr. Smith, for instance, could have gone on smoking and telling how he'd had a steamer "sink on him" on Lake Nipissing and a still bigger one, a side-wheeler, sink on him in Lake Abbitibbi.

Then, quite suddenly, with a quiver, down she went. You could feel the boat sink, sink,—down, down,—would it never get to the bottom? The water came flush up to the lower deck, and then,—thank heaven,—the sinking stopped and there was the Mariposa Belle safe and tight on a reed bank.

Really, it made one positively laugh! It seemed so queer and, anyway, if a man has a sort of natural courage, danger makes him laugh. Danger! pshaw! fiddlesticks! everybody scouted the idea. Why, it is just the little things like this that give zest to a day on the water.

Within half a minute they were all running round looking for sandwiches and cracking jokes and talking of making coffee over the remains of the engine fires.

~ ~ ~

I don't need to tell at length how it all happened after that.

I suppose the people on the Mariposa Belle would have had to settle down there all night or till help came from the town, but some of the men who had gone forward and were peering out into the dark said that it couldn't be more than a mile across the water to Miller's Point. You could almost see it over there to the left,—some of them, I think, said "off on the port bow," because you know when you get mixed up in these marine disasters, you soon catch the atmosphere of the thing.

So pretty soon they had the davits swung out over the side and were lowering the old lifeboat from the top deck into the water.

There were men leaning out over the rail of the Mariposa Belle with lanterns that threw the light as they let her down, and the glare fell on the water and the reeds. But when they got the boat lowered, it looked such a frail, clumsy thing as one saw it from the rail above, that the cry was raised: "Women and children first!" For what was the sense, if it should turn out that the boat wouldn't even hold women and children, of trying to jam a lot of heavy men into it?

So they put in mostly women and children and the boat pushed out into the darkness so freighted down it would hardly float.

In the bow of it was the Presbyterian student who was relieving the minister, and he called out that they were in the hands of Providence. But he was crouched and ready to spring out of them at the first moment.

So the boat went and was lost in the darkness except for the lantern in the bow that you could see bobbing on the water. Then presently it came back and they sent another load, till pretty soon the decks began to thin out and everybody got impatient to be gone.

It was about the time that the third boat-load put off that Mr. Smith took a bet with Mullins for twenty-five dollars, that he'd be home in Mariposa before the people in the boats had walked round the shore.

No one knew just what he meant, but pretty soon they saw Mr. Smith disappear down below into the lowest part of the steamer with a mallet in one hand and a big bundle of marline in the other.

They might have wondered more about it, but it was just at this time that they heard the shouts from the rescue boat—the big Mackinaw lifeboat—that had put out from the town with fourteen men at the sweeps when they saw the first rockets go up.

I suppose there is always something inspiring about a rescue at sea, or on the water.

After all, the bravery of the lifeboat man is the true bravery,—expended to save life, not to destroy it.

Certainly they told for months after of how the rescue boat came out to the Mariposa Belle.

I suppose that when they put her in the water the lifeboat touched it for the first time since the old Macdonald Government placed her on Lake Wissanotti.

Anyway, the water poured in at every seam. But not for a moment,—even with two miles of water between them and the steamer,—did the rowers pause for that.

By the time they were half-way there the water was almost up to the thwarts, but they drove her on. Panting and exhausted (for mind you, if you haven't been in a fool boat like that for years, rowing takes it out of you), the rowers stuck to their task. They threw the ballast over and chucked into the water the heavy cork jackets and lifebelts that encumbered their movements. There was no thought of turning back. They were nearer to the steamer than the shore.

"Hang to it, boys," called the crowd from the steamer's deck, and hang they did.

They were almost exhausted when they got them; men leaning from the steamer threw them ropes and one by one every man was hauled aboard just as the lifeboat sank under their feet.

Saved! by Heaven, saved, by one of the smartest pieces of rescue work ever seen on the lake.

There's no use describing it; you need to see rescue work of this kind by lifeboats to understand it.

Nor were the lifeboat crew the only ones that distinguished themselves.

Boat after boat and canoe after canoe had put out from Mariposa to the help of the steamer. They got them all.

Pupkin, the other bank teller, with a face like a horse, who hadn't gone on the excursion,—as soon as he knew that the boat was signalling for help and that Miss Lawson was sending up rockets,—rushed for a row boat, grabbed an oar (two would have hampered him), and paddled madly out into the lake. He struck right out into the dark with the crazy skiff almost sinking beneath his feet. But they got him. They rescued him. They watched him, almost dead with exhaustion, make his way to the steamer, where he was hauled up with ropes. Saved! Saved!!

❧ ❧ ❧

They might have gone on that way half the night, picking up the rescuers, only, at the very moment when the tenth load of people left for the shore,—just as suddenly and saucily as you please, up came the Mariposa Belle from the mud bottom and floated.

FLOATED?

Why, of course she did. If you take a hundred and fifty people off a steamer that has sunk, and if you get a man as shrewd as Mr. Smith to plug the timber seams with mallet and marline, and if you turn ten bandsmen of the Mariposa band on to your hand pump on the bow of the lower decks—float? why, what else can she do?

Then, if you stuff in hemlock into the embers of the fire that you were raking out, till it hums and crackles under the boiler, it won't be long before you hear the propeller thud—thudding at the stern again, and before the long roar of the steam whistle echoes over to the town.

And so the Mariposa Belle, with all steam up again and with the long train of sparks careering from the funnel, is heading for the town.

But no Christie Johnson at the wheel in the pilot house this time.

"Smith! Get Smith!" is the cry.

Can he take her in? Well, now! Ask a man who has had steamers sink on him in half the lakes from Temiscaming to the Bay, if he can take her in? Ask a man who has run a York boat down the rapids of the Moose when the ice is moving, if he can grip the steering wheel of the Mariposa Belle? So there she steams safe and sound to the town wharf!

Look at the lights and the crowd! If only the federal census taker could count us now! Hear them calling and shouting back and forward from the deck to the shore! Listen! There is the rattle of the shore ropes as they get them ready, and there's the Mariposa band,—actually forming in a circle on the upper deck just as she docks, and the leader with his baton,—one—two—ready now,—

"O CAN-A-DA!"

FOUR

The Ministrations of the Rev. Mr. Drone

THE CHURCH of England in Mariposa is on a side street, where the maple trees are thickest, a little up the hill from the heart of the town. The trees above the church and the grass plot that was once the cemetery, till they made the new one (the Necropolis, over the brow of the hill), fill out the whole corner. Down behind the church, with only the driving shed and a lane between, is the rectory. It is a little brick house with odd angles. There is a hedge and a little gate, and a weeping ash tree with red berries.

At the side of the rectory, churchward, is a little grass lawn with low hedges and at the side of that two wild plum trees, that are practically always in white blossom. Underneath them is a rustic table and chairs, and it is here that you may see Rural Dean Drone, the incumbent of the Church of England Church, sitting, in the chequered light of the plum tress that is neither sun nor shadow. Generally you will find him reading, and when I tell you that at the end of the grass plot where the hedge is highest there is a yellow bee hive with seven bees that belong to Dean Drone, you will realize that it is only fitting that the Dean is reading in the Greek. For what better could a man be reading beneath the blossom of the plum trees, within the very sound of the bees, than the Pastorals of Theocritus? The light trash of modern romance might put a man to sleep in such a spot, but with such food for reflection as Theocritus, a man may safely close his eyes and muse on what he reads without fear of dropping into slumber.

Some men, I suppose, terminate their education when they leave their college. Not so Dean Drone. I have often heard him say that if he couldn't take a book in the Greek out on the lawn in a spare half-hour, he would feel lost. It's a certain activity of the brain that must be stilled somehow. The Dean, too, seemed to have a native feeling for the Greek language. I have often heard people who might sit with him on the lawn, ask him to translate some of it. But he always refused. One couldn't translate it, he said. It lost so much in the translation that it was better not to try. It was far wiser not to attempt it. If you undertook to translate it, there was something gone, something missing immediately. I believe that many classical scholars feel this way, and like to read the Greek just as it is, without the hazard of trying to put it into so poor a medium as English. So that when Dean Drone said that he simply couldn't translate it, I believe he was perfectly sincere.

Sometimes, indeed, he would read it aloud. That was another matter. Whenever, for example, Dr. Gallagher—I mean, of course, old Dr. Gallagher, not the young doctor (who was always out in the country in the afternoon)—would come over and bring his latest Indian relics to show to the Dean, the latter always read to him a passage or two. As soon as the doctor laid his tomahawk on the table, the Dean would reach for his Theocritus. I remember that on the day when Dr. Gallagher brought over the Indian skull that they had dug out of the railway embankment, and placed it on the rustic table, the Dean read to him so long from Theocritus that the doctor, I truly believe, dozed off in his chair. The Dean had to wait and fold his hands with the book across his knee, and close his eyes till the doctor should wake up again. And the skull was on the table between them, and from above the plum blossoms fluttered down, till they made flakes on it as white as Dr. Gallagher's hair.

~ ~ ~

I don't want you to suppose that the Rev. Mr. Drone spent the whole of his time under the trees. Not at all. In point of fact, the rector's life was one round of activity which he himself might deplore but was powerless to prevent. He had hardly sat down beneath the trees of an afternoon after his mid-day meal when there was the Infant Class at three, and after that, with scarcely an hour between, the Mothers' Auxiliary at five, and the next morning the Book Club, and that evening the Bible Study Class, and the next morning the Early Workers' Guild at eleven-thirty. The whole week was like that, and if one found time to sit down for an hour or so to recuperate it was the most one could do. After all, if a busy man spends the little bit of leisure that he gets in advanced classical study, there is surely no harm in it. I suppose, take it all in all, there wasn't a busier man than the Rural Dean among the Anglican clergy of the diocese.

If the Dean ever did snatch a half-day from his incessant work, he spent it in fishing. But not always that, for as likely as not, instead of taking a real holiday he would put in the whole afternoon amusing the children and the boys that he knew, by making kites and toys and clockwork steamboats for them.

It was fortunate for the Dean that he had the strange interest and aptitude for mechanical advices which he possessed, or otherwise this kind of thing would have been too cruel an imposition. But the Rev. Mr. Drone had a curious liking for machinery. I think I never heard him preach a better sermon than the one on Aeroplanes (Lo, what now see you on high Jeremiah Two).

So it was that he spent two whole days making a kite with Chinese wings for Teddy Moore, the photographer's son, and closed down the infant class for forty-eight hours so that Teddy Moore should not miss the pleasure of flying it, or rather seeing it flown. It is foolish to trust a Chinese kite to the hands of a young child.

In the same way the Dean made a mechanical top for little Marjorie

Trewlaney, the cripple, to see spun: it would have been unwise to allow the afflicted girl to spin it. There was no end to the things that Mr. Drone could make, and always for the children. Even when he was making the sand-clock for poor little Willie Yodel (who died, you know) the Dean went right on with it and gave it to another child with just the same pleasure. Death, you know, to the clergy is a different thing from what it is to us. The Dean and Mr. Gingham used often to speak of it as they walked through the long grass of the new cemetery, the Necropolis. And when your Sunday walk is to your wife's grave, as the Dean's was, perhaps it seems different to anybody.

The Church of England Church, I said, stood close to the rectory, a tall, sweeping church, and inside a great reach of polished cedar beams that ran to the point of the roof. There used to stand on the same spot the little stone church that all the grown-up people in Mariposa still remember, a quaint little building in red and grey stone. About it was the old cemetery, but that was all smoothed out later into the grass plot round the new church, and the headstones laid out flat, and no new graves have been put there for ever so long. But the Mariposa children still walk round and read the headstones lying flat in the grass and look for the old ones,—because some of them are ever so old—forty or fifty years back.

Nor are you to think from all this that the Dean was not a man with serious perplexities. You could easily convince yourself of the contrary. For if you watched the Rev. Mr. Drone as he sat reading in the Greek, you would notice that no very long period every passed without his taking up a sheet or two of paper that lay between the leaves of the Theocritus and that were covered close with figures.

And these the Dean would lay upon the rustic table, and he would add them up forwards and backwards, going first up the column and then down it to see that nothing had been left out, and then down it again to see what it was that must have been left out.

Mathematics, you will understand, were not the Dean's forte. They never were the forte of the men who had been trained at the little

Anglican college with the clipped hedges and the cricket ground, where Rupert Drone had taken the gold medal in Greek fifty-two years ago. You will see the medal at any time lying there in its open box on the rectory table, in case of immediate need. Any of the Drone girls, Lilian, or Jocelyn, or Theodora, would show it to you. But, as I say, mathematics were not the rector's forte, and he blamed for it (in a Christian spirit, you will understand) the memory of his mathematical professor, and often he spoke with great bitterness. I have often heard him say that in his opinion the colleges ought to dismiss, of course in a Christian spirit, all the professors who are not, in the most reverential sense of the term, fit for their jobs.

No doubt many of the clergy of the diocese had suffered more or less just as the Dean had from lack of mathematical training. But the Dean always felt that his own case was especially to be lamented. For you see, if a man is trying to make a model aeroplane—for a poor family in the lower part of the town—and he is brought to a stop by the need of reckoning the coefficient of torsion of cast-iron rods, it shows plainly enough that the colleges are not truly filling their divine mission.

But the figures that I speak of were not those of the model aeroplane. These were far more serious. Night and day they had been with the rector now for the best part of ten years, and they grew, if anything, more intricate.

If, for example, you try to reckon the debt of a church—a large church with a great sweep of polished cedar beams inside, for the special glorification of the All Powerful, and with imported tiles on the roof for the greater glory of Heaven and with stained-glass windows for the exaltation of the All Seeing—if, I say, you try to reckon up the debt on such a church and figure out its interest and its present worth, less a fixed annual payment, it makes a pretty complicated sum. Then if you try to add to this the annual cost of insurance, and deduct from it three-quarters of a stipend, year by year, and then suddenly remember that three-quarters is too much, because you have forgotten the boarding-school fees of the littlest of the Drones (including French, as an extra—she must have it, all the older girls did), you have got a sum that pretty well defies ordinary arithmetic. The provoking part of it was that the Dean knew perfectly well that with the help of logarithms he could have done the thing in a moment. But at the Anglican college they had stopped short at that very place in the book. They had simply explained that Logos was a word and Arithmos a number, which at the time, seemed amply sufficient.

So the Dean was perpetually taking out his sheets of figures, and adding them upwards and downwards, and they never came the same. Very often Mr. Gingham, who was a warden, would come and sit beside the rector and ponder over the figures, and Mr. Drone would explain that with a book of logarithms you could work it out in a moment. You would simply open the book and run your finger up the columns (he illustrated exactly the way in which the finger was moved), and there you were. Mr. Gingham said that it was a caution, and that logarithms (I quote his exact phrase) must be a terror.

Very often, too, Nivens, the lawyer, who was a sidesman, and Mullins, the manager of the Exchange Bank, who was the chairman of the vestry, would come and take a look, at the figures. But they never could make much of them, because the stipend part was not a matter that one could discuss.

Mullins would notice the item for a hundred dollars due on fire insurance and would say, as a business man, that surely that couldn't be fire insurance, and the Dean would say surely not, and change it: and Mullins would say surely there couldn't be fifty dollars for taxes, because there weren't any taxes, and the Dean would admit that of course it couldn't be for the taxes. In fact, the truth is that the Dean's figures were badly mixed, and the fault lay indubitably with the mathematical professor of two generations back.

It was always Mullins's intention some day to look into the finances of the church, the more so as his father had been with Dean Drone at the little Anglican college with the cricket ground. But he was a busy man. As he explained to the rector himself, the banking business nowadays is getting to be such that a banker can hardly call even his Sunday mornings his own. Certainly Henry Mullins could not. They belonged largely to Smith's Hotel, and during the fishing season they belonged away down the lake, so far away that practically no one, unless it was George Duff of the Commercial Bank, could see them.

But to think that all this trouble had come through the building of the new church.

That was the bitterness of it.

For the twenty-five years that Rural Dean Drone had preached in the little stone church, it had been his one aim, as he often put it in his sermons, to rear a larger Ark in Gideon. His one hope had been to set up a greater Evidence, or, very simply stated, to kindle a Brighter Beacon.

After twenty-five years of waiting, he had been able at last to kindle it. Everybody in Mariposa remembers the building of the church. First of all they had demolished the little stone church to make way for the newer Evidence. It seemed almost a sacrilege, as the Dean himself said, to lay hands on it. Indeed it was at first proposed to take the stone of it and build it into a Sunday School, as a lesser testimony. Then, when that provided impracticable, it was suggested that the stone be reverently fashioned into a wall that should stand as a token. And when even that could not be managed, the stone of the little church was laid reverently into a stone pile; afterwards it was devoutly sold to a building contractor, and, like so much else in life, was forgotten.

But the building of the church, no one, I think, will forget. The Dean threw himself into the work. With his coat off and his white shirt-sleeves conspicuous among the gang that were working at the foundations, he set his hand to the shovel, himself guided the road-scraper, urging on the horses, cheering and encouraging the men, till they begged him to desist.

He mingled with the stone-masons, advising, helping, and giving counsel, till they pleaded with him to rest. He was among the carpenters, sawing, hammering, enquiring, suggesting, till they besought him to lay off. And he was night and day with the architect's assistants, drawing, planning, revising, till the architect told him to cut it out.

So great was his activity, that I doubt whether the new church would ever have been finished, had not the wardens and the vestry men insisted that Mr. Drone must take a holiday, and sent him on the Mackinaw trip up the lakes,—the only foreign travel of the Dean's life.

~ ~ ~

So in due time the New Church was built and it towered above the maple trees of Mariposa like a beacon on a hill. It stood so high that from the open steeple of it, where the bells were, you could see all the town lying at its feet, and the farmsteads to the south of it, and the railway like a double pencil line, and Lake Wissanotti spread out like a map. You could see and appreciate things from the height of the new church,—such as the size and the growing wealth of Mariposa,—that you never could have seen from the little stone church at all.

Presently the church was opened and the Dean preached his first sermon in it, and he called it a Greater Testimony, and he said that it was an earnest, or firstfruit of endeavour, and that it was a token or pledge, and he named it also a covenant. He said, too, that it was an anchorage and a harbour and a lighthouse as well as being a city set upon a hill; and he ended by declaring it an Ark of Refuge and notified them that the Bible Class would meet in the basement of it on that and every other third Wednesday.

In the opening months of preaching about it the Dean had called the church so often an earnest and a pledge and a guerdon and a tabernacle, that I think he used to forget that it wasn't paid for. It was only when the agent of the building society and a representative of the Hosanna Pipe and Steam Organ Co. (Limited), used to call for quarterly payments that he was suddenly reminded of the fact. Always after these men came round the Dean used to preach a special sermon on sin, in the course of which he would mention that the ancient Hebrews used to put unjust traders to death,—a thing of which he spoke with Christian serenity.

I don't think that at first anybody troubled much about the debt on the church. Dean Drone's figures showed that it was only a matter of time before it would be extinguished; only a little effort was needed, a little girding up of the loins of the congregation and they could shoulder the whole debt and trample it under their feet. Let them but set their hands to the plough and they could soon guide it into the deep water. Then they might furl their sails and sit every man under his own olive tree.

Meantime, while the congregation was waiting to gird up its loins, the interest on the debt was paid somehow, or, when it wasn't paid, was added to the principal.

I don't know whether you have had any experience with Greater Testimonies and with Beacons set on Hills. If you have, you will realize how, at first gradually, and then rapidly, their position from year to year grows more distressing. What with the building loan and the organ instalment, and the fire insurance,—a cruel charge,—and the heat and light, the rector began to realize as he added up the figures that nothing but logarithms could solve them. Then the time came when not only the rector, but all the wardens knew and the sidesmen knew that the debt was more than the church could carry; then the choir knew and the congregation knew and at last everybody knew; and there were special collections at Easter and special days of giving, and special weeks of tribulation, and special arrangements with the Hosanna Pipe and Steam Organ Co. And it was noticed that when the Rural Dean announced a service of Lenten Sorrow,—aimed more especially at the business men,—the congregation had diminished by forty per cent.

~ ~ ~

I suppose things are just the same elsewhere,—I mean the peculiar kind of discontent that crept into the Church of England congregation in Mariposa after the setting up of the Beacon. There were those who claimed that they had seen the error from the first, though they had kept quiet, as such people always do, from breadth of mind. There were those who had felt years before how it would end, but their lips were sealed from humility of spirit. What was worse was that there were others who grew dissatisfied with the whole conduct of the church.

Yodel, the auctioneer, for example, narrated how he had been to the city and had gone into a service of the Roman Catholic church: I believe, to state it more fairly, he had "dropped in,"—the only recognized means of access to such a service. He claimed that the music that he had heard there was music, and that (outside of his profession) the chanting and intoning could not be touched.

Ed Moore, the photographer, also related that he had listened to a sermon in the city, and that if anyone would guarantee him a sermon like that he would defy you to keep him away from church. Meanwhile, failing the guarantee, he stayed away.

The very doctrines were impeached. Some of the congregation began to cast doubts on eternal punishment,—doubts so grave as to keep them absent from the Lenten Services of Sorrow. Indeed, Lawyer Macartney took up the whole question of the Athanasian Creed one afternoon with Joe Milligan, the dentist, and hardly left a clause of it intact.

All this time, you will understand, Dean Drone kept on with his special services, and leaflets, calls, and appeals went out from the Ark of Gideon like rockets from a sinking ship. More and more with every month the debt of the church lay heavy on his mind. At times he forgot it. At other times he woke up in the night and thought about it. Sometimes as he went down the street from the lighted precincts of the Greater Testimony and passed the Salvation Army, praying around a naphtha lamp under the open sky, it smote him to the heart with a stab.

But the congregation were wrong, I think, in imputing fault to the sermons of Dean Drone. There I do think they were wrong. I can speak from personal knowledge when I say that the rector's sermons were not only stimulating in matters of faith, but contained valuable material in regard to the Greek language, to modern machinery and to a variety of things that should have proved of the highest advantage to the congregation.

There was, I say, the Greek language. The Dean always showed the greatest delicacy of feeling in regard to any translation in or out of it that he made from the pulpit. He was never willing to accept even the faintest shade of rendering different from that commonly given without being assured of the full concurrence of the congregation. Either the translation must be unanimous and without contradiction, or he could not pass it. He would pause in his sermon and would say: "The original Greek is 'Hoson,' but perhaps you will allow me to translate it as equivalent to 'Hoyon.'" And they did. So that if there was any fault to be found it was purely on the side of the congregation for not entering a protest at the time.

It was the same way in regard to machinery. After all, what better illustrates the supreme purpose of the All Wise than such a thing as the dynamo or the reciprocating marine engine or the pictures in the Scientific American?

Then, too, if a man has had the opportunity to travel and has seen the great lakes spread out by the hand of Providence from where one leaves the new dock at the Sound to where one arrives safe and thankful with one's dear fellow-passengers in the spirit at the concrete landing stage at Mackinaw—is not this fit and proper material for the construction of an analogy or illustration? Indeed, even apart from an analogy, is it not mighty interesting to narrate, anyway? In any case, why should the churchwardens have sent the rector on the Mackinaw trip, if they had not expected him to make some little return for it?

I lay some stress on this point because the criticisms directed against the Mackinaw sermons always seemed so unfair. If the rector had described his experiences in the crude language of the ordinary newspaper, there might, I admit, have been something unfitting about it. But he was always careful to express himself in a way that showed,—or, listen, let me explain with an example.

"It happened to be my lot some years ago," he would say, "to find myself a voyager, just as one is a voyager on the sea of life, on the broad expanse of water which has been spread out to the north-west of us by the hand of Providence, at a height of five hundred and eighty-one feet above the level of the sea,—I refer, I may say, to Lake Huron."

Now, how different that is from saying: "I'll never forget the time I went on the Mackinaw trip." The whole thing has a different sound entirely. In the same way the Dean would go on:

"I was voyaging on one of those magnificent leviathans of the water,—I refer to the boats of the Northern Navigation Company,—and was standing beside the forward rail talking with a dear brother in the faith who was journeying westward also—I may say he was a commercial traveller,—and beside us was a dear sister in the spirit seated in a deck chair, while near us were two other dear souls in grace engaged in Christian pastime on the deck,—I allude more particulary to the game of deck billiards."

I leave it to any reasonable man whether, with that complete and fair-minded explanation of the environment, it was not perfectly proper to close down the analogy, as the rector did, with the simple words: "In fact, it was an extremely fine morning."

Yet there were some people, even in Mariposa, that took exception and spent their Sunday dinner time in making out that they couldn't understand what Dean Drone was talking about, and asking one another if they knew. Once, as he passed out from the doors of the Greater Testimony, the rector heard some one say: "The Church would be all right if that old mugwump was out of the pulpit." It went to his heart like a barbed thorn, and stayed there.

You know, perhaps, how a remark of that sort can stay and rankle, and make you wish you could hear it again to make sure of it, because perhaps you didn't hear it aright, and it was a mistake after all. Perhaps no one said it, anyway. You ought to have written it down at the time. I have seen the Dean take down the encyclopaedia in the rectory, and move his finger slowly down the pages of the letter M, looking for mugwump. But it wasn't there. I have known him, in his little study upstairs, turn over the pages of the "Animals of Palestine," looking for a mugwump. But there was none there. It must have been unknown in the greater days of Judea.

So things went on from month to month, and from year to year, and the debt and the charges loomed like a dark and gathering cloud on the horizon. I don't mean to say that efforts were not made to face the difficulty and to fight it. They were. Time after time the workers of the congregation got together and thought out plans for the extinction of the debt. But somehow, after every trial, the debt grew larger with each year, and every system that could be devised turned out more hopeless than the last.

They began, I think, with the "endless chain" of letters of appeal. You may remember the device, for it was all-popular in clerical circles some ten or fifteen years ago. You got a number of people to write each of them three letters asking for ten cents from three each of their friends and asking each of them to send on three similar letters. Three each from three each, and three each more from each! Do you observe the wonderful ingenuity of it? Nobody, I think, has forgotten how the Willing Workers of the Church of England Church of Mariposa sat down in the vestry room in the basement with a pile of stationery three feet high, sending out the letters. Some, I know, will never forget it. Certainly not Mr. Pupkin, the teller in the Exchange Bank, for it was here that he met Zena Pepperleigh, the judge's daughter, for the first time; and they worked so busily that they wrote out ever so many letters—eight or nine—in a single afternoon, and they discovered that their handwritings were awfully alike, which was one of the most extraordinary and amazing coincidences, you will admit, in the history of chirography.

But the scheme failed—failed utterly. I don't know why. The letters went out and were copied broadcast and recopied, till you could see the Mariposa endless chain winding its way towards the Rocky Mountains. But they never got the ten cents. The Willing Workers wrote for it in thousands, but by some odd chance they never struck the person who had it.

Then after that there came a regular winter of effort. First of all they had a bazaar that was got up by the Girls' Auxiliary and held in the basement of the church. All the girls wore special costumes that were brought up from the city, and they had booths, where there was every imaginable thing for sale—pincushion covers, and chair covers, and sofa covers, everything that you can think of. If the people had once started buying them, the debt would have been lifted in no time. Even as it was the bazaar only lost twenty dollars.

After that, I think, was the magic lantern lecture that Dean Drone gave on "Italy and her Invaders." They got the lantern and the slides up from the city, and it was simply splendid. Some of the slides were perhaps a little confusing, but it was all there,—the pictures of the dense Italian jungle and the crocodiles and the naked invaders with their invading clubs. It was a pity that it was such a bad night, snowing hard, and a curling match on, or they would have made a lot of money out of the lecture. As it was the loss, apart from the breaking of the lantern, which was unavoidable, was quite trifling.

~ ~ ~

I can hardly remember all the things that there were after that. I recollect that it was always Mullins who arranged about renting the hall and printing the tickets and all that sort of thing. His father, you remember, had been at the Anglican college with Dean Drone, and though the rector was thirty-seven years older than Mullins, he leaned upon him, in matters of business, as upon a staff; and though Mullins was thirty-seven years younger than the Dean, he leaned against him, in matters of doctrine, as against a rock.

At one time they got the idea that what the public wanted was not anything instructive but something light and amusing. Mullins said that people loved to laugh. He said that if you get a lot of people all together and get them laughing you can do anything you like with them. Once they start to laugh they are lost. So they got Mr. Dreery, the English Literature teacher at the high school, to give an evening of readings from the Great Humorists from Chaucer to Adam Smith. They came mighty near to making a barrel of money out of that. If the people had once started laughing it would have been all over with them. As it was I heard a lot of them say that they simply wanted to scream with laughter: they said they just felt like bursting into peals of laughter all the time. Even when, in the more subtle parts, they didn't feel like bursting out laughing, they said they had all they could do to keep from smiling. They said they never had such a hard struggle in their lives not to smile.

In fact the chairman said when he put the vote of thanks that he was sure if people had known what the lecture was to be like there would have been a much better "turn-out." But you see all that the people had to go on was just the announcement of the name of the lecturer, Mr. Dreery, and that he would lecture on English Humour All Seats Twenty-five Cents. As the chairman expressed it himself, if the people had had any idea, any idea at all, of what the lecture would be like they would have been there in hundreds. But how could they get an idea that it would be so amusing with practically nothing to go upon?

After that attempt things seemed to go from bad to worse. Nearly everybody was disheartened about it. What would have happened to the debt, or whether they would have ever paid it off, is more than I can say, if it hadn't occurred that light broke in on Mullins in the strangest and most surprising way you can imagine. It happened that he went away for his bank holidays, and while he was away he happened to be present in one of the big cities and saw how they went at it there to raise money. He came home in such a state of excitement that he went straight up from the Mariposa station to the rectory, valise and all, and he burst in one April evening to where the Rural Dean was sitting with the three girls beside the lamp in the front room, and he cried out:

"Mr. Drone, I've got it,—I've got a way that will clear the debt before you're a fortnight older. We'll have a Whirlwind Campaign in Mariposa!"

But stay! The change from the depth of depression to the pinnacle of hope is too abrupt. I must pause and tell you in another chapter of the Whirlwind Campaign in Mariposa.

FIVE

The Whirlwind Campaign in Mariposa

IT WAS MULLINS, the banker, who told Mariposa all about the plan of a Whirlwind Campaign and explained how it was to be done. He'd happened to be in one of the big cities when they were raising money by a Whirlwind Campaign for one of the universities, and he saw it all.

He said he would never forget the scene on the last day of it, when the announcement was made that the total of the money raised was even more than what was needed. It was a splendid sight,—the business men of the town all cheering and laughing and shaking hands, and the professors with the tears streaming down their faces, and the Deans of the Faculties, who had given money themselves, sobbing aloud.

He said it was the most moving thing he ever saw.

So, as I said, Henry Mullins, who had seen it, explained to the others how it was done. He said that first of all a few of the business men got together quietly,—very quietly, indeed the more quietly the better,—and talked things over. Perhaps one of them would dine,—just quietly,—with another one and discuss the situation. Then these two would invite a third man,—possibly even a fourth,—to have lunch with them and talk in a general way,—even talk of other things part of the time. And so on in this way things would be discussed and looked at in different lights and viewed from different angles and then when everything was ready they would go at things with a rush. A central committee would be formed and sub-committees, with captains of each group and recorders and secretaries, and on a stated day the Whirlwind Campaign would begin.

Each day the crowd would all agree to meet at some stated place and each lunch together,—say at a restaurant or at a club or at some eating place. This would go on every day with the interest getting keener and keener, and everybody getting more and more excited, till presently the chairman would announce that the campaign had succeeded and there would be the kind of scene that Mullins had described.

So that was the plan that they set in motion in Mariposa.

I don't wish to say too much about the Whirlwind Campaign itself. I don't mean to say that it was a failure. On the contrary, in many ways it couldn't have been a greater success, and yet somehow it didn't seem to work out just as Henry Mullins had said it would. It may be that there are differences between Mariposa and the larger cities that one doesn't appreciate at first sight. Perhaps it would have been better to try some other plan.

Yet they followed along the usual line of things closely enough. They began with the regular system of some of the business men getting together in a quiet way.

First of all, for example, Henry Mullins came over quietly to Duff's rooms, over the Commercial Bank, with a bottle of rye whiskey, and they talked things over. And the night after that George Duff came over quietly to Mullins's rooms, over the Exchange Bank, with a bottle of Scotch whiskey. A few evenings after that Mullins and Duff went together, in a very unostentatious way, with perhaps a couple of bottles of rye, to Pete Glover's room over the hardware store. And then all three of them went up one night with Ed Moore, the photographer, to Judge

Pepperleigh's house under pretence of having a game of poker. The very day after that, Mullins and Duff and Ed Moore, and Pete Glover and the judge got Will Harrison, the harness maker, to go out without any formality on the lake on the pretext of fishing. And the next night after that Duff and Mullins and Ed Moore and Pete Glover and Pepperleigh and Will Harrison got Alf Trelawney, the postmaster, to come over, just in a casual way, to the Mariposa House, after the night mail, and the next day Mullins and Duff and—

But, pshaw! you see at once how the thing is worked. There's no need to follow that part of the Whirlwind Campaign further. But it just shows the power of organization.

And all this time, mind you, they were talking things over, and looking at things first in one light and then in another light,—in fact, just doing as the big city men do when there's an important thing like this under way.

So after things had been got pretty well into shape in this way, Duff asked Mullins one night, straight out, if he would be chairman of the Central Committee. He sprung it on him and Mullins had no time to refuse, but he put it to Duff straight whether he would be treasurer. And Duff had no time to refuse.

~ ~ ~

That gave things a start, and within a week they had the whole organization on foot. There was the Grand Central Committee and six groups or sub-committees of twenty men each, and a captain for every group. They had it all arranged on the lines most likely to be effective.

In one group there were all the bankers, Mullins and Duff and Pupkin (with the cameo pin), and about four others. They had their photographs taken at Ed Moore's studio, taken in a line with a background of icebergs—a winter scene—and a pretty penetrating crowd they looked, I can tell you. After all, you know, if you get a crowd of representative bank men together in any financial deal, you've got a pretty considerable leverage right away.

In the second group were the lawyers, Nivens and Macartney and the rest—about as level-headed a lot as you'd see anywhere. Get the lawyers of a town with you on a thing like this and you'll find you've got a sort of brain power with you that you'd never get without them.

Then there were the business men—there was a solid crowd for you,—Harrison, the harness maker, and Glover, the hardware man, and all that gang, not talkers, perhaps, but solid men who can tell you to a nicety how many cents there are in a dollar. It's all right to talk about education and that sort of thing, but if you want driving power and efficiency, get business men. They're seeing it every day in the city, and it's just the same in Mariposa. Why, in the big concerns in the city, if they found out a man was educated, they wouldn't have him,—wouldn't keep him there a minute. That's why the business men have to conceal it so much.

Then in the other teams there were the doctors and the newspaper men and the professional men like Judge Pepperleigh and Yodel the auctioneer.

❧ ❧ ❧

It was all organized so that every team had its headquarters, two of them in each of the three hotels—one upstairs and one down. And it was arranged that there would be a big lunch every day, to be held in Smith's caff, round the corner of Smith's Northern Health Resort and Home of the Wissanotti Angler,—you know the place. The lunch was divided up into tables, with a captain for each table to see about things to drink, and of course all the tables were in competition with one another. In fact the competition was the very life of the whole thing.

It's just wonderful how these things run when they're organized. Take the first luncheon, for example. There they all were, every man in his place, every captain at his post at the top of the table. It was hard, perhaps, for some of them to get there. They had very likely to be in their stores and banks and offices till the last minute and then make a dash for it. It was the cleanest piece of team work you ever saw.

You have noticed already, I am sure, that a good many of the captains and committee men didn't belong to the Church of England Church. Glover, for instance, was a Presbyterian, till they ran the picket fence of the manse two feet on to his property, and after that he became a freethinker. But in Mariposa, as I have said, everybody likes to be in everything and naturally a Whirlwind Campaign was a novelty. Anyway it would have been a poor business to keep a man out of the lunches merely on account of his religion. I trust that the day for that kind of religious bigotry is past.

Of course the excitement was when Henry Mullins at the head of the table began reading out the telegrams and letters and messages. First of all there was a telegram of good wishes from the Anglican Lord Bishop of the Diocese to Henry Mullins and calling him Dear Brother in Grace—the Mariposa telegraph office is a little unreliable and it read: "Dear Brother in grease," but that was good enough. The Bishop said that his most earnest wishes were with them.

Then Mullins read a letter from the Mayor of Mariposa—Pete Glover was mayor that year—stating that his keenest desires were with them: and then one from the Carriage Company saying that its heartiest good will was all theirs; and then one from the Meat Works saying that its nearest thoughts were next to them. Then he read one from himself, as head of the Exchange Bank, you understand, informing him that he had heard of his project and assuring him of his liveliest interest in what he proposed.

At each of these telegrams and messages there was round after round of applause, so that you could hardly hear yourself speak or give an order. But that was nothing to when Mullins got up again, and beat on the table for silence and made one of those crackling speeches—just the way business men speak—the kind of speech that a college man simply can't make. I wish I could repeat it all. I remember that it began: "Now boys, you know what we're here for, gentlemen," and it went on just as good as that all through.

When Mullins had done he took out a fountain pen and wrote out a cheque for a hundred dollars, conditional on the fund reaching fifty thousand. And there was a burst of cheers all over the room.

Just the moment he had done it, up sprang George Duff,—you know the keen competition there is, as a straight matter of business, between the banks in Mariposa,—up sprang George Duff, I say, and wrote out a cheque for another hundred conditional on the fund reaching seventy thousand. You never heard such cheering in your life.

And then when Netley walked up to the head of the table and laid down a cheque for a hundred dollars conditional on the fund reaching one hundred thousand the room was in an uproar. A hundred thousand dollars! Just think of it! The figures fairly stagger one. To think of a hundred thousand dollars raised in five minutes in a little place like Mariposa!

And even that was nothing! In less than no time there was such a crowd round Mullins trying to borrow his pen all at once that his waistcoat was all stained with ink. Finally when they got order at last, and Mullins stood up and announced that the conditional fund had reached a quarter of a million, the whole place was a perfect babel of cheering. Oh, these Whirlwind Campaigns are wonderful things!

~ ~ ~

I can tell you the Committee felt pretty proud that first day. There was Henry Mullins looking a little bit flushed and excited, with his white waistcoat and an American Beauty rose, and with ink marks all over him from the cheque signing; and he kept telling them that he'd known all along that all that was needed was to get the thing started and telling again about what he'd seen at the University Campaign and about the professors crying, and wondering if the high school teachers would come down for the last day of the meetings.

Looking back on the Mariposa Whirlwind, I can never feel that it was a failure. After all, there is a sympathy and a brotherhood in these things when men work shoulder to shoulder. If you had seen the canvassers of the Committee going round the town that evening shoulder to shoulder from the Mariposa House to the Continental and up to Mullins's rooms and over to Duff's, shoulder to shoulder, you'd have understood it.

I don't say that every lunch was quite such a success as the first. It's not always easy to get out of the store if you're a busy man, and a good many of the Whirlwind Committee found that they had just time to hurry down and snatch their lunch and get back again. Still, they came, and snatched it. As long as the lunches lasted, they came. Even if they had simply to rush it and grab something to eat and drink without time to talk to anybody, they came.

No, no, it was not lack of enthusiasm that killed the Whirlwind Campaign in Mariposa. It must have been something else. I don't just know what it was but I think it had something to do with the financial, the book-keeping side of the thing.

It may have been, too, that the organization was not quite correctly planned. You see, if practically everybody is on the committees, it is awfully hard to try to find men to canvass, and it is not allowable for the captains and the committee men to canvass one another, because their gifts are spontaneous. So the only thing that the different groups could do was to wait round in some likely place—say the bar parlour of Smith's Hotel—in the hope that somebody might come in who could be canvassed.

You might ask why they didn't canvass Mr. Smith himself, but of course they had done that at the very start, as I should have said. Mr. Smith had given them two hundred dollars in cash conditional on the lunches being held in the caff of his hotel; and it's awfully hard to get a proper lunch—I mean the kind to which a Bishop can express regret at not being there—under a dollar twenty-five. So Mr. Smith got back his own money, and the crowd began eating into the benefactions, and it got more and more complicated whether to hold another lunch in the hope of breaking even, or to stop the campaign.

It was disappointing, yes. In spite of all the success and the sympathy, it was disappointing. I don't say it didn't do good. No doubt a lot of the men got to know one another better than ever they had before. I have myself heard Judge Pepperleigh say that after the campaign he knew all of Pete Glover that he wanted to. There was a lot of that kind of complete satiety. The real trouble about the Whirlwind Campaign was that they never clearly understood which of them were the whirlwind and who were to be the campaign.

Some of them, I believe, took it pretty much to heart. I know that Henry Mullins did. You could see it. The first day he came down to the lunch, all dressed up with the American Beauty and the white waistcoat. The second day he only wore a pink carnation and a grey waistcoat. The third day he had on a dead daffodil and a cardigan undervest, and on the last day, when the high school teachers should have been there, he only wore his office suit and he hadn't even shaved. He looked beaten.

It was that night that he went up to the rectory to tell the news to Dean Drone. It had been arranged, you know, that the rector should not attend the lunches, so as to let the whole thing come as a surprise; so that all he knew about it was just scraps of information about the crowds at the lunch and how they cheered and all that. Once, I believe, he caught sight of the Newspacket with a two-inch headline: A QUARTER OF A MILLION, but he wouldn't let himself read further because it would have spoilt the surprise.

I saw Mullins, as I say, go up the street on his way to Dean Drone's. It was middle April and there was ragged snow on the streets, and the nights were dark still, and cold. I saw Mullins grit his teeth as he walked, and I know that he held in his coat pocket his own cheque for the hundred, with the condition taken off it, and he said that there were so many skunks in Mariposa that a man might as well be in the Head Office in the city.

The Dean came out to the little gate in the dark,—you could see the lamplight behind him from the open door of the rectory,—and he shook hands with Mullins and they went in together.

SIX

The Beacon on the Hill

MULLINS said afterward that it was ever so much easier than he thought it would have been. The Dean, he said, was so quiet. Of course if Mr. Drone had started to swear at Mullins, or tried to strike him, it would have been much harder. But as it was he was so quiet that part of the time he hardly seemed to follow what Mullins was saying. So Mullins was glad of that, because it proved that the Dean wasn't feeling disappointed as, in a way, he might have.

Indeed, the only time when the rector seemed animated and excited in the whole interview was when Mullins said that the campaign had been ruined by a lot of confounded mugwumps. Straight away the Dean asked if those mugwumps had really prejudiced the outcome of the campaign. Mullins said there was no doubt of it, and the Dean enquired if the presence of mugwumps was fatal in matters of endeavour, and Mullins said that it was. Then the rector asked if even one mugwump was, in the Christian sense, deleterious. Mullins said that one mugwump would kill anything. After that the Dean hardly spoke at all.

In fact, the rector presently said that he mustn't detain Mullins too long and that he had detained him too long already and that Mullins must be weary from his train journey and that in cases of extreme weariness nothing but a sound sleep was of any avail; he himself, unfortunately, would not be able to avail himself of the priceless boon of slumber until he had first retired to his study to write some letters; so that Mullins, who had a certain kind of social quickness of intuition, saw that it was time to leave, and went away.

It was midnight as he went down the street, and a dark, still night. That can be stated positively because it came out in court afterwards. Mullins swore that it was a dark night; he admitted, under examination, that there may have been the stars, or at least some of the less important of them, though he had made no attempt, as brought out on cross-examination, to count them: there may have been, too, the electric lights, and Mullins was not willing to deny that it was quite possible that there was more or less moonlight. But that there was no light that night in the form of sunlight, Mullins was absolutely certain. All that, I say, came out in court.

But meanwhile the rector had gone upstairs to his study and had seated himself in front of his table to write his letters. It was here always that he wrote his sermons. From the window of the room you looked through the bare white maple trees to the sweeping outline of the church shadowed against the night sky, and beyond that, though far off, was the new cemetery where the rector walked of a Sunday (I think I told you why): beyond that again, for the window faced the east, there lay, at no very great distance, the New Jerusalem. There were no better things that a man might look towards from his study window, nor anything that could serve as a better aid to writing.

But this night the Dean's letters must have been difficult indeed to write. For he sat beside the table holding his pen and with his head bent upon his other hand, and though he sometimes put a line or two on the paper, for the most part he sat motionless. The fact is that Dean Drone was not trying to write letters, but only one letter. He was writing a letter of resignation. If you have not done that for forty years it is extremely difficult to get the words.

So at least the Dean found it. First he wrote one set of words and then he sat and thought and wrote something else. But nothing seemed to suit.

The real truth was that Dean Drone, perhaps more than he knew himself, had a fine taste for words and effects, and when you feel that a situation is entirely out of the common, you naturally try, if you have that instinct, to give it the right sort of expression.

I believe that at the time when Rupert Drone had taken the medal in Greek over fifty years ago, it was only a twist of fate that had prevented him from becoming a great writer. There was a buried author in him just as there was a buried financier in Jefferson Thorpe. In fact, there were many people in Mariposa like that, and for all I know you may yourself have seen such elsewhere. For instance, I am certain that Billy Rawson, the telegraph operator at Mariposa, could easily have invented radium. In the same way one has only to read the advertisements of Mr. Gingham, the undertaker, to know that there is still in him a poet, who could have written on death far more attractive verses than the Thanatopsis of Cullen Bryant, and under a title less likely to offend the public and drive away custom. He has told me this himself.

So the Dean tried first this and then that and nothing would seem to suit. First of all he wrote:

"It is now forty years since I came among you, a youth full of life and hope and ardent in the work before me—" Then he paused, doubtful of the accuracy and clearness of the expression, read it over again and again in deep thought and then began again:

"It is now forty years since I came among you, a broken and melancholy boy, without life or hope, desiring only to devote to the service of this parish such few years as might remain of an existence blighted before it had truly begun—" And then again the Dean stopped. He read what he had written; he frowned; he crossed it through with his pen. This was no way to write, this thin egotistical strain of complaint. Once more he started:

"It is now forty years since I came among you, a man already tempered and trained, except possibly in mathematics—" And then again the rector paused and his mind drifted away to the memory of the Anglican professor that I spoke of, who had had so little sense of his higher mission as to omit the teaching of logarithms. And the rector mused so long that when he began again it seemed to him that it was simpler and better to discard the personal note altogether, and he wrote:

"There are times, gentlemen, in the life of a parish, when it comes to an epoch which brings it to a moment when it reaches a point—"

The Dean stuck fast again, but refusing this time to be beaten went resolutely on:

"—reaches a point where the circumstances of the moment make the epoch such as to focus the life of the parish in that time."

Then the Dean saw that he was beaten, and he knew that he not only couldn't manage the parish but couldn't say so in proper English, and of the two the last was the bitterer discovery.

He raised his head, and looked for a moment through the window at the shadow of the church against the night, so outlined that you could almost fancy that the light of the New Jerusalem was beyond it. Then he wrote, and this time not to the world at large but only to Mullins:

"My dear Harry, I want to resign my charge. Will you come over and help me?"

When the Dean at last rose from writing that, I think it was far on in the night. As he rose he looked again through the window, looked once and then once more, and so stood with widening eyes, and his face set towards what he saw.

What was that? That light in the sky there, eastward?—near or far he could not say. Was it already the dawn of the New Jerusalem brightening in the east, or was it—look—in the church itself,—what is that?—that dull red glow that shines behind the stained-glass windows, turning them to crimson? that fork of flame that breaks now from the casement and flashes upward, along the wood—and see—that sudden sheet of fire that springs the windows of the church with the roar of splintered glass and surges upward into the sky, till the dark night and the bare trees and sleeping street of Mariposa are all illumined with its glow!

Fire! Fire! and the sudden sound of the bell now, breaking upon the night.

So stood the Dean erect, with one hand pressed against the table for support, while the Mariposa fire bell struck out its warning to the sleeping town,—stood there while the street grew loud with the tumult of voices,—with the roaring gallop of the fire brigade,—with the harsh note of the gong—and over all other sounds, the great seething of the flames that tore their way into the beams and rafters of the pointed church and flared above it like a torch into the midnight sky.

So stood the Dean, and as the church broke thus into a very beacon kindled upon a hill,—sank forward without a sign, his face against the table, stricken.

You need to see a fire in a place such as Mariposa, a town still half of wood, to know what fire means. In the city it is all different. To the onlooker, at any rate, a fire is only a spectacle, nothing more. Everything is arranged, organized, certain. It is only once perhaps in a century that fire comes to a large city as it comes to the little wooden town like Mariposa as a great Terror of the Night.

That, at any rate, is what it meant in Mariposa that night in April, the night the Church of England Church burnt down. Had the fire gained but a hundred feet, or less, it could have reached from the driving shed behind the church to the backs of the wooden shops of the Main Street, and once there not all the waters of Lake Wissanotti could stay the course of its destruction. It was for that hundred feet that they fought, the men of Mariposa, from the midnight call of the bell till the slow coming of the day.

They fought the fire, not to save the church, for that was doomed from the first outbreak of the flames, but to stop the spread of it and save the town. They fought it at the windows, and at the blazing doors, and through the yawning furnace of the open belfry; fought it, with the Mariposa engine thumping and panting in the street, itself aglow with fire like a servant demon fighting its own kind, with tall ladders reaching to the very roof, and with hose that poured their streams of tossing water foaming into the flames.

Most of all they fought to save the wooden driving shed behind the church from which the fire could leap into the heart of Mariposa. That was where the real fight was, for the life of the town. I wish you could have seen how they turned the hose against the shingles, ripping and tearing them from their places with the force of the driven water: how they mounted on the roof, axe in hand, and cut madly at the rafters to bring the building down, while the black clouds of smoke rolled in volumes about the men as they worked. You could see the fire horses harnessed with logging chains to the uprights of the shed to tear the building from its place.

Most of all I wish you could have seen Mr. Smith, proprietor, as I think you know, of Smith's Hotel, there on the roof with a fireman's helmet on, cutting through the main beam of solid cedar, twelve by twelve, that held tight still when the rafters and the roof tree were down already, the shed on fire in a dozen places, and the other men driven from the work by the flaming sparks, and by the strangle of the smoke. Not so Mr. Smith! See him there as he plants himself firm at the angle of the beams, and with the full impact of his two hundred and eighty pounds drives his axe into the wood! I tell you it takes a man from the pine country of the north to handle an axe! Right, left, left, right, down it comes, with never a pause or stay, never missing by a fraction of an inch the line of the stroke! At it, Smith! Down with it! Till with a shout from the crowd the beam gapes asunder, and Mr. Smith is on the ground again, roaring his directions to the men and horses as they haul down the shed, in a voice that dominates the fire itself.

Who made Mr. Smith the head and chief of the Mariposa fire brigade that night, I cannot say. I do not know even where he got the huge red helmet that he wore, nor had I ever heard till the night the church burnt down that Mr. Smith was a member of the fire brigade at all. But it's always that way. Your little narrow-chested men may plan and organize, but when there is something to be done, something real, then it's the man of size and weight that steps to the front every time. Look at Bismarck and Mr. Gladstone and President Taft and Mr. Smith,—the same thing in each case.

I suppose it was perfectly natural that just as soon as Mr. Smith came on the scene he put on somebody's helmet and shouted his directions to the men and bossed the Mariposa fire brigade like Bismarck with the German parliament.

The fire had broken out late, late at night, and they fought it till the day. The flame of it lit up the town and the bare grey maple trees, and you could see in the light of it the broad sheet of the frozen lake, snow covered still. It kindled such a beacon as it burned that from the other side of the lake the people on the night express from the north could see it twenty miles away. It lit up such a testimony of flame that Mariposa has never seen the like of it before or since. Then when the roof crashed in and the tall steeple tottered and fell, so swift a darkness seemed to come that the grey trees and the frozen lake vanished in a moment as if blotted out of existence.

When the morning came the great church of Mariposa was nothing but a ragged group of walls with a sodden heap of bricks and blackened wood, still hissing here and there beneath the hose with the sullen anger of a conquered fire.

Round the ruins of the fire walked the people of Mariposa next morning, and they pointed out where the wreck of the steeple had fallen, and where the bells of the church lay in a molten heap among the bricks, and they talked of the loss that it was and how many dollars it would take to rebuild the church, and whether it was insured and for how much. And there were at least fourteen people who had seen the fire first, and more than that who had given the first alarm, and ever so many who knew how fires of this sort could be prevented.

Most noticeable of all you could see the sidesmen and the wardens and Mullins, the chairman of the vestry, talking in little groups about the fire. Later in the day there came from the city the insurance men and the fire appraisers, and they too walked about the ruins, and talked with the wardens and the vestry men. There was such a luxury of excitement in the town that day that it was just as good as a public holiday.

But the strangest part of it was the unexpected sequel. I don't know through what error of the Dean's figures it happened, through what lack of mathematical training the thing turned out as it did. No doubt the memory of the mathematical professor was heavily to blame for it, but the solid fact is that the Church of England Church of Mariposa turned out to be insured for a hundred thousand, and there were the receipts and the vouchers, all signed and regular, just as they found them in a drawer of the rector's study. There was no doubt about it. The insurance people might protest as they liked. The straight, plain fact was that the church was insured for about twice the whole amount of the cost and the debt and the rector's salary and the boarding-school fees of the littlest of the Drones all put together.

There was a Whirlwind Campaign for you! Talk of raising money,—that was something like! I wonder if the universities and the city institutions that go round trying to raise money by the slow and painful method called a Whirlwind Campaign, that takes perhaps all day to raise fifty thousand dollars, ever thought of anything so beautifully simple as this.

The Greater Testimony that had lain so heavily on the congregation went flaming to its end, and burned up its debts and its obligations and enriched its worshippers by its destruction. Talk of a beacon on a hill! You can hardly beat that one.

I wish you could have seen how the wardens and the sidesmen and Mullins, the chairman of the vestry, smiled and chuckled at the thought of it. Hadn't they said all along that all that was needed was a little faith and effort? And here it was, just as they said, and they'd been right after all.

Protest from the insurance people? Legal proceedings to prevent payment? My dear sir! I see you know nothing about the Mariposa court, in spite of the fact that I have already said that it was one of the most precise instruments of British fair play ever established. Why, Judge Pepperleigh disposed of the case and dismissed the protest of the company in less than fifteen minutes! Just what the jurisdiction of Judge Pepperleigh's court is I don't know, but I do know that in upholding the rights of a Christian congregation—I am quoting here the text of the decision—against the intrigues of a set of infernal skunks that make too much money, anyway, the Mariposa court is without an equal. Pepperleigh even threatened the plaintiffs with the penitentiary, or worse.

How the fire started no one ever knew. There was a queer story that went about to the effect that Mr. Smith and Mr. Gingham's assistant had been seen very late that night carrying an automobile can of kerosene up the street. But that was amply disproved by the proceedings of the court, and by the evidence of Mr. Smith himself. He took his dying oath,—not his ordinary one as used in the License cases, but his dying one,—that he had not carried a can of kerosene up the street, and that anyway it was the rottenest kind of kerosene he had ever seen and no more use than so much molasses. So that point was settled.

Dean Drone? Did he get well again? Why, what makes you ask that? You mean, was his head at all affected after the stroke? No, it was not. Absolutely not. It was not affected in the least, though how anybody who knows him now in Mariposa could have the faintest idea that his mind was in any way impaired by the stroke is more than I can tell. The engaging of Mr. Uttermost, the curate, whom perhaps you have heard preach in the new church, had nothing whatever to do with Dean Drone's head. It was merely a case of the pressure of overwork. It was felt very generally by the wardens that, in these days of specialization, the rector was covering too wide a field, and that if he should abandon some of the lesser duties of his office, he might devote his energies more intently to the Infant Class. That was all. You may hear him there any afternoon, talking to them, if you will stand under the maple trees and listen through the open windows of the new Infant School.

And, as for audiences, for intelligence, for attention—well, if I want to find listeners who can hear and understand about the great spaces of Lake Huron, let me tell of it, every time face to face with the blue eyes of the Infant Class, fresh from the infinity of spaces greater still. Talk of grown-up people all you like, but for listeners let me have the Infant Class with their pinafores and their Teddy Bears and their feet not even touching the floor, and Mr. Uttermost may preach to his heart's content of the newer forms of doubt revealed by the higher criticism.

So you will understand that the Dean's mind is, if anything, even keener, and his head even clearer than before. And if you want proof of it, notice him there beneath the plum blossoms reading in the Greek: he has told me that he finds that he can read, with the greatest ease, works in the Greek that seemed difficult before. Because his head is so clear now.

And sometimes,—when his head is very clear,—as he sits there reading beneath the plum blossoms he can hear them singing beyond, and his wife's voice.

SEVEN

The Extraordinary Entanglement of Mr. Pupkin

JUDGE PEPPERLEIGH lived in a big house with hardwood floors and a wide piazza that looked over the lake from the top of Oneida Street.

Every day about half-past five he used to come home from his office in the Mariposa Court House. On some days as he got near the house he would call out to his wife:

"Almighty Moses, Martha! who left the sprinkler on the grass?"

On other days he would call to her from quite a little distance off. "Hullo, mother! Got any supper for a hungry man?"

And Mrs. Pepperleigh never knew which it would be.

On the days when he swore at the sprinkler you could see his spectacles flash like dynamite. But on the days when he called: "Hullo, mother," they were simply irradiated with kindliness.

Some days, I say, he would cry out with a perfect whine of indignation: "Suffering Caesar! has that infernal dog torn up those geraniums again?" And other days you would hear him singing out: "Hullo, Rover! Well, doggie, well, old fellow!"

In the same way at breakfast, the judge, as he looked over the morning paper, would sometimes leap to his feet with a perfect howl of suffering, and cry: "Everlasting Moses! the Liberals have carried East Elgin." Or else he would lean back from the breakfast table with the most good-humoured laugh you ever heard and say: "Ha! ha! the Conservatives have carried South Norfolk."

And yet he was perfectly logical, when you come to think of it. After all, what is more annoying to a sensitive, highly-strung man than an infernal sprinkler playing all over the place, and what more agreeable to a good-natured, even-tempered fellow than a well-prepared supper? Or, what is more likeable than one's good, old, affectionate dog bounding down the path from sheer delight at seeing you,—or more execrable than an infernal whelp that has torn up the geraniums and is too old to keep, anyway?

As for politics, well, it all seemed reasonable enough. When the Conservatives got in anywhere, Pepperleigh laughed and enjoyed it, simply because it does one good to see a straight, fine, honest fight where the best man wins. When a Liberal got in, it made him mad, and he said so,—not, mind you, from any political bias, for his office forbid it,—but simply because one can't bear to see the country go absolutely to the devil.

I suppose, too, it was partly the effect of sitting in court all day listening to cases. One gets what you might call the judicial temper of mind. Pepperleigh had it so strongly developed that I've seen him kick a hydrangea pot to pieces with his foot because the accursed thing wouldn't flower. He once threw the canary cage clear into the lilac bushes because the "blasted bird wouldn't stop singing." It was a straight case of judicial temper. Lots of judges have it, developed in just the same broad, all-round way as with Judge Pepperleigh.

I think it must be passing sentences that does it. Anyway, Pepperleigh had the aptitude for passing sentences so highly perfected that he spent his whole time at it inside of court and out. I've heard him hand out sentences for the Sultan of Turkey and Mrs. Pankhurst and the Emperor of

Germany that made one's blood run cold. He would sit there on the piazza of a summer evening reading the paper, with dynamite sparks flying from his spectacles as he sentenced the Czar of Russia to ten years in the salt mines—and made it fifteen a few minutes afterwards. Pepperleigh always read the foreign news—the news of things that he couldn't alter—as a form of wild and stimulating torment.

So you can imagine that in some ways the judge's house was a pretty difficult house to go to. I mean you can see how awfully hard it must have been for Mr. Pupkin. I tell you it took some nerve to step up on that piazza and say, in a perfectly natural, off-hand way: "Oh, how do you do, judge? Is Miss Zena in? No, I won't stay, thanks; I think I ought to be going. I simply called." A man who can do that has got to have a pretty fair amount of savoir what do you call it, and he's got to be mighty well shaved and have his cameo pin put in his tie at a pretty undeniable angle before he can tackle it. Yes, and even then he may need to hang round behind the lilac bushes for half an hour first, and cool off. And he's apt to make pretty good time down Oneida Street on the way back.

Still, that's what you call love, and if you've got it, and are well shaved, and your boots well blacked, you can do things that seem almost impossible. Yes, you can do anything, even if you do trip over the dog in getting off the piazza.

Don't suppose for a moment that Judge Pepperleigh was an unapproachable or a harsh man always and to everybody. Even Mr. Pupkin had to admit that that couldn't be so. To know that, you had only to see Zena Pepperleigh put her arm round his neck and call him Daddy. She would do that even when there were two or three young men sitting on the edge of the piazza. You know, I think, the way they sit on the edge in Mariposa. It is meant to indicate what part of the family they have come to see. Thus when George Duff, the bank manager, came up to the Pepperleigh house, he always sat in a chair on the verandah and talked to the judge. But when Pupkin or Mallory Tompkins or any fellow like that came, he sat down in a sidelong fashion on the edge of the boards and then they knew exactly what he was there for. If he knew the house well, he leaned his back against the verandah post and smoked a cigarette. But that took nerve.

But I am afraid that this is a digression, and, of course, you know all about it just as well as I do. All that I was trying to say was that I don't suppose that the judge had ever spoken a cross word to Zena in his life.—Oh, he threw her novel over the grape-vine, I don't deny that, but then why on earth should a girl read trash like the *Errant Quest of the Palladin Pilgrim*, and the *Life of Sir Galahad*, when the house was full of good reading like *The Life of Sir John A. Macdonald*, and *Pioneer Days in Tecumseh Township*?

~ ~ ~

Still, what I mean is that the judge never spoke harshly to Zena, except perhaps under extreme provocation; and I am quite sure that he never, never had to Neil. But then what father ever would want to speak angrily to such a boy as Neil Pepperleigh? The judge took no credit himself for that; the finest grown boy in the whole county and so broad and big that they took him into the Missinaba Horse when he was only seventeen. And clever,—so clever that he didn't need to study; so clever that he used to come out at the foot of the class in mathematics at the Mariposa high school through sheer surplus of brain power. I've heard the judge explain it a dozen times. Why, Neil was so clever that he used to be able to play billiards at the Mariposa House all evening when the other boys had to stay at home and study.

Such a powerful looking fellow, too! Everybody in Mariposa remembers how Neil Pepperleigh smashed in the face of Peter McGinnis, the Liberal organizer, at the big election—you recall it—when the old Macdonald Government went out. Judge Pepperleigh had to try him for it the next morning—his own son. They say there never was such a scene even in the Mariposa court. There was, I believe, something like it on a smaller scale in Roman history, but it wasn't half as dramatic. I remember Judge Pepperleigh leaning forward to pass the sentence,—for a judge is bound, you know, by his oath,—and how grave he looked and yet so proud and happy, like a man doing his duty and sustained by it, and he said:

"My boy, you are innocent. You smashed in Peter McGinnis's face, but you did it without criminal intent. You put a face on him, by Jehoshaphat! that he won't lose for six months, but you did it without evil purpose or malign design. My boy, look up! Give me your hand! You leave this court without a stain upon your name."

They said it was one of the most moving scenes ever enacted in the Mariposa Court.

❧ ❧ ❧

But the strangest thing is that if the judge had known what every one else in Mariposa knew, it would have broken his heart. If he could have seen Neil with the drunken flush on his face in the billiard room of the Mariposa House,—if he had known, as every one else did, that Neil was crazed with drink the night he struck the Liberal organizer when the old Macdonald Government went out,—if he could have known that even on that last day Neil was drunk when he rode with the Missinaba Horse to the station to join the Third Contingent for the war, and all the street of the little town was one great roar of people—

But the judge never knew, and now he never will. For if you could find it in the meanness of your soul to tell him, it would serve no purpose now except to break his heart, and there would rise up to rebuke you the pictured vision of an untended grave somewhere in the great silences of South Africa.

Did I say above, or seem to imply, that the judge sometimes spoke harshly to his wife? Or did you gather for a minute that her lot was one to lament over or feel sorry for? If so, it just shows that you know nothing about such things, and that marriage, at least as it exists in Mariposa, is a sealed book to you. You are as ignorant as Miss Spiffkins, the biology teacher at the high school, who always says how sorry she is for Mrs. Pepperleigh. You get that impression simply because the judge howled like an Algonquin Indian when he saw the sprinkler running on the lawn. But are you sure you know the other side of it? Are you quite sure when you talk like Miss Spiffkins does about the rights of it, that you are taking all things into account? You might have thought differently perhaps of the Pepperleighs, anyway, if you had been there that evening when the judge came home to his wife with one hand pressed to his temple and in the other the cablegram that said that Neil had been killed in action in South Africa. That night they sat together with her hand in his, just as they had sat together thirty years ago when he was a law student in the city.

Go and tell Miss Spiffkins that! Hydrangeas,—canaries,—temper,—blazes! What does Miss Spiffkins know about it all?

But in any case, if you tried to tell Judge Pepperleigh about Neil now he wouldn't believe it. He'd laugh it to scorn. That is Neil's picture, in uniform, hanging in the dining-room beside the Fathers of Confederation. That military-looking man in the picture beside him is General Kitchener, whom you may perhaps have heard of, for he was very highly spoken of in Neil's letters. All round the room, in fact, and still more in the judge's library upstairs, you will see pictures of South Africa and the departure of the Canadians (there are none of the return), and of Mounted Infantry and of Unmounted Cavalry and a lot of things that only soldiers and the fathers of soldiers know about.

So you can realize that for a fellow who isn't military, and who wears nothing nearer to a uniform than a daffodil tennis blazer, the judge's house is a devil of a house to come to.

I think you remember young Mr. Pupkin, do you not? I have referred to him several times already as the junior teller in the Exchange Bank. But if you know Mariposa at all you have often seen him. You have noticed him, I am sure, going for the bank mail in the morning in an office suit effect of clinging grey with a gold necktie pin shaped like a riding whip.

You have seen him often enough going down to the lake front after supper, in tennis things, smoking a cigarette and with a paddle and a crimson canoe cushion under his arm. You have seen him entering Dean Drone's church in a top hat and a long frock coat nearly to his feet. You have seen him, perhaps, playing poker in Peter Glover's room over the hardware store and trying to look as if he didn't hold three aces,—in fact, giving absolutely no sign of it beyond the wild flush in his face and the fact that his hair stands on end.

That kind of reticence is a thing you simply have to learn in banking. I mean, if you've got to be in a position where you know for a fact that the Mariposa Packing Company's account is overdrawn by sixty-four dollars, and yet daren't say anything about it, not even to the girls that you play tennis with,—I don't say, not a casual hint as a reference, but not really tell them, not, for instance, bring down the bank ledger to the tennis court and show them,—you learn a sort of reticence and self-control that people outside of banking circles never can attain.

Why, I've known Pupkin at the Fireman's Ball lean against the wall in his dress suit and talk away to Jim Eliot, the druggist, without giving the faintest hint or indication that Eliot's note for twenty-seven dollars had been protested that very morning. Not a hint of it. I don't say he didn't mention it, in a sort of way, in the supper room, just to one or two, but I mean there was nothing in the way he leant up against the wall to suggest it.

But, however, I don't mention that as either for or against Mr. Pupkin. That sort of thing is merely the A B C of banking, as he himself told me when explaining why it was that he hesitated to divulge the exact standing of the Mariposa Carriage Company. Of course, once you get past the A B C you can learn a lot that is mighty interesting.

So I think that if you know Mariposa and understand even the rudiments of banking, you are perfectly acquainted with Mr. Pupkin. What? You remember him as being in love with Miss Lawson, the high school teacher? In love with HER? What a ridiculous idea. You mean merely because on the night when the Mariposa Belle sank with every soul on board, Pupkin put off from the town in a skiff to rescue Miss Lawson. Oh, but you're quite wrong. That wasn't LOVE. I've heard Pupkin explain it himself a dozen times. That sort of thing,—paddling out to a sinking steamer at night in a crazy skiff,—may indicate a sort of attraction, but not real love, not what Pupkin came to feel afterwards. Indeed, when he began to think of it, it wasn't even attraction, it was merely respect,—that's all it was. And anyway, that was long before, six or seven months back, and Pupkin admitted that at the time he was a mere boy.

~ ~ ~

Mr. Pupkin, I must explain, lived with Mallory Tompkins in rooms over the Exchange Bank, on the very top floor, the third, with Mullins's own rooms below them. Extremely comfortable quarters they were, with two bedrooms and a sitting-room that was all fixed up with snowshoes and tennis rackets on the walls and dance programmes and canoe club badges and all that sort of thing.

Mallory Tompkins was a young man with long legs and check trousers who worked on the Mariposa Times-Herald. That was what gave him his literary taste. He used to read Ibsen and that other Dutch author—Bumstone Bumstone, isn't it?—and you can judge that he was a mighty intellectual fellow. He was so intellectual that he was, as he himself admitted, a complete eggnostic. He and Pupkin used to have the most tremendous arguments about creation and evolution, and how if you study at a school of applied science you learn that there's no hell beyond the present life.

Mallory Tompkins used to prove absolutely that the miracles were only electricity, and Pupkin used to admit that it was an awfully good argument, but claimed that he had heard it awfully well answered in a sermon, though unfortunately he had forgotten how.

Tompkins used to show that the flood was contrary to geology, and Pupkin would acknowledge that the point was an excellent one, but that he had read a book,—the title of which he ought to have written down,—which explained geology away altogether.

Mallory Tompkins generally got the best of the merely logical side of the arguments, but Pupkin—who was a tremendous Christian—was much stronger in the things he had forgotten. So the discussions often lasted till far into the night, and Mr. Pupkin would fall asleep and dream of a splendid argument, which would have settled the whole controversy, only unfortunately he couldn't recall it in the morning.

Of course, Pupkin would never have thought of considering himself on an intellectual par with Mallory Tompkins. That would have been ridiculous. Mallory Tompkins had read all sorts of things and had half a mind to write a novel himself—either that or a play. All he needed, he said, was to have a chance to get away somewhere by himself and think. Every time he went away to the city Pupkin expected that he might return with the novel all finished; but though he often came back with his eyes red from thinking, the novel as yet remained incomplete.

Meantime, Mallory Tompkins, as I say, was a mighty intellectual fellow. You could see that from the books on the bamboo bookshelves in the sitting-room. There was, for instance, the "Encyclopaedia Metropolitana" in forty volumes, that he bought on the instalment plan for two dollars a month. Then when they took that away, there was the "History of Civilization," in fifty volumes at fifty cents a week for fifty years. Tompkins had read in it half-way through the Stone Age before they took it from him. After that there was the "Lives of the Painters," one volume at a time—a splendid thing in which you could read all about Aahrens, and Aachenthal, and Aax and men of that class. After all, there's nothing like educating oneself. Mallory Tompkins knew about the opening period of all sorts of things, and in regard to people whose names began with "A" you couldn't stick him.

I don't mean that he and Mr. Pupkin lived a mere routine of studious evenings. That would be untrue. Quite often their time was spent in much less commendable ways than that, and there were poker parties in their sitting-room that didn't break up till nearly midnight. Card-playing, after all, is a slow business, unless you put money on it, and, besides, if you are in a bank and are handling money all day, gambling has a fascination.

I've seen Pupkin and Mallory Tompkins and Joe Milligan, the dentist, and Mitchell the ticket agent, and the other "boys" sitting round the table with matches enough piled up in front of them to stock a factory. Ten matches counted for one chip and ten chips made a cent—so you see they weren't merely playing for the fun of the thing. Of course it's a hollow pleasure. You realize that when you wake up at night parched with thirst, ten thousand matches to the bad. But banking is a wild life and everybody knows it.

Sometimes Pupkin would swear off and keep away from the cursed thing for weeks, and then perhaps he'd see by sheer accident a pile of matches on the table, or a match lying on the floor and it would start the craze in him. I am using his own words—a "craze"—that's what he called it when he told Miss Lawson all about it, and she promised to cure him of it. She would have, too. Only, as I say, Pupkin found that what he had mistaken for attraction was only respect. And there's no use worrying a woman that you respect about your crazes.

It was from Mallory Tompkins that Pupkin learned all about the Mariposa people, because Pupkin came from away off—somewhere down in the Maritime Provinces—and didn't know a soul. Mallory Tompkins used to tell him about Judge Pepperleigh, and what a wonderfully clever man he was and how he would have been in the Supreme Court for certain if the Conservative Government had stayed in another fifteen or twenty years instead of coming to a premature end. He used to talk so much about the Pepperleighs, that Pupkin was sick of the very name. But just as soon as he had seen Zena Pepperleigh he couldn't hear enough of them. He would have talked with Tompkins for hours about the judge's dog Rover. And as for Zena, if he could have brought her name over his lips, he would have talked of her forever.

He first saw her—by one of the strangest coincidences in the world—on the Main Street of Mariposa. If he hadn't happened to be going up the street and she to be coming down it, the thing wouldn't have happened. Afterwards they both admitted that it was one of the most peculiar coincidences they ever heard of. Pupkin owned that he had had the strangest feeling that morning as if something were going to happen—a feeling not at all to be classed with the one of which he had once spoken to Miss Lawson, and which was, at the most, a mere anticipation of respect.

But, as I say, Pupkin met Zena Pepperleigh on the 26th of June, at twenty-five minutes to eleven. And at once the whole world changed. The past was all blotted out. Even in the new forty volume edition of the "Instalment Record of Humanity" that Mallory Tompkins had just received—Pupkin wouldn't have bothered with it.

She—that word henceforth meant Zena—had just come back from her boarding-school, and of all times of year coming back from a boarding-school and for wearing a white shirt waist and a crimson tie and for carrying a tennis racket on the stricken street of a town—commend me to the month of June in Mariposa.

And, for Pupkin, straight away the whole town was irradiated with sunshine, and there was such a singing of the birds, and such a dancing of the rippled waters of the lake, and such a kindliness in the faces of all the people, that only those who have lived in Mariposa, and been young there, can know at all what he felt.

The simple fact is that just the moment he saw Zena Pepperleigh, Mr. Pupkin was clean, plumb, straight, flat, absolutely in love with her.

Which fact is so important that it would be folly not to close the chapter and think about it.

EIGHT

The Fore-ordained Attachment of Zena Pepperleigh and Peter Pupkin

ZENA PEPPERLEIGH used to sit reading novels on the piazza of the judge's house, half hidden by the Virginia creepers. At times the book would fall upon her lap and there was such a look of unstilled yearning in her violet eyes that it did not entirely disappear even when she picked up the apple that lay beside her and took another bite out of it.

With hands clasped she would sit there dreaming all the beautiful day-dreams of girlhood. When you saw that faraway look in her eyes, it meant that she was dreaming that a plumed and armoured knight was rescuing her from the embattled keep of a castle beside the Danube. At other times she was being borne away by an Algerian corsair over the blue waters of the Mediterranean and was reaching out her arms towards France to say farewell to it.

Sometimes when you noticed a sweet look of resignation that seemed to rest upon her features, it meant that Lord Ronald de Chevereux was kneeling at her feet, and that she was telling him to rise, that her humbler birth must ever be a bar to their happiness, and Lord Ronald was getting into an awful state about it, as English peers do at the least suggestion of anything of the sort.

Or, if it wasn't that, then her lover had just returned to her side, tall and soldierly and sunburned, after fighting for ten years in the Soudan for her sake, and had come back to ask her for her answer and to tell her that for ten years her face had been with him even in the watches of the night. He was asking her for a sign, any kind of sign,—ten years in the Soudan entitles them to a sign,—and Zena was plucking a white rose, just one, from her hair, when she would hear her father's step on the piazza and make a grab for the *Pioneers of Tecumseh Township*, and start reading it like mad.

She was always, as I say, being rescued and being borne away, and being parted, and reaching out her arms to France and to Spain, and saying good-bye forever to Valladolid or the old grey towers of Hohenbranntwein.

And I don't mean that she was in the least exceptional or romantic, because all the girls in Mariposa were just like that. An Algerian corsair could have come into the town and had a dozen of them for the asking, and as for a wounded English officer,—well, perhaps it's better not to talk about it outside or the little town would become a regular military hospital.

Because, mind you, the Mariposa girls are all right. You've only to look at them to realize that. You see, you can get in Mariposa a print dress of pale blue or pale pink for a dollar twenty that looks infinitely better than anything you ever see in the city,—especially if you can wear with it a broad straw hat and a background of maple trees and the green grass of a tennis court. And if you remember, too, that these are cultivated girls who have all been to the Mariposa high school and can do decimal fractions, you will understand that an Algerian corsair would sharpen his scimitar at the very sight of them.

Don't think either that they are all dying to get married; because they are not. I don't say they wouldn't take an errant knight, or a buccaneer or a Hungarian refugee, but for the ordinary marriages of ordinary people they feel nothing but a pitying disdain. So it is that each one of them in due time marries an enchanted prince and goes to live in one of the little enchanted houses in the lower part of the town.

I don't know whether you know it, but you can rent an enchanted house in Mariposa for eight dollars a month, and some of the most completely enchanted are the cheapest. As for the enchanted princes, they find them in the strangest places, where you never expected to see them, working—under a spell, you understand,—in drug-stores and printing offices, and even selling things in shops. But to be able to find them you have first to read ever so many novels about Sir Galahad and the Errant Quest and that sort of thing.

Naturally then Zena Pepperleigh, as she sat on the piazza, dreamed of bandits and of wounded officers and of Lord Ronalds riding on foam-flecked chargers. But that she ever dreamed of a junior bank teller in a daffodil blazer riding past on a bicycle, is pretty hard to imagine. So, when Mr. Pupkin came tearing past up the slope of Oneida Street at a speed that proved that he wasn't riding there merely to pass the house, I don't suppose that Zena Pepperleigh was aware of his existence.

That may be a slight exaggeration. She knew, perhaps, that he was the new junior teller in the Exchange Bank and that he came from the Maritime Provinces, and that nobody knew who his people were, and that he had never been in a canoe in his life till he came to Mariposa, and that he sat four pews back in Dean Drone's church, and that his salary was eight hundred dollars. Beyond that, she didn't know a thing about him. She presumed, however, that the reason why he went past so fast was because he didn't dare to go slow.

This, of course, was perfectly correct. Ever since the day when Mr. Pupkin met Zena in the Main Street he used to come past the house on his bicycle just after bank hours. He would have gone past twenty times a day but he was afraid to. As he came up Oneida Street, he used to pedal faster and faster,—he never meant to, but he couldn't help it,—till he went past the piazza where Zena was sitting at an awful speed with his little yellow blazer flying in the wind. In a second he had disappeared in a buzz and a cloud of dust, and the momentum of it carried him clear out into the country for miles and miles before he ever dared to pause or look back.

Then Mr. Pupkin would ride in a huge circuit about the country, trying to think he was looking at the crops, and sooner or later his bicycle would be turned towards the town again and headed for Oneida Street, and would get going quicker and quicker and quicker, till the pedals whirled round with a buzz and he came past the judge's house again, like a bullet out of a gun. He rode fifteen miles to pass the house twice, and even then it took all the nerve that he had.

The people on Oneida Street thought that Mr. Pupkin was crazy, but Zena Pepperleigh knew that he was not. Already, you see, there was a sort of dim parallel between the passing of the bicycle and the last ride of Tancred the Inconsolable along the banks of the Danube.

I have already mentioned, I think, how Mr. Pupkin and Zena Pepperleigh first came to know one another. Like everything else about them, it was a sheer matter of coincidence, quite inexplicable unless you understand that these things are fore-ordained.

That, of course, is the way with fore-ordained affairs and that's where they differ from ordinary love.

~ ~ ~

I won't even try to describe how Mr. Pupkin felt when he first spoke with Zena and sat beside her as they copied out the "endless chain" letter asking for ten cents. They wrote out, as I said, no less than eight of the letters between them, and they found out that their handwritings were so alike that you could hardly tell them apart, except that Pupkin's letters were round and Zena's letters were pointed and Pupkin wrote straight up and down and Zena wrote on a slant. Beyond that the writing was so alike that it was the strangest coincidence in the world. Of course when they made figures it was different and Pupkin explained to Zena that in the bank you have to be able to make a seven so that it doesn't look like a nine.

So, as I say, they wrote the letters all afternoon and when it was over they walked up Oneida Street together, ever so slowly. When they got near the house, Zena asked Pupkin to come in to tea, with such an easy off-hand way that you couldn't have told that she was half an hour late and was taking awful chances on the judge. Pupkin hadn't had time to say yes before the judge appeared at the door, just as they were stepping up on to the piazza, and he had a table napkin in his hand and the dynamite sparks were flying from his spectacles as he called out:

"Great heaven! Zena, why in everlasting blazes can't you get in to tea at a Christian hour?"

Zena gave one look of appeal to Pupkin, and Pupkin looked one glance of comprehension, and turned and fled down Oneida Street. And if the scene wasn't quite as dramatic as the renunciation of Tancred the Troubadour, it at least had something of the same elements in it.

Pupkin walked home to his supper at the Mariposa House on air, and that evening there was a gentle distance in his manner towards Sadie, the dining-room girl, that I suppose no bank clerk in Mariposa ever showed before. It was like Sir Galahad talking with the tire-women of Queen Guinevere and receiving huckleberry pie at their hands.

After that Mr. Pupkin and Zena Pepperleigh constantly met together. They played tennis as partners on the grass court behind Dr. Gallagher's house,—the Mariposa Tennis Club rent it, you remember, for fifty cents a month,—and Pupkin used to perform perfect prodigies of valour, leaping in the air to serve with his little body hooked like a letter S. Sometimes, too, they went out on Lake Wissanotti in the evening in Pupkin's canoe, with Zena sitting in the bow and Pupkin paddling in the stern and they went out ever so far and it was after dark and the stars were shining before they came home. Zena would look at the stars and say how infinitely far away they seemed, and Pupkin would realize that a girl with a mind like that couldn't have any use for a fool such as him. Zena used to ask him to point out the Pleiades and Jupiter and Ursa minor, and Pupkin showed her exactly where they were. That impressed them both tremendously, because Pupkin didn't know that Zena remembered the names out of the astronomy book at her boarding-school, and Zena didn't know that Pupkin simply took a chance on where the stars were.

And ever so many times they talked so intimately that Pupkin came mighty near telling her about his home in the Maritime Provinces and about his father and mother, and then kicked himself that he hadn't the manliness to speak straight out about it and take the consequences.

Please don't imagine from any of this that the course of Mr. Pupkin's love ran smooth. On the contrary, Pupkin himself felt that it was absolutely hopeless from the start.

There were, it might be admitted, certain things that seemed to indicate progress.

In the course of the months of June and July and August, he had taken Zena out in his canoe thirty-one times. Allowing an average of two miles for each evening, Pupkin had paddled Zena sixty-two miles, or more than a hundred thousand yards. That surely was something.

He had played tennis with her on sixteen afternoons. Three times he had left his tennis racket up at the judge's house in Zena's charge, and once he had, with her full consent, left his bicycle there all night. This must count for something. No girl could trifle with a man to the extent of having his bicycle leaning against the verandah post all night and mean nothing by it.

More than that—he had been to tea at the judge's house fourteen times, and seven times he had been asked by Lilian Drone to the rectory when Zena was coming, and five times by Nora Gallagher to tea at the doctor's house because Zena was there.

Altogether he had eaten so many meals where Zena was that his meal ticket at the Mariposa lasted nearly double its proper time, and the face of Sadie, the dining-room girl, had grown to wear a look of melancholy resignation, sadder than romance.

Still more than that, Pupkin had bought for Zena, reckoning it altogether, about two buckets of ice cream and perhaps half a bushel of chocolate. Not that Pupkin grudged the expense of it. On the contrary, over and above the ice cream and the chocolate he had bought her a white waistcoat and a walking stick with a gold top, a lot of new neckties and a pair of patent leather boots—that is, they were all bought on account of her, which is the same thing.

Add to all this that Pupkin and Zena had been to the Church of England Church nearly every Sunday evening for two months, and one evening they had even gone to the Presbyterian Church "for fun," which, if you know Mariposa, you will realize to be a wild sort of escapade that ought to speak volumes.

❧ ❧ ❧

Yet in spite of this, Pupkin felt that the thing was hopeless: which only illustrates the dreadful ups and downs, the wild alternations of hope and despair that characterise an exceptional affair of this sort.

Yes, it was hopeless.

Every time that Pupkin watched Zena praying in church, he knew that she was too good for him. Every time that he came to call for her and found her reading Browning and Omar Khayyam he knew that she was too clever for him. And every time that he saw her at all he realized that she was too beautiful for him.

You see, Pupkin knew that he wasn't a hero. When Zena would clasp her hands and talk rapturously about crusaders and soldiers and firemen and heroes generally, Pupkin knew just where he came in. Not in it, that was all. If a war could have broken out in Mariposa, or the judge's house been invaded by the Germans, he might have had a chance, but as it was—hopeless.

Then there was Zena's father. Heaven knows Pupkin tried hard to please the judge. He agreed with every theory that Judge Pepperleigh advanced, and that took a pretty pliable intellect in itself. They denounced female suffrage one day and they favoured it the next. One day the judge would claim that the labour movement was eating out the heart of the country, and the next day he would hold that the hope of the world lay in the organization of the toiling masses. Pupkin shifted his opinions like the glass in a kaleidoscope. Indeed, the only things on which he was allowed to maintain a steadfast conviction were the purity of the Conservative party of Canada and the awful wickedness of the recall of judges.

But with all that the judge was hardly civil to Pupkin. He hadn't asked him to the house till Zena brought him there, though, as a rule, all the bank clerks in Mariposa treated Judge Pepperleigh's premises as their own. He used to sit and sneer at Pupkin after he had gone till Zena would throw down the *Pioneers of Tecumseh Township* in a temper and flounce off the piazza to her room. After which the judge's manner would change instantly and he would relight his corn cob pipe and sit and positively beam with contentment. In all of which there was something so mysterious as to prove that Mr. Pupkin's chances were hopeless.

Nor was that all of it. Pupkin's salary was eight hundred dollars a year and the Exchange Bank limit for marriage was a thousand.

I suppose you are aware of the grinding capitalistic tyranny of the banks in Mariposa whereby marriage is put beyond the reach of ever so many mature and experienced men of nineteen and twenty and twenty-one, who are compelled to go on eating on a meal ticket at the Mariposa House and living over the bank to suit the whim of a group of capitalists.

Whenever Pupkin thought of this two hundred dollars he understood all that it meant by social unrest. In fact, he interpreted all forms of social discontent in terms of it. Russian Anarchism, German Socialism, the Labour Movement, Henry George, Lloyd George,—he understood the whole lot of them by thinking of his two hundred dollars.

When I tell you that at this period Mr. Pupkin read *Memoirs of the Great Revolutionists* and even thought of blowing up Henry Mullins with dynamite, you can appreciate his state of mind.

~ ~ ~

But not even by all these hindrances and obstacles to his love for Zena Pepperleigh would Peter Pupkin have been driven to commit suicide (oh, yes; he committed it three times, as I'm going to tell you), had it not been for another thing that he knew stood once and for all and in cold reality between him and Zena.

He felt it in a sort of way, as soon as he knew her. Each time that he tried to talk to her about his home and his father and mother and found that something held him back, he realized more and more the kind of thing that stood between them. Most of all did he realize it, with a sudden sickness of heart, when he got word that his father and mother wanted to come to Mariposa to see him and he had all he could do to head them off from it.

Why? Why stop them? The reason was, simple enough, that Pupkin was ashamed of them, bitterly ashamed. The picture of his mother and father turning up in Mariposa and being seen by his friends there and going up to the Pepperleigh's house made him feel faint with shame.

No, I don't say it wasn't wrong. It only shows what difference of fortune, the difference of being rich and being poor, means in this world. You perhaps have been so lucky that you cannot appreciate what it means to feel shame at the station of your own father and mother. You think it doesn't matter, that honesty and kindliness of heart are all that counts. That only shows that you have never known some of the bitterest feelings of people less fortunate than yourself.

So it was with Mr. Pupkin. When he thought of his father and mother turning up in Mariposa, his face reddened with unworthy shame.

He could just picture the scene! He could see them getting out of their Limousine touring car, with the chauffeur holding open the door for them, and his father asking for a suite of rooms,—just think of it, a suite of rooms!—at the Mariposa House.

The very thought of it turned him ill.

What! You have mistaken my meaning? Ashamed of them because they were poor? Good heavens, no, but because they were rich! And not rich in the sense in which they use the term in Mariposa, where a rich person merely means a man who has money enough to build a house with a piazza and to have everything he wants; but rich in the other sense,—motor cars, Ritz hotels, steam yachts, summer islands and all that sort of thing.

Why, Pupkin's father,—what's the use of trying to conceal it any longer?—was the senior partner in the law firm of Pupkin, Pupkin and Pupkin. If you know the Maritime Provinces at all, you've heard of the Pupkins. The name is a household word from Chedabucto to Chidabecto. And, for the matter of that, the law firm and the fact that Pupkin senior had been an Attorney General was the least part of it. Attorney General! Why, there's no money in that! It's no better than the Senate. No, no, Pupkin senior, like so many lawyers, was practically a promoter, and he blew companies like bubbles, and when he wasn't in the Maritime Provinces he was in Boston and New York raising money and floating loans, and when they had no money left in New York he floated it in London: and when he had it, he floated on top of it big rafts of lumber on the Miramichi and codfish on the Grand Banks and lesser fish in the Fundy Bay. You've heard perhaps of the Tidal Transportation Company, and Fundy Fisheries Corporation, and the Paspebiac Pulp and Paper Unlimited? Well, all of those were Pupkin senior under other names. So just imagine him in Mariposa! Wouldn't he be utterly foolish there? Just imagine him meeting Jim Eliot and treating him like a druggist merely because he ran a drug store! or speaking to Jefferson Thorpe as if he were a barber simply because he shaved for money! Why, a man like that could ruin young Pupkin in Mariposa in half a day, and Pupkin knew it.

That wouldn't matter so much, but think of the Pepperleighs and Zena! Everything would be over with them at once. Pupkin knew just what the judge thought of riches and luxuries. How often had he heard the judge pass sentences of life imprisonment on Pierpont Morgan and Mr. Rockefeller. How often had Pupkin heard him say that any man who received more than three thousand dollars a year (that was the judicial salary in the Missinaba district) was a mere robber, unfit to shake the hand of an honest man. Bitter! I should think he was! He was not so bitter, perhaps, as Mr. Muddleson, the principal of the Mariposa high school, who said that any man who received more than fifteen hundred dollars was a public enemy. He was certainly not so bitter as Trelawney, the post-master, who said that any man who got from society more than thirteen hundred dollars (apart from a legitimate increase in recognition of a successful election) was a danger to society. Still, he was bitter. They all were in Mariposa. Pupkin could just imagine how they would despise his father!

And Zena! That was the worst of all. How often had Pupkin heard her say that she simply hated diamonds, wouldn't wear them, despised them, wouldn't give a thank you for a whole tiara of them! As for motor cars and steam yachts,—well, it was pretty plain that that sort of thing had no chance with Zena Pepperleigh. Why, she had told Pupkin one night in the canoe that she would only marry a man who was poor and had his way to make and would hew down difficulties for her sake. And when Pupkin couldn't answer the argument she was quite cross and silent all the way home.

What was Peter Pupkin doing, then, at eight hundred dollars in a bank in Mariposa? If you ask that, it means that you know nothing of the life of the Maritime Provinces and the sturdy temper of the people. I suppose there are no people in the world who hate luxury and extravagance and that sort of thing quite as much as the Maritime Province people, and, of them, no one hated luxury more than Pupkin senior.

Don't mistake the man. He wore a long sealskin coat in winter, yes; but mark you, not as a matter of luxury, but merely as a question of his lungs. He smoked, I admit it, a thirty-five cent cigar, not because he preferred it, but merely through a delicacy of the thorax that made it imperative. He drank champagne at lunch, I concede the point, not in the least from the enjoyment of it, but simply on account of a peculiar affection of the tongue and lips that positively dictated it. His own longing—and his wife shared it—was for the simple, simple life—an island somewhere, with birds and trees. They had bought three or four islands—one in the St. Lawrence, and two in the Gulf, and one off the coast of Maine—looking for this sort of thing. Pupkin senior often said that he wanted to have some place that would remind him of the little old farm up the Aroostook where he was brought up. He often bought little old farms, just to try them, but they always turned out to be so near a city that he cut them into real estate lots, without even having had time to look at them.

But—and this is where the emphasis lay—in the matter of luxury for his only son, Peter, Pupkin senior was a Maritime Province man right to the core, with all the hardihood of the United Empire Loyalists ingrained in him. No luxury for that boy! No, sir! From his childhood, Pupkin senior had undertaken, at the least sign of luxury, to "tan it out of him," after the fashion still in vogue in the provinces. Then he sent him to an old-fashioned school to get it "thumped out of him," and after that he had put him for a year on a Nova Scotia schooner to get it "knocked out of him." If, after all that, young Pupkin, even when he came to Mariposa, wore cameo pins and daffodil blazers, and broke out into ribbed silk saffron ties on pay day, it only shows that the old Adam still needs further tanning even in the Maritime Provinces.

Young Pupkin, of course, was to have gone into law. That was his father's cherished dream and would have made the firm Pupkin, Pupkin, Pupkin, and Pupkin, as it ought to have been. But young Peter was kept out of the law by the fool system of examinations devised since his father's time. Hence there was nothing for it but to sling him into a bank; "sling him" was, I think, the expression. So his father decided that if Pupkin was to be slung, he should be slung good and far—clean into Canada (you know the way they use that word in the Maritime Provinces). And to sling Pupkin he called in the services of an old friend, a man after his own heart, just as violent as himself, who used to be at the law school in the city with Pupkin senior thirty years ago. So this friend, who happened to live in Mariposa, and who was a violent man, said at once: "Edward, by Jehoshaphat! send the boy up here."

So that is how Pupkin came to Mariposa. And if, when he got there, his father's friend gave no sign, and treated the boy with roughness and incivility, that may have been, for all I know, a continuation of the "tanning" process of the Maritime people.

Did I mention that the Pepperleigh family, generations ago, had taken up land near the Aroostook, and that it was from there the judge's father came to Tecumseh township? Perhaps not, but it doesn't matter.

But surely after such reminiscences as these the awful things that are impending over Mr. Pupkin must be kept for another chapter.

NINE

The Mariposa Bank Mystery

SUICIDE is a thing that ought not to be committed without very careful thought. It often involves serious consequences, and in some cases brings pain to others than oneself.

I don't say that there is no justification for it. There often is. Anybody who has listened to certain kinds of music, or read certain kinds of poetry, or heard certain kinds of performances upon the concertina, will admit that there are some lives which ought not to be continued, and that even suicide has its brighter aspects.

But to commit suicide on grounds of love is at the best a very dubious experiment. I know that in this I am expressing an opinion contrary to that of most true lovers who embrace suicide on the slightest provocation as the only honourable termination of an existence that never ought to have begun.

I quite admit that there is a glamour and a sensation about the thing which has its charm, and that there is nothing like it for causing a girl to realize the value of the heart that she has broken and which breathed forgiveness upon her at the very moment when it held in its hand the half-pint of prussic acid that was to terminate its beating for ever.

But apart from the general merits of the question, I suppose there are few people, outside of lovers, who know what it is to commit suicide four times in five weeks.

Yet this was what happened to Mr. Pupkin, of the Exchange Bank of Mariposa.

Ever since he had known Zena Pepperleigh he had realized that his love for her was hopeless. She was too beautiful for him and too good for him; her father hated him and her mother despised him; his salary was too small and his own people were too rich.

If you add to all that that he came up to the judge's house one night and found a poet reciting verses to Zena, you will understand the suicide at once. It was one of those regular poets with a solemn jackass face, and lank parted hair and eyes like puddles of molasses. I don't know how he came there—up from the city, probably—but there he was on the Pepperleighs' verandah that August evening. He was reciting poetry—either Tennyson's or Shelley's, or his own, you couldn't tell—and about him sat Zena with her hands clasped and Nora Gallagher looking at the sky and Jocelyn Drone gazing into infinity, and a little tubby woman looking at the poet with her head falling over sideways—in fact, there was a whole group of them.

I don't know what it is about poets that draws women to them in this way. But everybody knows that a poet has only to sit and saw the air with his hands and recite verses in a deep stupid voice, and all the women are crazy over him. Men despise him and would kick him off the verandah if they dared, but the women simply rave over him.

So Pupkin sat there in the gloom and listened to this poet reciting Browning and he realized that everybody understood it but him. He could see Zena with her eyes fixed on the poet as if she were hanging on to every syllable (she was; she needed to), and he stood it just about fifteen minutes and then slid off the side of the verandah and disappeared without even saying good-night.

He walked straight down Oneida Street and along the Main Street just as hard as he could go. There was only one purpose in his mind,—suicide. He was heading straight for Jim Eliot's drug store on the main corner and his idea was to buy a drink of chloroform and drink it and die right there on the spot.

As Pupkin walked down the street, the whole thing was so vivid in his mind that he could picture it to the remotest detail. He could even see it all in type, in big headings in the newspapers of the following day:

APPALLING SUICIDE.
PETER PUPKIN POISONED.

He perhaps hoped that the thing might lead to some kind of public enquiry and that the question of Browning's poetry and whether it is altogether fair to allow of its general circulation would be fully ventilated in the newspapers.

Thinking of that, Pupkin came to the main corner.

On a warm August evening the drug store of Mariposa, as you know, is all a blaze of lights. You can hear the hissing of the soda-water fountain half a block away, and inside the store there are ever so many people—boys and girls and old people too—all drinking sarsaparilla and chocolate sundaes and lemon sours and foaming drinks that you take out of long straws. There is such a laughing and a talking as you never heard, and the girls are all in white and pink and cambridge blue, and the soda fountain is of white marble with silver taps, and it hisses and sputters, and Jim Eliot and his assistant wear white coats with red geraniums in them, and it's just as gay as gay.

The foyer of the opera in Paris may be a fine sight, but I doubt if it can compare with the inside of Eliot's drug store in Mariposa—for real gaiety and joy of living.

This night the store was especially crowded because it was a Saturday and that meant early closing for all the hotels, except, of course, Smith's. So as the hotels were shut, the people were all in the drug store, drinking like fishes. It just shows the folly of Local Option and the Temperance Movement and all that. Why, if you shut the hotels you simply drive the people to the soda fountains and there's more drinking than ever, and not only of the men, too, but the girls and young boys and children. I've seen little things of eight and nine that had to be lifted up on the high stools at Eliot's drug store, drinking great goblets of lemon soda, enough to burst them—brought there by their own fathers, and why? Simply because the hotel bars were shut.

What's the use of thinking you can stop people drinking merely by cutting off whiskey and brandy? The only effect is to drive them to taking lemon sour and sarsaparilla and cherry pectoral and caroka cordial and things they wouldn't have touched before. So in the long run they drink more than ever. The point is that you can't prevent people having a good time, no matter how hard you try. If they can't have it with lager beer and brandy, they'll have it with plain soda and lemon pop, and so the whole gloomy scheme of the temperance people breaks down, anyway.

But I was only saying that Eliot's drug store in Mariposa on a Saturday night is the gayest and brightest spot in the world.

And just imagine what a fool of a place to commit suicide in!

Just imagine going up to the soda-water fountain and asking for five cents' worth of chloroform and soda! Well, you simply can't, that's all.

That's the way Pupkin found it. You see, as soon as he came in, somebody called out: "Hello, Pete!" and one or two others called: "Hullo, Pup!" and some said: "How goes it?" and others: "How are you toughing it?" and so on, because you see they had all been drinking more or less and naturally they felt jolly and glad-hearted.

So the upshot of it was that instead of taking chloroform, Pupkin stepped up to the counter of the fountain and he had a bromo-seltzer with cherry soda, and after that he had one of those aerated seltzers, and then a couple of lemon seltzers and a bromophizzer.

I don't know if you know the mental effect of a bromo-seltzer.

But it's a hard thing to commit suicide on.

You can't.

You feel so buoyant.

Anyway, what with the phizzing of the seltzer and the lights and the girls, Pupkin began to feel so fine that he didn't care a cuss for all the Browning in the world, and as for the poet—oh, to blazes with him! What's poetry, anyway?—only rhymes.

So, would you believe it, in about ten minutes Peter Pupkin was off again and heading straight for the Pepperleighs' house, poet or no poet, and, what was more to the point, he carried with him three great bricks of Eliot's ice cream—in green, pink and brown layers. He struck the verandah just at the moment when Browning was getting too stale and dreary for words. His brain was all sizzling and jolly with the bromo-seltzer, and when he fetched out the ice cream bricks and Zena ran to get plates and spoons to eat it with, and Pupkin went with her to help fetch them and they picked out the spoons together, they were so laughing and happy that it was just a marvel. Girls, you know, need no bromo-seltzer. They're full of it all the time.

And as for the poet—well, can you imagine how Pupkin felt when Zena told him that the poet was married, and that the tubby little woman with her head on sideways was his wife?

So they had the ice cream, and the poet ate it in bucketsful. Poets always do. They need it. And after it the poet recited some stanzas of his own and Pupkin saw that he had misjudged the man, because it was dandy poetry, the very best. That night Pupkin walked home on air and there was no thought of chloroform, and it turned out that he hadn't committed suicide, but like all lovers he had commuted it.

~ ~ ~

I don't need to describe in full the later suicides of Mr. Pupkin, because they were all conducted on the same plan and rested on something the same reasons as above.

Sometimes he would go down at night to the offices of the bank below his bedroom and bring up his bank revolver in order to make an end of himself with it. This, too, he could see headed up in the newspapers as:

BRILLIANT BOY BANKER
BLOWS OUT BRAINS.

But blowing your brains out is a noisy, rackety performance, and Pupkin soon found that only special kinds of brains are suited for it. So he always sneaked back again later in the night and put the revolver in its place, deciding to drown himself instead. Yet every time that he walked down to the Trestle Bridge over the Ossawippi he found it was quite unsuitable for drowning—too high, and the water too swift and black, and the rushes too gruesome—in fact, not at all the kind of place for a drowning.

Far better, he realized, to wait there on the railroad track and throw himself under the wheels of the express and be done with it. Yet, though Pupkin often waited in this way for the train, he was never able to pick out a pair of wheels that suited him. Anyhow, it's awfully hard to tell an express from a fast freight.

I wouldn't mention these attempts at suicide if one of them hadn't finally culminated in making Peter Pupkin a hero and solving for him the whole perplexed entanglement of his love affair with Zena Pepperleigh. Incidentally it threw him into the very centre of one of the most impenetrable bank mysteries that ever baffled the ingenuity of some of the finest legal talent that ever adorned one of the most enterprising communities in the country.

It happened one night, as I say, that Pupkin decided to go down into the office of the bank and get his revolver and see if it would blow his brains out. It was the night of the Firemen's Ball and Zena had danced four times with a visitor from the city, a man who was in the fourth year at the University and who knew everything. It was more than Peter Pupkin could bear. Mallory Tompkins was away that night, and when Pupkin came home he was all alone in the building, except for Gillis, the caretaker, who lived in the extension at the back.

He sat in his room for hours brooding. Two or three times he picked up a book—he remembered afterwards distinctly that it was *Kant's Critique of Pure Reason*—and tried to read it, but it seemed meaningless and trivial. Then with a sudden access of resolution he started from his chair and made his way down the stairs and into the office room of the bank, meaning to get a revolver and kill himself on the spot and let them find his body lying on the floor.

It was then far on in the night and the empty building of the bank was as still as death. Pupkin could hear the stairs creak under his feet, and as he went he thought he heard another sound like the opening or closing of a door. But it sounded not like the sharp ordinary noise of a closing door but with a dull muffled noise as if someone had shut the iron door of a safe in a room under the ground. For a moment Pupkin stood and listened with his heart thumping against his ribs. Then he kicked his slippers from his feet and without a sound stole into the office on the ground floor and took the revolver from his teller's desk. As he gripped it, he listened to the sounds on the back-stairway and in the vaults below.

I should explain that in the Exchange Bank of Mariposa the offices are on the ground floor level with the street. Below this is another floor with low dark rooms paved with flagstones, with unused office desks and with piles of papers stored in boxes. On this floor are the vaults of the bank, and lying in them in the autumn—the grain season—there is anything from fifty to a hundred thousand dollars in currency tied in bundles. There is no other light down there than the dim reflection from the lights out on the street, that lies in patches on the stone floor.

I think as Peter Pupkin stood, revolver in hand, in the office of the bank, he had forgotten all about the maudlin purpose of his first coming. He had forgotten for the moment all about heroes and love affairs, and his whole mind was focussed, sharp and alert, with the intensity of the night-time, on the sounds that he heard in the vault and on the back-stairway of the bank.

Straight away, Pupkin knew what it meant as plainly as if it were written in print. He had forgotten, I say, about being a hero and he only knew that there was sixty thousand dollars in the vault of the bank below, and that he was paid eight hundred dollars a year to look after it.

As Peter Pupkin stood there listening to the sounds in his stockinged feet, his faced showed grey as ashes in the light that fell through the window from the street. His heart beat like a hammer against his ribs. But behind its beatings was the blood of four generations of Loyalists, and the robber who would take that sixty thousand dollars from the Mariposa bank must take it over the dead body of Peter Pupkin, teller.

Pupkin walked down the stairs to the lower room, the one below the ground with the bank vault in it, with as fine a step as any of his ancestors showed on parade. And if he had known it, as he came down the stairway in the front of the vault room, there was a man crouched in the shadow of the passage way by the stairs at the back. This man, too, held a revolver in his hand, and, criminal or not, his face was as resolute as Pupkin's own. As he heard the teller's step on the stair, he turned and waited in the shadow of the doorway without a sound.

There is no need really to mention all these details. They are only of interest as showing how sometimes a bank teller in a corded smoking jacket and stockinged feet may be turned into such a hero as even the Mariposa girls might dream about.

All of this must have happened at about three o'clock in the night.

This much was established afterwards from the evidence of Gillis, the caretaker. When he first heard the sounds he had looked at his watch and noticed that it was half-past two; the watch he knew was three-quarters of an hour slow three days before and had been gaining since. The exact time at which Gillis heard footsteps in the bank and started downstairs, pistol in hand, became a nice point afterwards in the cross-examination.

But one must not anticipate. Pupkin reached the iron door of the bank safe, and knelt in front of it, feeling in the dark to find the fracture of the lock. As he knelt, he heard a sound behind him, and swung round on his knees and saw the bank robber in the half light of the passage way and the glitter of a pistol in his hand. The rest was over in an instant. Pupkin heard a voice that was his own, but that sounded strange and hollow, call out: "Drop that, or I'll fire!" and then just as he raised his revolver, there came a blinding flash of light before his eyes, and Peter Pupkin, junior teller of the bank, fell forward on the floor and knew no more.

~ ~ ~

At that point, of course, I ought to close down a chapter, or volume, or, at least, strike the reader over the head with a sandbag to force him to stop and think. In common fairness one ought to stop here and count a hundred or get up and walk round a block, or, at any rate, picture to oneself Peter Pupkin lying on the floor of the bank, motionless, his arms distended, the revolver still grasped in his hand. But I must go on.

By half-past seven on the following morning it was known all over Mariposa that Peter Pupkin the junior teller of the Exchange had been shot dead by a bank robber in the vault of the building. It was known also that Gillis, the caretaker, had been shot and killed at the foot of the stairs, and that the robber had made off with fifty thousand dollars in currency; that he had left a trail of blood on the sidewalk and that the men were out tracking him with bloodhounds in the great swamps to the north of the town.

This, I say, and it is important to note it, was what they knew at half-past seven. Of course as each hour went past they learned more and more. At eight o'clock it was known that Pupkin was not dead, but dangerously wounded in the lungs. At eight-thirty it was known that he was not shot in the lungs, but that the ball had traversed the pit of his stomach.

At nine o'clock it was learned that the pit of Pupkin's stomach was all right, but that the bullet had struck his right ear and carried it away. Finally it was learned that his ear had not exactly been carried away, that is, not precisely removed by the bullet, but that it had grazed Pupkin's head in such a way that it had stunned him, and if it had been an inch or two more to the left it might have reached his brain. This, of course, was just as good as being killed from the point of view of public interest.

Indeed, by nine o'clock Pupkin could be himself seen on the Main Street with a great bandage sideways on his head, pointing out the traces of the robber. Gillis, the caretaker, too, it was known by eight, had not been killed. He had been shot through the brain, but whether the injury was serious or not was only a matter of conjecture. In fact, by ten o'clock it was understood that the bullet from the robber's second shot had grazed the side of the caretaker's head, but as far as could be known his brain was just as before. I should add that the first report about the bloodstains and the swamp and the bloodhounds turned out to be inaccurate. The stains may have been blood, but as they led to the cellar way of Netley's store they may have also been molasses, though it was argued, to be sure, that the robber might well have poured molasses over the bloodstains from sheer cunning.

It was remembered, too, that there were no bloodhounds in Mariposa, although, mind you, there are any amount of dogs there.

So you see that by ten o'clock in the morning the whole affair was settling into the impenetrable mystery which it ever since remained.

Not that there wasn't evidence enough. There was Pupkin's own story and Gillis's story, and the stories of all the people who had heard the shots and seen the robber (some said, the bunch of robbers) go running past (others said, walking past), in the night. Apparently the robber ran up and down half the streets of Mariposa before he vanished.

But the stories of Pupkin and Gillis were plain enough. Pupkin related that he heard sounds in the bank and came downstairs just in time to see the robber crouching in the passage way, and that the robber was a large, hulking, villainous looking man, wearing a heavy coat. Gillis told exactly the same story, having heard the noises at the same time, except that he first described the robber as a small thin fellow (peculiarly villainous looking, however, even in the dark), wearing a short jacket; but on thinking it over, Gillis realized that he had been wrong about the size of the criminal, and that he was even bigger, if anything, than what Mr. Pupkin thought. Gillis had fired at the robber; just at the same moment had Mr. Pupkin.

Beyond that, all was mystery, absolute and impenetrable.

By eleven o'clock the detectives had come up from the city under orders from the head of the bank.

I wish you could have seen the two detectives as they moved to and fro in Mariposa—fine looking, stern, impenetrable men that they were. They seemed to take in the whole town by instinct and so quietly. They found their way to Mr. Smith's Hotel just as quietly as if it wasn't design at all and stood there at the bar, picking up scraps of conversation—you know the way detectives do it. Occasionally they allowed one or two bystanders—confederates, perhaps,—to buy a drink for them, and you could see from the way they drank it that they were still listening for a clue. If there had been the faintest clue in Smith's Hotel or in the Mariposa House or in the Continental, those fellows would have been at it like a flash.

To see them moving round the town that day—silent, massive, imperturbable—gave one a great idea of their strange, dangerous calling. They went about the town all day and yet in such a quiet peculiar way that you couldn't have realized that they were working at all. They ate their dinner together at Smith's café and took an hour and a half over it to throw people off the scent. Then when they got them off it, they sat and talked with Josh Smith in the back bar to keep them off. Mr. Smith seemed to take to them right away. They were men of his own size, or near it, and anyway hotel men and detectives have a general affinity and share in the same impenetrable silence and in their confidential knowledge of the weaknesses of the public.

Mr. Smith, too, was of great use to the detectives. "Boys," he said, "I wouldn't ask too close as to what folks was out late at night: in this town it don't do."

When those two great brains finally left for the city on the five-thirty, it was hard to realize that behind each grand, impassible face a perfect vortex of clues was seething.

But if the detectives were heroes, what was Pupkin? Imagine him with his bandage on his head standing in front of the bank and talking of the midnight robbery with that peculiar false modesty that only heroes are entitled to use.

I don't know whether you have ever been a hero, but for sheer exhilaration there is nothing like it. And for Mr. Pupkin, who had gone through life thinking himself no good, to be suddenly exalted into the class of Napoleon Bonaparte and John Maynard and the Charge of the Light Brigade—oh, it was wonderful. Because Pupkin was a brave man now and he knew it and acquired with it all the brave man's modesty. In fact, I believe he was heard to say that he had only done his duty, and that what he did was what any other man would have done: though when somebody else said: "That's so, when you come to think of it," Pupkin turned on him that quiet look of the wounded hero, bitterer than words.

And if Pupkin had known that all of the afternoon papers in the city reported him dead, he would have felt more luxurious still.

That afternoon the Mariposa court sat in enquiry,—technically it was summoned in inquest on the dead robber—though they hadn't found the body—and it was wonderful to see them lining up the witnesses and holding cross-examinations. There is something in the cross-examination of great criminal lawyers like Nivens, of Mariposa, and in the counter examinations of presiding judges like Pepperleigh that thrills you to the core with the astuteness of it.

They had Henry Mullins, the manager, on the stand for an hour and a half, and the excitement was so breathless that you could have heard a pin drop. Nivens took him on first.

"What is your name?" he said.

"Henry August Mullins."

"What position do you hold?"

"I am manager of the Exchange Bank."

"When were you born?"

"December 30, 1869."

After that, Nivens stood looking quietly at Mullins. You could feel that he was thinking pretty deeply before he shot the next question at him.

"Where did you go to school?"

Mullins answered straight off: "The high school down home," and Nivens thought again for a while and then asked:

"How many boys were at the school?"

"About sixty."

"How many masters?"

"About three."

After that Nivens paused a long while and seemed to be digesting the evidence, but at last an idea seemed to strike him and he said:

"I understand you were not on the bank premises last night. Where were you?"

"Down the lake duck shooting."

You should have seen the excitement in the court when Mullins said this. The judge leaned forward in his chair and broke in at once.

"Did you get any, Harry?" he asked.

"Yes," Mullins said, "about six."

"Where did you get them? What? In the wild rice marsh past the river? You don't say so! Did you get them on the sit or how?"

All of these questions were fired off at the witness from the court in a single breath. In fact, it was the knowledge that the first ducks of the season had been seen in the Ossawippi marsh that led to the termination of the proceedings before the afternoon was a quarter over. Mullins and George Duff and half the witnesses were off with shotguns as soon as the court was cleared.

❧ ❧ ❧

I may as well state at once that the full story of the robbery of the bank of Mariposa never came to the light. A number of arrests—mostly of vagrants and suspicious characters—were made, but the guilt of the robbery was never brought home to them. One man was arrested twenty miles away, at the other end of Missinaba county, who not only corresponded exactly with the description of the robber, but, in addition to this, had a wooden leg. Vagrants with one leg are always regarded with suspicion in places like Mariposa, and whenever a robbery or a murder happens they are arrested in batches.

It was never even known just how much money was stolen from the bank. Some people said ten thousand dollars, others more. The bank, no doubt for business motives, claimed that the contents of the safe were intact and that the robber had been foiled in his design.

But none of this matters to the exaltation of Mr. Pupkin. Good fortune, like bad, never comes in small instalments. On that wonderful day, every good thing happened to Peter Pupkin at once. The morning saw him a hero. At the sitting of the court, the judge publicly told him that his conduct was fit to rank among the annals of the pioneers of Tecumseh Township, and asked him to his house for supper. At five o'clock he received the telegram of promotion from the head office that raised his salary to a thousand dollars, and made him not only a hero but a marriageable man. At six o'clock he started up to the judge's house with his resolution nerved to the most momentous step of his life.

His mind was made up.

He would do a thing seldom if ever done in Mariposa. He would propose to Zena Pepperleigh. In Mariposa this kind of step, I say, is seldom taken. The course of love runs on and on through all its stages of tennis playing and dancing and sleigh riding, till by sheer notoriety of circumstance an understanding is reached. To propose straight out would be thought priggish and affected and is supposed to belong only to people in books.

But Pupkin felt that what ordinary people dare not do, heroes are allowed to attempt. He would propose to Zena, and more than that, he would tell her in a straight, manly way that he was rich and take the consequences.

And he did it.

That night on the piazza, where the hammock hangs in the shadow of the Virginia creeper, he did it. By sheer good luck the judge had gone indoors to the library, and by a piece of rare good fortune Mrs. Pepperleigh had gone indoors to the sewing room, and by a happy trick of coincidence the servant was out and the dog was tied up—in fact, no such chain of circumstances was ever offered in favour of mortal man before.

What Zena said—beyond saying yes—I do not know. I am sure that when Pupkin told her of the money, she bore up as bravely as so fine a girl as Zena would, and when he spoke of diamonds she said she would wear them for his sake.

They were saying these things and other things—ever so many other things—when there was such a roar and a clatter up Oneida Street as you never heard, and there came bounding up to the house one of the most marvellous Limousine touring cars that ever drew up at the home of a judge on a modest salary of three thousand dollars. When it stopped there sprang from it an excited man in a long sealskin coat—worn not for the luxury of it at all but from the sheer chilliness of the autumn evening. And it was, as of course you know, Pupkin's father. He had seen the news of his son's death in the evening paper in the city. They drove the car through, so the chauffeur said, in two hours and a quarter, and behind them there was to follow a special trainload of detectives and emergency men, but Pupkin senior had cancelled all that by telegram half way up when he heard that Peter was still living.

For a moment as his eye rested on young Pupkin you would almost have imagined, had you not known that he came from the Maritime Provinces, that there were tears in them and that he was about to hug his son to his heart. But if he didn't hug Peter to his heart, he certainly did within a few moments clasp Zena to it, in that fine fatherly way in which they clasp pretty girls in the Maritime Provinces. The strangest thing is that Pupkin senior seemed to understand the whole situation without any explanations at all.

Judge Pepperleigh, I think, would have shaken both of Pupkin senior's arms off when he saw him; and when you heard them call one another "Ned" and "Phillip" it made you feel that they were boys again attending classes together at the old law school in the city.

If Pupkin thought that his father wouldn't make a hit in Mariposa, it only showed his ignorance. Pupkin senior sat there on the judge's verandah smoking a corn cob pipe as if he had never heard of Havana cigars in his life. In the three days that he spent in Mariposa that autumn, he went in and out of Jeff Thorpe's barber shop and Eliot's drug store, shot black ducks in the marsh and played poker every evening at a hundred matches for a cent as if he had never lived any other life in all his days. They had to send him telegrams enough to fill a satchel to make him come away.

So Pupkin and Zena in due course of time were married, and went to live in one of the enchanted houses on the hillside in the newer part of the town, where you may find them to this day.

You may see Pupkin there at any time cutting enchanted grass on a little lawn in as gaudy a blazer as ever.

But if you step up to speak to him or walk with him into the enchanted house, pray modulate your voice a little—musical though it is—for there is said to be an enchanted baby on the premises whose sleep must not lightly be disturbed.

TEN

The Great Election in Missinaba County

DON'T ASK me what election it was, whether Dominion or Provincial or Imperial or Universal, for I scarcely know.

It must, of course, have been going on in other parts of the country as well, but I saw it all from Missinaba County which, with the town of Mariposa, was, of course, the storm centre and focus point of the whole turmoil.

I only know that it was a huge election and that on it turned issues of the most tremendous importance, such as whether or not Mariposa should become part of the United States, and whether the flag that had waved over the school house at Tecumseh Township for ten centuries should be trampled under the hoof of an alien invader, and whether Britons should be slaves, and whether Canadians should be Britons, and whether the farming class would prove themselves Canadians, and tremendous questions of that kind.

And there was such a roar and a tumult to it, and such a waving of flags and beating of drums and flaring of torchlights that such parts of the election as may have been going on elsewhere than in Missinaba county must have been quite unimportant and didn't really matter.

Now that it is all over, we can look back at it without heat or passion.

We can see,—it's plain enough now,—that in the great election Canada saved the British Empire, and that Missinaba saved Canada and that the vote of the Third Concession of Tecumseh Township saved Missinaba County, and that those of us who carried the third concession,—well, there's no need to push it further. We prefer to be modest about it. If we still speak of it, it is only quietly and simply and not more than three or four times a day.

But you can't understand the election at all, and the conventions and the campaigns and the nominations and the balloting, unless you first appreciate the peculiar complexion of politics in Mariposa.

Let me begin at the beginning. Everybody in Mariposa is either a Liberal or a Conservative or else is both. Some of the people are or have been Liberals or Conservatives all their lives and are called dyed-in-the-wool Grits or old-time Tories and things of that sort. These people get from long training such a swift penetrating insight into national issues that they can decide the most complicated question in four seconds: in fact, just as soon as they grab the city papers out of the morning mail, they know the whole solution of any problem you can put to them. There are other people whose aim it is to be broad-minded and judicious and who vote Liberal or Conservative according to their judgment of the questions of the day. If their judgment of these questions tells them that there is something in it for them in voting Liberal, then they do so. But if not, they refuse to be the slaves of a party or the henchmen of any political leader. So that anybody looking for henches has got to keep away from them.

But the one thing that nobody is allowed to do in Mariposa is to have no politics. Of course there are always some people whose circumstances compel them to say that they have no politics. But that is easily understood. Take the case of Trelawney, the postmaster. Long ago he was a letter carrier under the old Mackenzie Government, and later he was a letter sorter under the old Macdonald Government, and after that a letter stamper under the old Tupper Government, and so on. Trelawney always says that he has no politics, but the truth is that he has too many.

So, too, with the clergy in Mariposa. They have no politics—absolutely none. Yet Dean Drone round election time always announces as his text such a verse as: "Lo! is there not one righteous man in Israel?" or: "What ho! is it not time for a change?" And that is a signal for all the Liberal business men to get up and leave their pews.

Similarly over at the Presbyterian Church, the minister says that his sacred calling will not allow him to take part in politics and that his sacred calling prevents him from breathing even a word of harshness against his fellow man, but that when it comes to the elevation of the ungodly into high places in the commonwealth (this means, of course, the nomination of the Conservative candidate) then he's not going to allow his sacred calling to prevent him from saying just what he thinks of it. And by that time, having pretty well cleared the church of Conservatives, he proceeds to show from the scriptures that the ancient Hebrews were Liberals to a man, except those who were drowned in the flood or who perished, more or less deservedly, in the desert.

There are, I say, some people who are allowed to claim to have no politics,—the office holders, and the clergy and the school teachers and the hotel keepers. But beyond them, anybody in Mariposa who says that he has no politics is looked upon as crooked, and people wonder what it is that he is "out after."

In fact, the whole town and county is a hive of politics, and people who have only witnessed gatherings such as the House of Commons at Westminster and the Senate at Washington and never seen a Conservative Convention at Tecumseh Corners or a Liberal Rally at the Concession school house, don't know what politics means.

So you may imagine the excitement in Mariposa when it became known that King George had dissolved the parliament of Canada and had sent out a writ or command for Missinaba County to elect for him some other person than John Henry Bagshaw because he no longer had confidence in him.

The king, of course, is very well known, very favourably known, in

Mariposa. Everybody remembers how he visited the town on his great tour in Canada, and stopped off at the Mariposa station. Although he was only a prince at the time, there was quite a big crowd down at the depôt and everybody felt what a shame it was that the prince had no time to see more of Mariposa, because he would get such a false idea of it, seeing only the station and the lumber yards. Still, they all came to the station and all the Liberals and Conservatives mixed together perfectly freely and stood side by side without any distinction, so that the prince should not observe any party differences among them. And he didn't,—you could see that he didn't. They read him an address all about the tranquillity and loyalty of the Empire, and they purposely left out any reference to the trouble over the town wharf or the big row there had been about the location of the new post-office. There was a general decent feeling that it wouldn't be fair to disturb the prince with these things: later on, as king, he would, of course, *have* to know all about them, but meanwhile it was better to leave him with the idea that his empire was tranquil.

So they deliberately couched the address in terms that were just as reassuring as possible and the prince was simply delighted with it. I am certain that he slept pretty soundly after hearing that address. Why, you could see it taking effect even on his aides-de-camp and the people round him, so imagine how the prince must have felt!

I think in Mariposa they understand kings perfectly. Every time that a king or a prince comes, they try to make him see the bright side of everything and let him think that they're all united. Judge Pepperleigh walked up and down arm in arm with Dr. Gallagher, the worst Grit in the town, just to make the prince feel fine.

So when they got the news that the king had lost confidence in John Henry Bagshaw, the sitting member, they never questioned it a bit. Lost confidence? All right, they'd elect him another right away. They'd elect him half a dozen if he needed them. They don't mind; they'd elect the whole town man after man rather than have the king worried about it.

In any case, all the Conservatives had been wondering for years how the king and the governor-general and men like that had tolerated such a man as Bagshaw so long.

Missinaba County, I say, is a regular hive of politics, and not the miserable, crooked, money-ridden politics of the cities, but the straight, real old-fashioned thing that is an honour to the country side. Any man who would offer to take a bribe or sell his convictions for money, would be an object of scorn. I don't say they wouldn't take money,—they would, of course, why not?—but if they did they would take it in a straight fearless way and say nothing about it. They might,—it's only human,—accept a job or a contract from the government, but if they did, rest assured it would be in a broad national spirit and not for the sake of the work itself. No, sir. Not for a minute.

Any man who wants to get the votes of the Missinaba farmers and the Mariposa business men has got to persuade them that he's the right man. If he can do that,—if he can persuade any one of them that he is the right man and that all the rest know it, then they'll vote for him.

The division, I repeat, between the Liberals and the Conservatives, is intense. Yet you might live for a long while in the town, between elections, and never know it. It is only when you get to understand the people that you begin to see that there is a cross division running through them that nothing can ever remove. You gradually become aware of fine subtle distinctions that miss your observation at first. Outwardly, they are all friendly enough. For instance, Joe Milligan the dentist is a Conservative, and has been for six years, and yet he shares the same boat-house with young Dr. Gallagher, who is a Liberal, and they even bought a motor boat between them. Pete Glover and Alf McNichol were in partnership in the hardware and paint store, though they belonged on different sides.

But just as soon as elections drew near, the differences in politics became perfectly apparent. Liberals and Conservatives drew away from one another. Joe Milligan used the motor boat one Saturday and Dr. Gallagher the next, and Pete Glover sold hardware on one side of the store and Alf McNichol sold paint on the other. You soon realized too that one of the newspapers was Conservative and the other was Liberal, and that there was a Liberal drug store and a Conservative drug store, and so on. Similarly round election time, the Mariposa House was the Liberal Hotel, and the Continental Conservative, though Mr. Smith's place, where they always put on a couple of extra bar tenders, was what you might call Independent-Liberal-Conservative, with a dash of Imperialism thrown in. Mr. Gingham, the undertaker, was, as a natural effect of his calling, an advanced Liberal, but at election time he always engaged a special assistant for embalming Conservative customers.

So now, I think, you understand something of the general political surroundings of the great election in Missinaba County.

John Henry Bagshaw was the sitting member, the Liberal member, for Missinaba County.

The Liberals called him the old war horse, and the old battle-axe, and the old charger and the old champion and all sorts of things of that kind. The Conservatives called him the old jackass and the old army mule and the old booze fighter and the old grafter and the old scoundrel.

John Henry Bagshaw was, I suppose, one of the greatest political forces in the world. He had flowing white hair crowned with a fedora hat, and a smooth statesmanlike face which it cost the country twenty-five cents a day to shave.

Altogether the Dominion of Canada had spent over two thousand dollars in shaving that face during the twenty years that Bagshaw had represented Missinaba County. But the result had been well worth it.

Bagshaw wore a long political overcoat that it cost the country twenty cents a day to brush, and boots that cost the Dominion fifteen cents every morning to shine.

But it was money well spent.

Bagshaw of Mariposa was one of the most representative men of the age, and it's no wonder that he had been returned for the county for five elections running, leaving the Conservatives nowhere. Just think how representative he was. He owned two hundred acres out on the Third

Concession and kept two men working on it all the time to prove that he was a practical farmer. They sent in fat hogs to the Missinaba County Agricultural Exposition and the World's Fair every autumn, and Bagshaw himself stood beside the pig pens with the judges, and wore a pair of corduroy breeches and chewed a straw all afternoon. After that if any farmer thought that he was not properly represented in Parliament, it showed that he was an ass.

Bagshaw owned a half share in the harness business and a quarter share in the tannery and that made him a business man. He paid for a pew in the Presbyterian Church and that represented religion in Parliament. He attended college for two sessions thirty years ago, and that represented education and kept him abreast with modern science, if not ahead of it. He kept a little account in one bank and a big account in the other, so that he was a rich man or a poor man at the same time.

Add to that that John Henry Bagshaw was perhaps the finest orator in Mariposa. That, of course, is saying a great deal. There are speakers there, lots of them that can talk two or three hours at a stretch, but the old war horse could beat them all. They say that when John Henry Bagshaw got well started, say after a couple of hours of talk, he could speak as Pericles or Demosthenes or Cicero never could have spoken.

You could tell Bagshaw a hundred yards off as a member of the House of Commons. He wore a pepper-and-salt suit to show that he came from a rural constituency, and he wore a broad gold watch-chain with dangling seals to show that he also represents a town. You could see from his quiet low collar and white tie that his electorate were a God-fearing, religious people, while the horseshoe pin that he wore showed that his electorate were not without sporting instincts and knew a horse from a jackass.

Most of the time, John Henry Bagshaw had to be at Ottawa (though he preferred the quiet of his farm and always left it, as he said, with a sigh). If he was not in Ottawa, he was in Washington, and of course at any time they might need him in London, so that it was no wonder that he could only be in Mariposa about two months of the year.

That is why everybody knew, when Bagshaw got off the afternoon train one day early in the spring, that there must be something very important coming and that the rumours about a new election must be perfectly true.

Everything that he did showed this. He gave the baggage man twenty-five cents to take the check off his trunk, the 'bus driver fifty cents to drive him up to the Main Street, and he went into Callahan's tobacco store and bought two ten-cent cigars and took them across the street and gave them to Mallory Tompkins of the Times-Herald as a present from the Prime Minister.

All that afternoon, Bagshaw went up and down the Main Street of Mariposa, and you could see, if you knew the signs of it, that there was politics in the air. He bought nails and putty and glass in the hardware store, and harness in the harness shop, and drugs in the drug store and toys in the toy shop, and all the things like that that are needed for a big campaign.

Then when he had done all this he went over with McGinnis the Liberal organizer and Mallory Tompkins, the Times-Herald man, and Gingham (the great Independent-Liberal undertaker) to the back parlour in the Mariposa House.

You could tell from the way John Henry Bagshaw closed the door before he sat down that he was in a pretty serious frame of mind.

"Gentlemen," he said, "the election is a certainty. We're going to have a big fight on our hands and we've got to get ready for it."

"Is it going to be on the tariff?" asked Tompkins.

"Yes, gentlemen, I'm afraid it is. The whole thing is going to turn on the tariff question. I wish it were otherwise. I think it madness, but they're bent on it, and we got to fight it on that line. Why they can't fight it merely on the question of graft," continued the old war horse, rising from his seat and walking up and down, "Heaven only knows. I warned them. I appealed to them. I said, fight the thing on graft and we can win easy. Take this constituency,—why not have fought the thing out on whether I spent too much money on the town wharf or the post-office?

What better issues could a man want? Let them claim that I am crooked, and let me claim that I'm not. Surely that was good enough without dragging in the tariff. But now, gentlemen, tell me about things in the constituency. Is there any talk yet of who is to run?"

Mallory Tompkins lighted up the second of his Prime Minister's cigars and then answered for the group:

"Everybody says that Edward Drone is going to run."

"Ah!" said the old war horse, and there was joy upon his face, "is he? At last! That's good, that's good—now what platform will he run on?"

"Independent."

"Excellent," said Mr. Bagshaw. "Independent, that's fine. On a programme of what?"

"Just simple honesty and public morality."

"Come now," said the member, "that's splendid: that will help enormously. Honesty and public morality! The very thing! If Drone runs and makes a good showing, we win for a certainty. Tompkins, you must lose no time over this. Can't you manage to get some articles in the other papers hinting that at the last election we bribed all the voters in the county, and that we gave out enough contracts to simply pervert the whole constituency. Imply that we poured the public money into this county in bucketsful and that we are bound to do it again. Let Drone have plenty of material of this sort and he'll draw off every honest unbiassed vote in the Conservative party.

"My only fear is," continued the old war horse, losing some of his animation, "that Drone won't run after all. He's said it so often before and never has. He hasn't got the money. But we must see to that. Gingham, you know his brother well; you must work it so that we pay Drone's deposit and his campaign expenses. But how like Drone it is to come out at this time!"

It was indeed very like Edward Drone to attempt so misguided a thing as to come out an Independent candidate in Missinaba County on a platform of public honesty. It was just the sort of thing that anyone in Mariposa would expect from him.

Edward Drone was the Rural Dean's younger brother,—young Mr. Drone, they used to call him, years ago, to distinguish him from the rector. He was a somewhat weaker copy of his elder brother, with a simple, inefficient face and kind blue eyes. Edward Drone was, and always had been, a failure. In training he had been, once upon a time, an engineer and built dams that broke and bridges that fell down and wharves that floated away in the spring floods. He had been a manufacturer and failed, had been a contractor and failed, and now lived a meagre life as a sort of surveyor or land expert on goodness knows what.

In his political ideas Edward Drone was and, as everybody in Mariposa knew, always had been crazy. He used to come up to the autumn exercises at the high school and make speeches about the ancient Romans and Titus Manlius and Quintus Curtius at the same time when John Henry Bagshaw used to make a speech about the Maple Leaf and ask for an extra half holiday. Drone used to tell the boys about the lessons to be learned from the lives of the truly great, and Bagshaw used to talk to them about the lessons learned from the lives of the extremely rich. Drone used to say that his heart filled whenever he thought of the splendid patriotism of the ancient Romans, and Bagshaw said that whenever he looked out over this wide Dominion his heart overflowed.

Even the youngest boy in the school could tell that Drone was foolish. Not even the school teachers would have voted for him.

"What about the Conservatives?" asked Bagshaw presently; "is there any talk yet as to who they'll bring out?"

Gingham and Mallory Tompkins looked at one another. They were almost afraid to speak.

"Hadn't you heard?" said Gingham; "they've got their man already."

"Who is it?" said Bagshaw quickly.

"They're going to put up Josh Smith."

"Great Heaven!" said Bagshaw, jumping to his feet; "Smith! the hotel keeper."

"Yes, sir," said Mr. Gingham, "that's the man."

Do you remember, in history, how Napoleon turned pale when he heard that the Duke of Wellington was to lead the allies in Belgium? Do you remember how when Themistocles heard that Aristogiton was to lead the Spartans, he jumped into the sea? Possibly you don't, but it may help you to form some idea of what John Henry Bagshaw felt when he heard that the Conservatives had selected Josh Smith, proprietor of Smith's Hotel.

You remember Smith. You've seen him there on the steps of his hotel,—two hundred and eighty pounds in his stockinged feet. You've seen him selling liquor after hours through sheer public spirit, and you recall how he saved the lives of hundreds of people on the day when the steamer sank, and how he saved the town from being destroyed the night when the Church of England Church burnt down. You know that hotel of his, too, half way down the street, Smith's Northern Health Resort, though already they were beginning to call it Smith's British Arms.

So you can imagine that Bagshaw came as near to turning pale as a man in federal politics can.

"I never knew Smith was a Conservative," he said faintly; "he always subscribed to our fund."

"He is now," said Mr. Gingham ominously; "he says the idea of this reciprocity business cuts him to the heart."

"The infernal liar!" said Mr. Bagshaw.

There was silence for a few moments. Then Bagshaw spoke again.

"Will Smith have anything else in his platform besides the trade question?"

"Yes," said Mr. Gingham gloomily, "he will."

"What is it?"

"Temperance and total prohibition!"

John Henry Bagshaw sank back in his chair as if struck with a club. There let me leave him for a chapter.

ELEVEN

The Candidacy of Mr. Smith

"Boys," said Mr. Smith to the two hostlers, stepping out on to the sidewalk in front of the hotel,—"hoist that there British Jack over the place and hoist her up good."

Then he stood and watched the flag fluttering in the wind.

"Billy," he said to the desk clerk, "get a couple more and put them up on the roof of the caff behind the hotel. Wire down to the city and get a quotation on a hundred of them. Take them signs '*American Drinks*' out of the bar. Put up noo ones with '*British Beer at all Hours*'; clear out the rye whiskey and order in Scotch and Irish, and then go up to the printing office and get me them placards."

Then another thought struck Mr. Smith.

"Say, Billy," he said, "wire to the city for fifty pictures of King George. Get 'em good, and get 'em coloured. It don't matter what they cost."

"All right, sir," said Billy.

"And Billy," called Mr. Smith, as still another thought struck him (indeed, the moment Mr. Smith went into politics you could see these thoughts strike him like waves), "get fifty pictures of his father, old King Albert."

"All right, sir."

"And say, I tell you, while you're at it, get some of the old queen, Victorina, if you can. Get 'em in mourning, with a harp and one of them lions and a three-pointed prong."

❧ ❧ ❧

It was on the morning after the Conservative Convention. Josh Smith had been chosen the candidate. And now the whole town was covered with flags and placards and there were bands in the streets every evening, and noise and music and excitement that went on from morning till night.

Election times are exciting enough even in the city. But there the excitement dies down in business hours. In Mariposa there aren't any business hours and the excitement goes on *all* the time.

Mr. Smith had carried the Convention before him. There had been a feeble attempt to put up Nivens. But everybody knew that he was a lawyer and a college man and wouldn't have a chance by a man with a broader outlook like Josh Smith.

So the result was that Smith was the candidate and there were placards out all over the town with SMITH AND BRITISH ALLEGIANCE in big letters, and people were wearing badges with Mr. Smith's face on one side and King George's on the other, and the fruit store next to the hotel had been cleaned out and turned into committee rooms with a gang of workers smoking cigars in it all day and half the night.

There were other placards, too, with BAGSHAW AND LIBERTY, BAGSHAW AND PROSPERITY, VOTE FOR THE OLD MISSINABA STANDARD BEARER, and up town beside the Mariposa House there were the Bagshaw committee rooms with a huge white streamer across the street, and with a gang of Bagshaw workers smoking their heads off.

But Mr. Smith had an estimate made which showed that nearly two cigars to one were smoked in his committee rooms as compared with the Liberals. It was the first time in five elections that the Conservative had been able to make such a showing as that.

One might mention, too, that there were Drone placards out,—five or six of them,—little things about the size of a pocket handkerchief, with a statement that "Mr. Edward Drone solicits the votes of the electors of Missinaba County." But you would never notice them. And when Drone tried to put up a streamer across the Main Street with DRONE AND HONESTY the wind carried it away into the lake.

The fight was really between Smith and Bagshaw, and everybody knew it from the start.

I wish that I were able to narrate all the phases and the turns of the great contest from the opening of the campaign till the final polling day. But it would take volumes.

First of all, of course, the trade question was hotly discussed in the two newspapers of Mariposa, and the Newspacket and the Times-Herald literally bristled with statistics. Then came interviews with the candidates and the expression of their convictions in regard to tariff questions.

"Mr. Smith," said the reporter of the Mariposa Newspacket, "we'd like to get your views of the effect of the proposed reduction of the differential duties."

"By gosh, Pete," said Mr. Smith, "you can search me. Have a cigar."

"What do you think, Mr. Smith, would be the result of lowering the *ad valorem* British preference and admitting American goods at a reciprocal rate?"

"It's a corker, ain't it?" answered Mr. Smith. "What'll you take, lager or domestic?"

And in that short dialogue Mr. Smith showed that he had instantaneously grasped the whole method of dealing with the press. The interview in the paper next day said that Mr. Smith, while unwilling to state positively that the principle of tariff discrimination was at variance with sound fiscal science, was firmly of opinion that any reciprocal interchange of tariff preferences with the United States must inevitably lead to a serious per capita reduction of the national industry.

❧ ❧ ❧

"Mr. Smith," said the chairman of a delegation of the manufacturers of Mariposa, "what do you propose to do in regard to the tariff if you're elected?"

"Boys," answered Mr. Smith, "I'll put her up so darned high they won't never get her down again."

❧ ❧ ❧

"Mr. Smith," said the chairman of another delegation, "I'm an old free trader—"

"Put it there," said Mr. Smith, "so'm I. There ain't nothing like it."

❧ ❧ ❧

"What do you think about imperial defence?" asked another questioner.

"Which?" said Mr. Smith.

"Imperial defence."

"Of what?"

"Of everything."

"Who says it?" said Mr. Smith.

"Everybody is talking of it."

"What do the Conservative boys at Ottaway think about it?" answered Mr. Smith.

"They're all for it."

"Well, I'm fer it too," said Mr. Smith.

❧ ❧ ❧

These little conversations represented only the first stage, the argumentative stage of the great contest. It was during this period, for example, that the Mariposa Newspacket absolutely proved that the price of hogs in Mariposa was decimal six higher than the price of oranges in Southern California and that the average decennial import of eggs into Missinaba County had increased four decimal six eight two in the last fifteen years more than the import of lemons in New Orleans.

Figures of this kind made the people think. Most certainly.

After all this came the organizing stage and after that the big public meetings and the rallies. Perhaps you have never seen a county being "organized." It is a wonderful sight. First of all the Bagshaw men drove through crosswise in top buggies and then drove through it again lengthwise. Whenever they met a farmer they went in and ate a meal with him, and after the meal they took him out to the buggy and gave him a drink. After that the man's vote was absolutely solid until it was tampered with by feeding a Conservative.

In fact, the only way to show a farmer that you are in earnest is to go in and eat a meal with him. If you won't eat it, he won't vote for you. That is the recognized political test.

But, of course, just as soon as the Bagshaw men had begun to get the farming vote solidified, the Smith buggies came driving through in the other direction, eating meals and distributing cigars and turning all the farmers back into Conservatives.

Here and there you might see Edward Drone, the Independent candidate, wandering round from farm to farm in the dust of the political buggies. To each of the farmers he explained that he pledged himself to give no bribes, to spend no money and to offer no jobs, and each one of them gripped him warmly by the hand and showed him the way to the next farm.

After the organization of the county there came the period of the public meetings and the rallies and the joint debates between the candidates and their supporters.

I suppose there was no place in the whole Dominion where the trade question—the Reciprocity question—was threshed out quite so thoroughly and in quite such a national patriotic spirit as in Mariposa. For a month, at least, people talked of nothing else. A man would stop another in the street and tell him that he had read last night that the average price of an egg in New York was decimal ought one more than the price of an egg in Mariposa, and the other man would stop the first one later in the day and tell him that the average price of a hog in Idaho was point six of a cent per pound less (or more,—he couldn't remember which for the moment) than the average price of beef in Mariposa.

People lived on figures of this sort, and the man who could remember most of them stood out as a born leader.

But of course it was at the public meetings that these things were most fully discussed. It would take volumes to do full justice to all the meetings that they held in Missinaba County. But here and there single speeches stood out as masterpieces of convincing oratory. Take, for example, the speech of John Henry Bagshaw at the Tecumseh Corners School House. The Mariposa Times-Herald said next day that that speech would go down in history, and so it will,—ever so far down.

Anyone who has heard Bagshaw knows what an impressive speaker he is, and on this night when he spoke with the quiet dignity of a man old in years and anxious only to serve his country, he almost surpassed himself. Near the end of his speech somebody dropped a pin, and the noise it made in falling fairly rattled the windows.

"I am an old man now, gentlemen," Bagshaw said, "and the time must soon come when I must not only leave politics, but must take my way towards that goal from which no traveller returns."

There was a deep hush when Bagshaw said this. It was understood to imply that he thought of going to the United States.

"Yes, gentlemen, I am an old man, and I wish, when my time comes to go, to depart leaving as little animosity behind me as possible. But before I *do* go, I want it pretty clearly understood that there are more darn scoundrels in the Conservative party than ought to be tolerated in any decent community. I bear," he continued, "malice towards none and

I wish to speak with gentleness to all, but what I will say is that how any set of rational responsible men could nominate such a skunk as the Conservative candidate passes the bounds of my comprehension. Gentlemen, in the present campaign there is no room for vindictive abuse. Let us rise to a higher level than that. They tell me that my opponent, Smith, is a common saloon keeper. Let it pass. They tell me that he has stood convicted of horse stealing, that he is a notable perjurer, that he is known as the blackest-hearted liar in Missinaba County. Let us not speak of it. Let no whisper of it pass our lips.

"No, gentlemen," continued Bagshaw, pausing to take a drink of water, "let us rather consider this question on the high plane of national welfare. Let us not think of our own particular interests but let us consider the good of the country at large. And to do this, let me present to you some facts in regard to the price of barley in Tecumseh Township."

Then, amid a deep stillness, Bagshaw read off the list of prices of sixteen kinds of grain in sixteen different places during sixteen years.

"But let me turn," Bagshaw went on to another phase of the national subject, "and view for a moment the price of marsh hay in Missinaba County—"

When Bagshaw sat down that night it was felt that a Liberal vote in Tecumseh Township was a foregone conclusion.

But here they hadn't reckoned on the political genius of Mr. Smith. When he heard next day of the meeting, he summoned some of his leading speakers to him and he said:

"Boys, they're beating us on them statissicks. Ourn ain't good enough."

Then he turned to Nivens and he said:

"What was them figures you had here the other night?"

Nivens took out a paper and began reading.

"Stop," said Mr. Smith, "what was that figure for bacon?"

"Fourteen million dollars," said Nivens.

"Not enough," said Mr. Smith, "make it twenty. They'll stand for it, them farmers."

Nivens changed it.

"And what was that for hay?"

"Two dollars a ton."

"Shove it up to four," said Mr. Smith. "And I tell you," he added, "if any of them farmers says the figures ain't correct, tell them to go to Washington and see for themselves; say that if any man wants the proof of your figures let him go over to England and ask,—tell him to go straight to London and see it all for himself in the books."

❧ ❧ ❧

After this, there was no more trouble over statistics. I must say though that it is a wonderfully convincing thing to hear trade figures of this kind properly handled. Perhaps the best man on this sort of thing in the campaign was Mullins, the banker. A man of his profession simply has to have figures of trade and population and money at his fingers' ends and the effect of it in public speaking is wonderful.

No doubt you have listened to speakers of this kind, but I question whether you have ever heard anything more typical of the sort of effect that I allude to than Mullins's speech at the big rally at the Fourth Concession.

Mullins himself, of course, knows the figures so well that he never bothers to write them into notes and the effect is very striking.

"Now, gentlemen," he said very earnestly, "how many of you know just to what extent the exports of this country have increased in the last ten years? How many could tell what per cent of increase there has been in one decade of our national importation?"—then Mullins paused and looked round. Not a man knew it.

"I don't recall," he said, "exactly the precise amount myself,—not at this moment,—but it must be simply tremendous. Or take the question of population," Mullins went on, warming up again as a born statistician always does at the proximity of figures, "how many of you know, how many of you can state, what has been the decennial percentage increase in our leading cities—?"

There he paused, and would you believe it, not a man could state it.

"I don't recall the exact figures," said Mullins, "but I have them at home and they are positively colossal."

But just in one phase of the public speaking, the candidacy of Mr. Smith received a serious set-back.

It had been arranged that Mr. Smith should run on a platform of total prohibition. But they soon found that it was a mistake. They had imported a special speaker from the city, a grave man with a white tie, who put his whole heart into the work and would take nothing for it except his expenses and a sum of money for each speech. But beyond the money, I say, he would take nothing.

He spoke one night at the Tecumseh Corners social hall at the same time when the Liberal meeting was going on at the Tecumseh Corners school house.

"Gentlemen," he said, as he paused half way in his speech,—"while we are gathered here in earnest discussion, do you know what is happening over at the meeting place of our opponents? Do you know that seventeen bottles of rye whiskey were sent out from the town this afternoon to that innocent and unsuspecting school house? Seventeen bottles of whiskey hidden in between the blackboard and the wall, and every single man that attends that meeting,—mark my words, every single man,—will drink his fill of the abominable stuff at the expense of the Liberal candidate!"

Just as soon as the speaker said this, you could see the Smith men at the meeting look at one another in injured surprise, and before the speech was half over the hall was practically emptied.

After that the total prohibition plank was changed and the committee substituted a declaration in favour of such a form of restrictive license as should promote temperance while encouraging the manufacture of spirituous liquors, and by a severe regulation of the liquor traffic should place intoxicants only in the hands of those fitted to use them.

~ ~ ~

Finally there came the great day itself, the Election Day that brought, as everybody knows, the crowning triumph of Mr. Smith's career. There is no need to speak of it at any length, because it has become a matter of history.

In any case, everybody who has ever seen Mariposa knows just what election day is like. The shops, of course, are, as a matter of custom, all closed, and the bar rooms are all closed by law so that you have to go in by the back way. All the people are in their best clothes and at first they walk up and down the street in a solemn way just as they do on the twelfth of July and on St. Patrick's Day, before the fun begins. Everybody keeps looking in at the different polling places to see if anybody else has voted yet, because, of course, nobody cares to vote first for fear of being fooled after all and voting on the wrong side.

Most of all did the supporters of Mr. Smith, acting under his instructions, hang back from the poll in the early hours. To Mr. Smith's mind, voting was to be conducted on the same plan as bear-shooting.

"Hold back your votes, boys," he said, "and don't be too eager. Wait till she begins to warm up and then let 'em have it good and hard."

In each of the polling places in Mariposa there is a returning officer and with him are two scrutineers, and the electors, I say, peep in and out like mice looking into a trap. But if once the scrutineers get a man well into the polling booth, they push him in behind a little curtain and make him vote. The voting, of course, is by secret ballot, so that no one except the scrutineers and the returning officer and the two or three people who may be round the poll can possibly tell how a man has voted.

That's how it comes about that the first results are often so contradictory and conflicting. Sometimes the poll is badly arranged and the scrutineers are unable to see properly just how the ballots are being marked and they count up the Liberals and Conservatives in different ways. Often, too, a voter makes his mark so hurriedly and carelessly that they have to pick it out of the ballot box and look at it to see what it is.

I suppose that may have been why it was that in Mariposa the results came out at first in such a conflicting way.

Perhaps that was how it was that the first reports showed that Edward Drone the Independent candidate was certain to win. You should have seen how the excitement grew upon the streets when the news was circulated. In the big rallies and meetings of the Liberals and Conservatives, everybody had pretty well forgotten all about Drone, and when the news got round at about four o'clock that the Drone vote was carrying the poll, the people were simply astounded. Not that they were not pleased. On the contrary. They were delighted. Everybody came up to Drone and shook hands and congratulated him and told him that they had known all along that what the country wanted was a straight, honest, non-partisan representation. The Conservatives said openly that they were sick of party, utterly done with it, and the Liberals said that they hated it. Already three or four of them had taken Drone aside and explained that what was needed in the town was a straight, clean, non-partisan post-office, built on a piece of ground of a strictly non-partisan character, and constructed under contracts that were not tainted and smirched with party affiliation. Two or three men were willing to show to Drone just where a piece of ground of this character could be bought. They told him too that in the matter of the postmastership itself they had nothing against Trelawney, the present postmaster, in any personal sense, and would say nothing against him except merely that he was utterly and hopelessly unfit for his job and that if Drone believed, as he had said he did, in a purified civil service, he ought to begin by purifying Trelawney.

Already Edward Drone was beginning to feel something of what it meant to hold office and there was creeping into his manner the quiet self-importance which is the first sign of conscious power.

In fact, in that brief half-hour of office, Drone had a chance to see something of what it meant. Henry McGinnis came to him and asked straight out for a job as federal census-taker on the ground that he was hard up and had been crippled with rheumatism all winter. Nelson Williamson asked for the post of wharf master on the plea that he had been laid up with sciatica all winter and was absolutely fit for nothing. Erasmus Archer asked him if he could get his boy Pete into one of the departments at Ottawa, and made a strong case of it by explaining that he had tried his cussedest to get Pete a job anywhere else and it was simply impossible. Not that Pete wasn't a willing boy, but he was slow,—even his father admitted it,—slow as the devil, blast him, and with no head for figures and unfortunately he'd never had the schooling to bring him on. But if Drone could get him in at Ottawa, his father truly believed it would be the very place for him. Surely in the Indian Department or in the Astronomical Branch or in the New Canadian Navy there must be any amount of opening for a boy like this? And to all of these requests Drone found himself explaining that he would take the matter under his very earnest consideration and that they must remember that he had to consult his colleagues and not merely follow the dictates of his own wishes. In fact, if he had ever in his life had any envy of Cabinet Ministers, he lost it in this hour.

But Drone's hour was short. Even before the poll had closed in Mariposa, the news came sweeping in, true or false, that Bagshaw was carrying the county. The second concession had gone for Bagshaw in a regular landslide,—six votes to only two for Smith,—and all down the township line road (where the hay farms are) Bagshaw was said to be carrying all before him.

Just as soon as that news went round the town, they launched the Mariposa band of the Knights of Pythias (every man in it is a Liberal) down the Main Street with big red banners in front of it with the motto BAGSHAW FOREVER in letters a foot high. Such rejoicing and enthusiasm began to set in as you never saw. Everybody crowded round Bagshaw on the steps of the Mariposa House and shook his hand and said they were proud to see the day and that the Liberal party was the glory of the Dominion and that as for this idea of non-partisan politics the very thought of it made them sick. Right away in the committee rooms they began to organize the demonstration for the evening with lantern slides and speeches and they arranged for a huge bouquet to be presented to Bagshaw on the platform by four little girls (all Liberals) all dressed in white.

And it was just at this juncture, with one hour of voting left, that Mr. Smith emerged from his committee rooms and turned his voters on the town, much as the Duke of Wellington sent the whole line to the charge at Waterloo. From every committee room and sub-committee room they poured out in flocks with blue badges fluttering on their coats.

"Get at it, boys," said Mr. Smith, "vote and keep on voting till they make you quit."

Then he turned to his campaign assistant. "Billy," he said, "wire down to the city that I'm elected by an overwhelming majority and tell them to wire it right back. Send word by telephone to all the polling places in the county that the hull town has gone solid Conservative and tell them to send the same news back here. Get carpenters and tell them to run up a platform in front of the hotel; tell them to take the bar door clean off its hinges and be all ready the minute the poll quits."

It was that last hour that did it. Just as soon as the big posters went up in the windows of the Mariposa Newspacket with the telegraphic despatch that Josh Smith was reported in the city to be elected, and was followed by the messages from all over the county, the voters hesitated no longer. They had waited, most of them, all through the day, not wanting to make any error in their vote, but when they saw the Smith men crowding into the polls and heard the news from the outside, they went solid in one great stampede, and by the time the poll was declared closed at five o'clock there was no shadow of doubt that the county was saved and that Josh Smith was elected for Missinaba.

I wish you could have witnessed the scene in Mariposa that evening. It would have done your heart good,—such joy, such public rejoicing as you never saw. It turned out that there wasn't really a Liberal in the whole town and that there never had been. They were all Conservatives and had been for years and years. Men who had voted, with pain and sorrow in their hearts, for the Liberal party for twenty years, came out that evening and owned up straight that they were Conservatives. They said they could stand the strain no longer and simply had to confess. Whatever the sacrifice might mean, they were prepared to make it.

Even Mr. Golgotha Gingham, the undertaker, came out and admitted that in working for John Henry Bagshaw he'd been going straight against his conscience. He said that right from the first he had had his misgivings. He said it had haunted him. Often at night when he would be working away quietly, one of these sudden misgivings would overcome him so that he could hardly go on with his embalming. Why, it appeared that on the very first day when reciprocity was proposed, he had come home and said to Mrs. Gingham that he thought it simply meant selling out the country. And the strange thing was that ever so many others had just the same misgivings. Trelawney admitted that he had said to Mrs. Trelawney that it was madness, and Jeff Thorpe, the barber, had, he admitted, gone home to his dinner, the first day reciprocity was talked of, and said to Mrs. Thorpe that it would simply kill business in the country and introduce a cheap, shoddy, American form of haircut that would render true loyalty impossible. To think that Mrs. Gingham and Mrs. Trelawney and Mrs. Thorpe had known all this for six months and kept quiet about it! Yet I think there were a good many Mrs. Ginghams in the country. It is merely another proof that no woman is fit for politics.

The demonstration that night in Mariposa will never be forgotten. The excitement in the streets, the torchlights, the music of the band of the Knights of Pythias (an organization which is conservative in all but name), and above all the speeches and the patriotism.

They had put up a big platform in front of the hotel, and on it were Mr. Smith and his chief workers, and behind them was a perfect forest of flags. They presented a huge bouquet of flowers to Mr. Smith, handed to him by four little girls in white,—the same four that I spoke of above, for it turned out that they were all Conservatives.

Then there were the speeches. Judge Pepperleigh spoke and said that there was no need to dwell on the victory that they had achieved, because it was history; there was no occasion to speak of what part he himself had played, within the limits of his official position, because what he had done was henceforth a matter of history; and Nivens, the lawyer, said that he would only say just a few words, because anything that he might have done was now history; later generations, he said, might read it but it was not for him to speak of it, because it belonged now to the history of the country. And, after them, others spoke in the same strain and all refused absolutely to dwell on the subject (for more than half an hour) on the ground that anything that they might have done was better left for future generations to investigate. And no doubt this was very true, as to some things, anyway.

Mr. Smith, of course, said nothing. He didn't have to,—not for four years,—and he knew it.

TWELVE

L'Envoi. The Train to Mariposa

IT LEAVES the city every day about five o'clock in the evening, the train for Mariposa.

Strange that you did not know of it, though you come from the little town—or did, long years ago.

Odd that you never knew, in all these years, that the train was there every afternoon, puffing up steam in the city station, and that you might have boarded it any day and gone home. No, not "home,"—of course you couldn't call it "home" now; "home" means that big red sandstone house of yours in the costlier part of the city. "Home" means, in a way, this Mausoleum Club where you sometimes talk with me of the times that you had as a boy in Mariposa.

But of course "home" would hardly be the word you would apply to the little town, unless perhaps, late at night, when you'd been sitting reading in a quiet corner somewhere such a book as the present one.

Naturally you don't know of the Mariposa train now. Years ago, when you first came to the city as a boy with your way to make, you knew of it well enough, only too well. The price of a ticket counted in those days, and though you knew of the train you couldn't take it, but sometimes from sheer homesickness you used to wander down to the station on a

Friday afternoon after your work, and watch the Mariposa people getting on the train and wish that you could go.

Why, you knew that train at one time better, I suppose, than any other single thing in the city, and loved it too for the little town in the sunshine that it ran to.

Do you remember how when you first began to make money you used to plan that just as soon as you were rich, really rich, you'd go back home again to the little town and build a great big house with a fine verandah,—no stint about it, the best that money could buy, planed lumber, every square foot of it, and a fine picket fence in front of it.

It was to be one of the grandest and finest houses that thought could conceive; much finer, in true reality, than that vast palace of sandstone with the porte cochère and the sweeping conservatories that you afterwards built in the costlier part of the city.

But if you have half forgotten Mariposa, and long since lost the way to it, you are only like the greater part of the men here in this Mausoleum Club in the city. Would you believe it that practically every one of them came from Mariposa once upon a time, and that there isn't one of them that doesn't sometimes dream in the dull quiet of the long evening here in the club, that some day he will go back and see the place.

They all do. Only they're half ashamed to own it.

Ask your neighbour there at the next table whether the partridge that they sometimes serve to you here can be compared for a moment to the birds that he and you, or he and some one else, used to shoot as boys in the spruce thickets along the lake. Ask him if he ever tasted duck that could for a moment be compared to the black ducks in the rice marsh along the Ossawippi. And as for fish, and fishing,—no, don't ask him about that, for if he ever starts telling you of the chub they used to catch below the mill dam and the green bass that used to lie in the water-shadow of the rocks beside the Indian's Island, not even the long dull evening in this club would be long enough for the telling of it.

But no wonder they don't know about the five o'clock train for

Mariposa. Very few people know about it. Hundreds of them know that there is a train that goes out at five o'clock, but they mistake it. Ever so many of them think it's just a suburban train. Lots of people that take it every day think it's only the train to the golf grounds, but the joke is that after it passes out of the city and the suburbs and the golf grounds, it turns itself little by little into the Mariposa train, thundering and pounding towards the north with hemlock sparks pouring out into the darkness from the funnel of it.

Of course you can't tell it just at first. All those people that are crowding into it with golf clubs, and wearing knickerbockers and flat caps, would deceive anybody. That crowd of suburban people going home on commutation tickets and sometimes standing thick in the aisles, those are, of course, not Mariposa people. But look round a little bit and you'll find them easily enough. Here and there in the crowd those people with the clothes that are perfectly all right and yet look odd in some way, the women with the peculiar hats and the—what do you say?—last year's fashions? Ah yes, of course, that must be it.

Anyway, those are the Mariposa people all right enough. That man with the two-dollar panama and the glaring spectacles is one of the greatest judges that ever adorned the bench of Missinaba County. That clerical gentleman with the wide black hat, who is explaining to the man with him the marvellous mechanism of the new air brake (one of the most conspicuous illustrations of the divine structure of the physical universe), surely you have seen him before. Mariposa people! Oh yes, there are any number of them on the train every day.

But of course you hardly recognize them while the train is still passing through the suburbs and the golf district and the outlying parts of the city area. But wait a little, and you will see that when the city is well behind you, bit by bit the train changes its character. The electric locomotive that took you through the city tunnels is off now and the old wood engine is hitched on in its place. I suppose, very probably, you haven't seen one of these wood engines since you were a boy forty years ago,—the old engine with a wide top like a hat on its funnel, and with sparks enough to light up a suit for damages once in every mile.

Do you see, too, that the trim little cars that came out of the city on the electric suburban express are being discarded now at the way stations, one by one, and in their place is the old familiar car with the stuff cushions in red plush (how gorgeous it once seemed!) and with a box stove set up in one end of it? The stove is burning furiously at its sticks this autumn evening, for the air sets in chill as you get clear away from the city and are rising up to the higher ground of the country of the pines and the lakes.

Look from the window as you go. The city is far behind now and right and left of you there are trim farms with elms and maples near them and with tall windmills beside the barns that you can still see in the gathering dusk. There is a dull red light from the windows of the farmstead. It must be comfortable there after the roar and clatter of the city, and only think of the still quiet of it.

As you sit back half dreaming in the car, you keep wondering why it is that you never came up before in all these years. Ever so many times you planned that just as soon as the rush and strain of business eased up a little, you would take the train and go back to the little town to see what it was like now, and if things had changed much since your day. But each time when your holidays came, somehow you changed your mind and went down to Naragansett or Nagahuckett or Nagasomething, and left over the visit to Mariposa for another time.

It is almost night now. You can still see the trees and the fences and the farmsteads, but they are fading fast in the twilight. They have lengthened out the train by this time with a string of flat cars and freight cars between where we are sitting and the engine. But at every crossway we can hear the long muffled roar of the whistle, dying to a melancholy wail that echoes into the woods; the woods, I say, for the farms are thinning out and the track plunges here and there into great stretches of bush,—tall tamerack and red scrub willow and with a tangled undergrowth of bush that has defied for two generations all attempts to clear it into the form of fields.

Why, look, that great space that seems to open out in the half-dark of the falling evening,—why, surely yes,—Lake Ossawippi, the big lake, as they used to call it, from which the river runs down to the smaller lake,—Lake Wissanotti,—where the town of Mariposa has lain waiting for you there for thirty years.

This is Lake Ossawippi surely enough. You would know it anywhere by the broad, still, black water with hardly a ripple, and with the grip of the coming frost already on it. Such a great sheet of blackness it looks as the train thunders along the side, swinging the curve of the embankment at a breakneck speed as it rounds the corner of the lake.

How fast the train goes this autumn night! You have travelled, I know you have; in the Empire State Express, and the New Limited and the Maritime Express that holds the record of six hundred whirling miles from Paris to Marseilles. But what are they to this, this mad career, this breakneck speed, this thundering roar of the Mariposa local driving hard to its home! Don't tell me that the speed is only twenty-five miles an hour. I don't care what it is. I tell you, and you can prove it for yourself if you will, that that train of mingled flat cars and coaches that goes tearing into the night, its engine whistle shrieking out its warning into the silent woods and echoing over the dull still lake, is the fastest train in the whole world.

Yes, and the best too,—the most comfortable, the most reliable, the most luxurious and the speediest train that ever turned a wheel.

And the most genial, the most sociable too. See how the passengers all turn and talk to one another now as they get nearer and nearer to the little town. That dull reserve that seemed to hold the passengers in the electric suburban has clean vanished and gone. They are talking,—listen,—of the harvest, and the late election, and of how the local member is mentioned for the cabinet and all the old familiar topics of the sort. Already the conductor has changed his glazed hat for an ordinary round

Christie and you can hear the passengers calling him and the brakesman "Bill" and "Sam" as if they were all one family.

What is it now—nine thirty? Ah, then we must be nearing the town,—this big bush that we are passing through, you remember it surely as the great swamp just this side of the bridge over the Ossawippi? There is the bridge itself, and the long roar of the train as it rushes sounding over the trestle work that rises above the marsh. Hear the clatter as we pass the semaphores and switch lights! We must be close in now!

What? it feels nervous and strange to be coming here again after all these years? It must indeed. No, don't bother to look at the reflection of your face in the window-pane shadowed by the night outside. Nobody could tell you now after all these years. Your face has changed in these long years of money-getting in the city. Perhaps if you had come back now and again, just at odd times, it wouldn't have been so.

There,—you hear it?—the long whistle of the locomotive, one, two, three! You feel the sharp slackening of the train as it swings round the curve of the last embankment that brings it to the Mariposa station. See, too, as we round the curve, the row of the flashing lights, the bright windows of the depôt.

How vivid and plain it all is. Just as it used to be thirty years ago. There is the string of the hotel 'buses, drawn up all ready for the train, and as the train rounds in and stops hissing and panting at the platform, you can hear above all other sounds the cry of the brakesmen and the porters:

"MARIPOSA! MARIPOSA!"

And as we listen, the cry grows fainter and fainter in our ears and we are sitting here again in the leather chairs of the Mausoleum Club, talking of the little Town in the Sunshine that once we knew.

Winnowed Wisdom

Contents

Author's Preface

An Appeal to the Average Man

It is the especial aim of this book to make an appeal to the average man. To do this the better, I have made a study of the census of the United States and of the census of Canada, in order to find out who and what the average man is.

In point of residence, it seems only logical to suppose that the average man lives at the centre of population, in other words, in the United States he lives at Honkville, Indiana, and in Canada at Red Hat, Saskatchewan.

In the matter of height the average man is five feet, eight inches, decimal four one seven, and in avoirdupois weight he represents 139 pounds, two ounces, and three pennyweights. Eight-tenths of his head is covered with hair and his whiskers if spread over his face could cover it to the extent of one-tenth of an inch. This ought to be a promising sign to a reader.

The average man goes to church six times a year and has attended Sunday School for two afternoons and can sing half a hymn.

Although it thus appears that the average man is rather weak on religion, in point of morals the fellow is decidedly strong. He has spent only one week of his whole life in the penitentiary. Taking an average of theft and dividing it by the population it appears that he has stolen only two dollars and a quarter. And he never tells a lie except where there is some definite material advantage.

The average man is not, by statistics, a great traveller. The poor fellow has been only sixty-two miles away from his own home. He owns nine-tenths of a Ford car, punctures a tire once every twenty-two days, and spends, in the course of his whole life, a month and a half underneath his car.

The education of the average man cost $350. But it didn't get him far. He stopped—according to the educational statistics—within one year of being ready for a college. Most of the things he learned had no meaning for him. He gave up algebra without yet knowing what it was about.

By the time I had got to this point of the investigation I began to realize what a poor shrimp the average man is. Think of him with his mean stature and his little chin and his Ford car and his fear of the dark and his home in Honkville, Indiana, or Red Hat, Saskatchewan. And think of his limited little mind! The average man, it seems, never forms an opinion for himself. The poor nut can't do it. He just follows the opinions of other men.

I would like ever so much to start a movement for getting above the average. Surely if we all try hard, we can all lift ourselves up high above the average. It looks a little difficult mathematically, but that's nothing.

Think how fine it would be to get away from the average—to mingle with men seven feet high and women six feet round, to consort with people who wouldn't tell a lie except for big money, and to have friends who could solve crossword puzzles without having to buy the Encyclopaedia Britannica!

But the only trouble with such a movement is that if I did really start it, and if I could, with great labor and persuasion, get it going and it began to succeed, then who would come flocking into it but the darned little average man himself. As long as it was unsuccessful, he'd keep out of it. But let it once succeed and in he'd come. That's exactly his dirty little nature.

In short, now that I think of it I am not so keen on appealing to the average man. Nothing ever does appeal to him, until it has made a terrible hit somewhere else.

I had just brought my investigation to this point when I realized that I had forgotten about the average woman. What about her? Where does she come out?

So I picked up the census volumes again and took another little run through them.

The average woman, it seems, does not live at Honkville, Indiana, or at Red Hat, Saskatchewan. The percentage of women in the population being much greater in the eastern part of the country, the average woman lives one hundred and five miles east of the average man. But she is getting nearer to him every day. Oh, yes, she is after him, all right!

It is also clear that the average woman is about half an inch taller than the average man. Women, taken individually, are no doubt not so tall as men, but, on the average, a woman is just a little taller. Men will find it a little difficult to understand how this can be, but any woman can see it at once.

In point of personal appearance, it may be estimated that women, taken as an average, wear their hair just below their shirt collar and have their skirts, at an average, always two inches higher than they were a year before.

The average woman gets married at twenty-seven, has two children and a quarter, and is divorced once in every eight years.

In morals the average woman is away ahead of the man. Everybody knows this in a general way, but it is very pleasing to see it corroborated by cold, hard statistics.

The man as we have seen above, spends a week in the penitentiary. But the woman is there only half a day. In her whole life she consumes only one and a half gills of whiskey, but, on the other hand, she eats, according to the director of the census, four tons of candy. She is devoted to her two and a quarter children, but she makes more fuss over the quarter of a child than she does over the two whole ones.

In point of intellect, the average woman cannot reason and cannot think. But she can argue. The average woman, according to the educational section of the census, only got as far in arithmetic as improper fractions. Those stopped her.

And yet, take her as she is—even with her hair bobbed round her ears and her skirt higher than it was, and her inability to add or to reason—she is all right. The average man comes out of the investigation as a poor insignificant shrimp. But with the average woman, the more you think about her, the better she appears.

Perhaps on second thoughts I might dedicate this book to the average woman. But then, unfortunately, the average woman reads nothing—or nothing except love stories.

STEPHEN LEACOCK
McGill University
1926

I

The Outlines of Everything

The Outlines of Everything

Designed for Busy People at Their Busiest

A Preface to the Outlines

Within recent years it is becoming clear that a university is now a superfluous institution. College teaching is being replaced by such excellent little manuals as the "Fireside University Series," the "World's Tiniest Books," the "Boys Own Comic Sections," and the "Little Folks Spherical Trigonometry." Thanks to books such as these no young man in any station of life need suffer from an unsatisfied desire for learning. He can get rid of it in a day. In the same way any business man who wishes to follow the main currents of history, philosophy and radio-activity may do so while changing his shirt for dinner.

The world's knowledge is thus reduced to a very short compass. But I doubt if even now it is sufficiently concentrated. Even the briefest outlines yet produced are too long for the modern business man. We have to remember that the man is busy. And when not busy he is tired. He has no time to go wading through five whole pages of print just to find out when Greece rose and fell. It has got to fall quicker than that if it wants to reach him. As to reading up a long account, with diagrams, of how the protozoa differentiated itself during the twenty million years of the Pleistocene era into the first invertebrate, the thing is out of the question. The man hasn't got twenty million years. The whole process is too long. We need something shorter, snappier, something that brings more immediate results.

From this point of view I have prepared a set of Outlines of Everything covering the whole field of science and literature. Each section is so written as to give the busy man *enough* and just exactly enough of each of the higher branches of learning. At the moment when he has had enough, I stop. The reader can judge for himself with what accuracy the point of complete satiety has been calculated.

Volume One—The Outline of Shakespeare

Designed to make Research Students in Fifteen Minutes. A Ph.D. degree granted immediately after reading it.

1. *Life of Shakespeare.* We do not know when Shaksper was born nor where he was born. But he is dead.

From internal evidence taken off his works after his death we know that he followed for a time the profession of a lawyer, a sailor and a scrivener and he was also an actor, a bartender and an ostler. His wide experience of men and manners was probably gained while a bartender. (Compare: *Henry V*, Act V, Scene 2. *"Say now, gentlemen, what shall yours be?"*)

But the technical knowledge which is evident upon every page shows also the intellectual training of a lawyer. (Compare: *Macbeth*, Act VI, Scene 4. *"What is there in it for me?"*) At the same time we are reminded by many passages of Shakspere's intimate knowledge of the sea. (*Romeo and Juliet.* Act VIII, Scene 14. *"How is her head now, nurse?"*)

We know, from his use of English, that Shagsper had no college education.

His Probable Probabilities

As an actor Shicksper, according to the current legend, was of no great talent. He is said to have acted the part of a ghost and he also probably took parts as *Enter a citizen, a Tucket sounds, a Dog barks, or a Bell is heard within.* (Note. We ourselves also have been a Tucket, a Bell, a Dog and so forth in our college dramatics days. Ed.)

In regard to the personality of Shakespere, or what we might call in the language of the day Shakespere the Man, we cannot do better than to quote the following excellent analysis done, we think, by Professor Gilbert Murray, though we believe that Brander Matthews helped him a little on the side.

"Shakespere was probably a genial man who probably liked his friends and probably spent a good deal of time in probable social intercourse. He was probably good tempered and easy going with very likely a bad temper. We know that he drank (Compare: *Titus Andronicus*, Act I, Scene I. "*What is there to drink?*"), but most likely not to excess. (Compare: *King Lear*, Act II, Scene I. "*Stop!*" and see also *Macbeth*, Act X, Scene 20. "*Hold! Enough!*") Shakespere was probably fond of children and most likely of dogs, but we don't know how he stood on porcupines.

"We imagine Shakespeare sitting among his cronies in Mitre Tavern, joining in the chorus of their probable songs, and draining a probable glass of ale, or at times falling into reverie in which the majestic pageant of Julius Caesar passes across his brooding mind."

To this excellent analysis we will only add. We can also imagine him sitting anywhere else we like—that in fact is the chief charm of Shakesperian criticism.

The one certain thing which we know about Shakespere is that in his will he left his second best bed to his wife.

Since the death of S. his native town—either Stratford upon Avon or somewhere else—has become a hallowed spot for the educated tourist. It is strange to stand today in the quiet street of the little town and to think that here Shakespeare actually lived—either here or elsewhere—and that England's noblest bard once mused among these willows—or others.

Works of Shakespeare

Our first mention must be of the Sonnets, written probably, according to Professor Matthews, during Shakesbur's life and not after his death. There is a haunting beauty about these sonnets which prevents us from remembering what they are about. But for the busy man of today it is enough to mention, "Drink to Me Only With Thine Eyes," "Rock Me to Sleep Mother," "Hark, Hark the Dogs do Bark." Oh, yes, quite enough. It will get past him every time.

The Historical Plays

Among the greatest of Shakespeare's achievements are his historical plays,—Henry I, Henry II, Henry III, Henry IV, Henry V, Henry VI, Henry VII and Henry VIII. It is thought that Shakespeare was engaged on a play dealing with Henry IX when he died. It is said to have been his opinion that having struck a good thing he had better stay with it.

There is doubt as to authorship of part, or all, of some of these historical plays. In the case of Henry V, for example, it is held by the best critics that the opening scene (100 lines) was done by Ben Jonson. Then Shakespeare wrote 200 lines (all but half a line in the middle) which undoubtedly is Marlowe's.

Then Jonson, with a little help from Fletcher, wrote 100 lines. After that Shakespear, Massinger and Marlowe put in 10 lines each. But from this point the authorship is confused, each sticking in what he could.

But we ourselves are under no misapprehension as to what is Shakespeare's and what is not. There is a touch which we recognize every time. When we see the real Shakespeare, we know it. Thus, whenever it says "*A Tucket Sounds, Enter Gloucester with Hoboes*," we know that Shakespeare, and only Shakespeare, could have thought of that. In fact Shakespeare could bring in things that were all his own, such as:—"*Enter Cambridge followed by An Axe.*" "*Enter Oxford followed by a Link.*" His lesser collaborators could never get the same niceness of touch. Thus, when we read, "Enter the Earl of Richmond followed by a pup," we realize that it is poor work.

Another way in which we are able to test whether or not a historical play is from Shakespeare's own pen is by the mode of address used by the characters. They are made to call one another by place designations instead of by their real names. "What says our brother France?" or "Well, Belgium, how looks it to you?" "Speak on, good Burgundy, our ears are yours." We ourselves have tried to imitate this but could never quite get it; our attempt to call our friends "Apartment B, the Grosvenor," and to say "Go to it, the Marlborough, Top Floor No. 6" has practically ended in failure.

The Great Tragedies

Every educated person should carry in his mind an outline idea of the greatest of Shakespeare's tragedies. This outline when reduced to what is actually remembered by playgoers and students is not difficult to acquire. Sample:

Hamlet (not to be confused with *Omelette* which was written by Voltaire). Hamlet, Prince of Denmark, lived among priceless scenery and was all dressed in black velvet. He was deeply melancholy. Either because he was mad, or because he was not, Hamlet killed his uncle and destroyed various other people whose names one does not recall.

The shock of this drove Ophelia to drown herself, but oddly enough when she threw herself in the water she floated, and went down the river singing and shouting. In the end Hamlet killed Laertes and himself, and others leaped into his grave until it was quite full when the play ends. People who possess this accurate recollection rightly consider themselves superior to others.

Shakespeare and Comparative Literature

Modern scholarship has added greatly to the interest in Shakespeare's work by investigating the sources from which he took his plays. It appears that in practically all cases they were old stuff already. Hamlet quite evidently can be traced to an old Babylonian play called *Humlid* and this itself is perhaps only a version of a Hindoo tragedy, *The Life of William Johnson.*

The play of Lear was very likely taken by S. from the old Chinese drama of *Li-Po*, while Macbeth, under the skilled investigation of modern scholars, shows distinct traces of a Scottish origin.

In effect, Shakespeare, instead of sitting down and making up a play out of his head, appears to have rummaged among sagas, myths, legends, archives and folk lore, much of which must have taken him years to find.

Personal Appearance

In person Shakespeare is generally represented as having a pointed beard and bobbed hair, with a bald forehead, large wide eyes, a salient nose, a retreating chin and a general expression of vacuity, verging on imbecility.

Summary

The following characteristics of Shakespeare's work should be memorized—majesty, sublimity, grace, harmony, altitude, also scope, range, reach, together with grasp, comprehension, force and light, heat and power.

Conclusion: Shakespeare is a very good writer.

Volume Two—The Outline of Evolution

Specially Revised to Suit Everybody, and Particularly Adapted for the Schools of Tennessee.

It seems that recently there has been a lot of new trouble about the theory of evolution in the schools. Either the theory is being taught all wrong or else there is something the matter with it. For years it had seemed as if the doctrine of Evolution was so universally accepted as to lose all its charm. It was running as a close second to Spherical Trigonometry and Comparative Religion and there was no more excitement about it than there is over Anthropology.

Then suddenly something seems to have happened. A boy in a Kansas public school threw down his book and said that the next time he was called a protozoon he'd quit the class. A parent in Ostaboola, Oklahoma, wrote to the local school board to say that for anyone to teach his children that they were descended from monkeys cast a doubt upon himself which he found intolerable. After that the wave of protest swept through the colleges.

The students marched in processions carrying banners with the motto "Are we baboons? Rah, Rah, Apes!" The Rotary Clubs of town after town voted by a standing vote that they were unable to support (or to understand) the doctrine of biological biogenesis, and they wanted it taken away.

The Woman's Culture Club of Winona, Utah, moved that the name of Charles Darwin be changed in the text books of the state to that of W. J. Bryan.

The Anti-Saloon League voted that the amount of Darwinianism that should be licensed in the schools should not be more than one-half of one per cent.

It is to meet this difficult situation that the present outline of Evolution has been prepared. It is intended so to revise and modify the rigid character of the theory as to make it acceptable to everybody.

The obvious beginning of the matter is to present the theory of evolution as it stood before the trouble began in Tennessee. Each of us at that time carried in his head an outline, a little bit hazy, but still usable, of the Doctrine of Evolution as we remembered it from our college training.

Outline of Evolution as Dimly Recalled from College Education

We are all descended from monkeys. This descent, however, took place a long time ago and there is no shame in it now. It happened two or three thousand years ago and must have been after and not before the Trojan war.

We have to remember also that there are several kinds of monkeys. There is the ordinary monkey seen in the street with the hand organ (*communis monacus*), the baboon, the giboon (not Edward,) the, bright, merry, little chimpanzee, and the hairy ourang-outang with the long arms. Ours is probably the hairy ourang-outang.

But the monkey business is only part of it. At an earlier stage men were not even that. They probably began as worms. From that they worked up to being oysters; after that they were fish, then snakes, then birds, then flying squirrels, and at last monkeys.

The same kind of change passed over all the animals. All the animals are descended from one another. The horse is really a bird, and is the same animal as the crow. The differences between them are purely superficial. If a crow had two more feet and no feathers it would be a horse except for its size.

The whole of these changes were brought about by what is called the

Survival of the Fittest. The crookedest snake outlived the others. Each creature had to adapt itself or bust.

The giraffe lengthened its neck. The stork went in for long legs. The hedgehog developed prickles. The skunk struck out an independent line of its own. Hence the animals that we see about us—as the skunk, the toad, the octopus, and the canary—are a highly selected lot.

This wonderful theory was discovered by Charles Darwin. After a five-year voyage in the *Beagle* as a naturalist in the Southern Seas, Darwin returned to England and wrote a book called *Sartor Resartus* which definitely established the descent of mankind from the avoirdupois apes.

One must admit that in this form the theory does not seem calculated to give any great offense to anybody. One must therefore suppose that the whole of the present bitter controversy arose out of what Darwin himself must have written. But this is obviously not so. I have not actually before me the text of Darwin's own writings, but I recall the general run of what he wrote with sufficient accuracy to reproduce it here.

Darwin's Own Statement

Personal Recollection of the Work of the Great Naturalist

"On the Antilles the common crow, or decapod, has two feet while in the Galapagos Islands it has a third. This third foot, however, does not appear to be used for locomotion, but merely for conversation. Dr. Anderson of H.M.S. *Unspeakable* during his visit to the Galapagos Islands in 1834 saw two crows sitting on a tree. One was, apparently, larger than the other. Dr. Anderson also saw a lizard at Guayaquil in Ecuador which had lost one toe. In fact, he had quite a good time.

"It would be too much to say that the crow and the lizard are the same bird. But there seems little doubt that the apex cervicus of the lizard is of the same structure as the rudimentary dorsal fin of the crow. I put forward this statement however with the modesty which it deserves and am only led to it with deep reluctance and with a full sense of its fatal character.

"I may say that I myself while off the Oesophagus Islands in H.M.S. *Impossible* in the year 1835 saw a flock of birds of the kind called by the sailors "bum-birds," which alighted on the masts and held on by their feet. In fact, I saw a lot of interesting things like that.

"While I was in the *Beagle*, I recall that on one occasion we landed on the Marquesas Islands where our captain and his party were entertained by the chief on hams and yams. After the feast a group of native women performed a hula-hula dance during which I wandered out into the woods and secured a fine collection of toads.

"On the next island—while the captain and his officers were watching a hitchi-kitchi dance—I picked up some admirable specimens of lizards and was fortunate enough to bring back a pocketful of potato bugs."

After reading this plain account as quoted, or at least as remembered, direct from Darwin, one must admit that there is no reason to try to rob him of his discoveries.

But to make the case still plainer, let us set alongside of this a clear simple statement of the Theory of Evolution as it is now held by the scientists in our colleges. I have before me the enunciation of the doctrine as stated at the request of the press by a distinguished biologist during the height of the present controversy. What he says runs, as follows—or very nearly as follows:

"All controversy apart, we must at least admit the existence of a continuous morphological protoplasmic differentiation—"

That seems to me a fair, manly statement of a plain fact.

"Cytology is still in its infancy—"

This is too bad, but it will grow.

"But at least it involves the admission of a primitive conformity which removes any *a priori* difficulty in the way of evolution."

So there we are. After that one would think that the Tennessee schools would have no further difficulty about the thing.

The Time of Evolution

But even if we reach a definite conclusion as to the nature of the process by which life gradually appeared and assumed higher and higher forms, the question still remains—over how great a period did the process last? What time element must be interposed? In other words as Henri Bergson once stated it with a characteristic flash of genius, "How long did it take?"

The earlier estimates of evolutionary scientists placed the age of man at about 500,000 years. This was ridiculously low. You can't evolve any kind of real man in that time. Huxley boldly raised the figures to 1,000,000. Lord Kelvin, amid unusual applause, put it up to 2,000,000 years. The cheers had hardly died away when Sir Ray Lankester disturbed the whole universe by declaring that man was 4,000,000 years old. Two years later a professor of the Smithsonian Institute raised it to 5,000,000. This estimate was seen and raised to 10,000,000 years. This again was raised from year to year amid universal enthusiasm.

The latest advices are that a student in Schenectady Technical High School places the age of man at 100,000,000 years. For a rough working estimate, therefore, the business man will not be far wrong in assuming (for practical purposes) that the age of man is anything from 100,000,000 to 1,000,000,000. Night watchmen are perhaps a little older.

Postscript: Up-to-Date Corrections of the Darwinian Theory

A still more cheerful light is thrown on the evolution controversy by the fact that modern biologists do not entirely hold with the theory of Charles Darwin. I find on inquiry that they are prepared to amend his evolution doctrine in a variety of points.

It seems that Darwin laid too much stress on what he called natural selection and the survival of the fittest. The modern biologist attaches no importance to either of these. It seems also that Darwin overestimated very much the part played by heredity. He was moreover mistaken in his idea of the changes of the species. It is probable, too, that his notion of a monkey is inadequate. It is doubtful also whether Darwin ever actually sailed on the *Beagle.* He may have been in the *Phineas Q. Fletcher* of Duluth. Nor is it certain that his name was Darwin.

Volume Three—The Business Outline of Astronomy

The world or universe in which we do our business consists of an infinite number, perhaps a hundred billion, perhaps not, of blazing stars accompanied by comets, dark planets, asteroids, asterisks, meteors, meteorites and dust clouds whirling in vast circles in all directions and at all velocities. How many of these bodies are habitable and fit for business we do not know.

The light emitted from these stars comes from distances so vast that most of it is not here yet. But owing to the great distance involved the light from the stars is of no commercial value. One has only to stand and look up at the sky on a clear starlight night to realize that the stars are of no use.

Practically all our efficient light, heat and power comes from the sun. Small though the sun is, it gives out an intense heat. The business man may form some idea of its intensity by imagining the entire lighting system of any two great American cities grouped into a single bulb; it would be but little superior to the sun.

The earth revolves around the sun and at the same time revolves on its own axis, the period of its revolution and the rising and setting of the sun being regulated at Washington, D.C. Some years ago the United States government decided to make time uniform and adopted the system of standard time; an agitation is now on foot—in Tennessee—for the lengthening of the year.

The moon, situated quite close to the earth but of no value, revolves around the earth and can be distinctly seen on a clear night outside the city limits. During a temporary breakdown of the lighting plant in New York city a few years ago the moon was quite plainly seen moving past the tower of the Metropolitan Life building. It cleared the Flatiron building by a narrow margin. Those who saw it reported it as somewhat round but not well shaped, and emitting an inferior light which showed that it was probably out of order.

The planets, like the earth, move around the sun. Some of them are so far away as to be of no consequence and, like the stars, may be dismissed. But one or two are so close to the earth that they may turn out to be fit for business. The planet Mars is of special interest inasmuch as its surface shows traces of what are evidently canals which come together at junction points where there must be hotels. It has been frequently proposed to interest enough capital to signal to Mars, and it is ingeniously suggested that the signals be sent in six languages.

Volume Four—Outline of Recent Advances in Science

Specially Designed for Members of Women's Culture Clubs, and Representing Exactly the Quantity of Information Carried Away From Lectures on Scientific Progress

Einstein's Theory of Relativity: Einstein himself is not what one would call a handsome man. When seen by members of the Fortnightly Women's Scientific Society in Boston he was pronounced by many of them to be quite insignificant in appearance. Some thought, however, that he had a certain air of distinction, something which they found it hard to explain but which they *felt*. It is certain that Einstein knows nothing of dress. His clothes appear as if taken out of the rag bag, and it is reported by two ladies who heard him speak at the University of Pennsylvania on the measurement of rays of light that he wore an absolutely atrocious red tie. It is declared to be a matter of wonder that no one has ever told him; and it is suggested that some one ought to take hold of him.

Einstein is not married. It has been reported, by members of the Trenton (New Jersey) Five O'clock Astronomical Investigation Club that there is a romance in his life. He is thought to have been thrown over by a girl who had a lot of money when he was a poor student, and it was this that turned his mind to physics. It is held that things work that way. Whether married or not he certainly behaved himself like a perfect gentleman at all the clubs where he spoke. He drinks nothing but black coffee.

Einstein's theories seem to have made a great stir.

Madame Curie's Discoveries in Radio-Activity: Madame Curie may be a great scientist but it is doubted whether she is a likeable woman or a woman who could make a home. Two members of the Omaha Woman's Astronomical and Physical Afternoon Tea Society heard her when she spoke in Washington on the Radiation of Gamma Particles from Helium. They say that they had some difficulty in following her. They say she was wearing just a plain coat and skirt but had quite a good French blouse which certainly had style to it. But they think that she lacks charm.

Rutherford's Researches in the Atomic Theory: Ernest Rutherford, or rather Sir Ernest Rutherford as it is right to call him because he was made a knight a few years ago for something he did with molecules, is a strikingly handsome man in early middle age. Some people might consider him as beginning to get old but that depends on the point of view. If you consider a man of fifty an old man then Sir Ernest is old. But the assertion is made by many members of various societies that in their opinion a man is at his *best* at fifty. Members who take that point of view would be interested in Rutherford. He has eyes of just that pale steely blue which suggest to members something powerful and strong, though members are unable to name it. Certainly he made a perfectly wonderful impression on The Ladies' Chemico-Physical Research and Amusement Society in Toronto, when he was there with that large British body.

Members of clubs meeting Sir Ernest should remember that he won the Nobel Prize and that it is not awarded for character but is spelled differently.

II

Brotherly Love Among the Nations

The Next War

From everything which I read in the press, I feel certain that it is coming. There doesn't seem the slightest doubt about it. It may not come for a month and it might be a year in coming, but there is no doubt the Next War is already looming in sight.

I have gathered together all the documents that prove it—interviews and discussions with the leading men concerned in it, who simply must know what they are talking about. Let me lay some of them before the reader and he can see for himself, on the very best authority, the situation that confronts us:

DOCUMENT NO. 1

The Alignment in the Next War

New York, July 25: Colonel The Honourable Fizzle Bangspark of the British General Army Staff, who arrived in New York on the *Megalomania*, expressed his views to the representatives of the press on the prospects of the Next War. The Colonel is confident that in the Next War, which he thinks may begin at any time, it is most likely the alignment will be that of Great Britain, France, and the United States against Germany and Russia.

But he may think it equally likely that it may be fought as between Great Britain, Russia, and Germany against France, the United States, and Portugal. Colonel Bangspark states, however, that though the war is certain the exact alignment of the nations will be very difficult to foresee.

He thinks it possible that England and Switzerland, if they get a good opportunity, may unite against France and Scotland. But it is altogether likely that in a war of magnitude, such as Colonel Bangspark hopes to see, the United States and China will insist on coming in, either on one side or the other. "If they do," continued Colonel Bangspark, "it will be hard to keep them out."

The distinguished officer considers it difficult to say what part Japan will play in the Next War, but he is sure that it will get into it somewhere. When asked about the part that would be played by the races of Africa in the coming conflict, Colonel Bangspark expressed a certain amount of doubt. "It is hard to say," he stated, "whether they can get in in time. They number of course a great many millions, but the question really turns on whether they have had a training sufficient to let them in. As yet their armies would be hardly destructive enough, and it would be very poor policy to let them in if they do not turn out to be deadly enough when they get in.

"The black," said the colonel, "is a good fellow and I like him. If he were put under first class European officers, he might prove fairly murderous. But I am not as yet prepared to say that we can make a profitable use of him in the Next War."

Asked if the Chinese would play a large part in the coming struggle, the distinguished officer again hesitated. "The Chinaman," he claims, "has not yet had enough contact with European civilizations. The Chinaman is by nature a pacifist and it will be hard to get him away from the idea of peace."

Asked finally if the South Sea Islanders would be in the struggle,

Colonel Bangspark spoke warmly and emphatically in their favor. "They will be in it from the start," he said. "I know the Polynesians well, having helped to organize native troops in the Marquesas Islands where I was quartered at Popo Popo for two years, and in the Friendly Islands and in the Society Islands and in the Paradise Group, where I was the first man to introduce gunpowder.

"The Marquesas Islander," the colonel went on, "is a splendid fellow. In many ways he is ahead of us Europeans. His work with the blowpipe and the poison dart antedates the use of poison in European warfare and compares favorably with the best work of our scientific colleges."

When questioned as to which side the Marquesas Islanders would come in on, the colonel stated that he did not regard that as a matter of prime importance. He was convinced, however, that a place would be found for them and he hoped to see them in the front trenches (on one side or the other) on the first day.

Colonel Bangspark expressed himself as delighted with all that he has seen on this side of the water. He says that he was immensely pleased with the powder works on the Hudson, and though he had not yet seen the powder works on the Potomac, he was convinced that they were just as delightful.

The colonel, whose sojourn in our country is to last for some weeks, will shortly leave New York to visit the powder works at South Chicago. He is accompanied on his journey by his wife and little daughter, both of whom he expects will be blown up in the Next War.

DOCUMENT NO. 2

The Peril from the Air

New York, July 25: General de Rochambeau-Lafayette, Director-in-Chief of the French Aerial forces, was interviewed yesterday at the Ritzmore Hotel as to the prospects of world peace. The General, whose full name is the Marquis de Rochambeau-Lafayette de Liancourt de la Rochefoucauld, belongs to the old noblesse of France, and is a cultivated French gentleman of the old school. He is himself a veteran of seven wars and is decorated with the *croix militaire*, the *croix de guerre*, the *nom de plume*, and the *cri de Paris.*

The Next War will, the count thinks, be opened, if not preceded, by the bombing of New York from the air. The hotels, which the count considers comfortable and luxurious above anything in Europe, will probably be blown up on the first day. The Metropolitan Museum of Art which General de Rochambeau visited yesterday and which he regards as equal to anything in the south of France, would undoubtedly afford an admirable target for a bomb.

The general expressed his unbounded astonishment at the size and beauty of the Pennsylvania and the Grand Central stations. Both, he said, would be blown up immediately. No air squadron could afford to neglect them.

"And your great mercantile houses," the count continued enthusiastically, "are admirable. Combining as they do, a wide superficies with an outline sufficiently *a pic* to make it an excellent *point de mire*, they could undoubtedly be lifted into the air at one bombing."

DOCUMENT NO. 3

The Coming Conflict on the Sea

New York, July 25: Admirable Breezy, who represents the jolliest type of the hearty British sailor and who makes a delightful impression everywhere, is of the opinion that the Next War will be fought not only on land but on the sea and in the sky and also under the sea.

"It will be fought all over the shop," said the Admirable, "but I do trust that the navy will have its fair share." The big battleship, he says, is after all the great arm of defense. "We are carrying guns now forty feet long and with an effective range of twenty-five miles." "Give me a gun ten feet longer," said the Admirable, "and I will stand off New York and knock down your bally city for you."

He offered further, if given a gun sixty feet long, to reach Philadelphia, and that if he were given the right gun platform he could perhaps hit Pittsburgh.

"I don't despair even of Chicago," said the Admirable. "We are moving forward in naval gunnery every year. It is merely a matter of size, length, and range. I could almost promise you that in ten years I could have a smack at St. Louis and Omaha. Canada, unfortunately, will mostly be on our side; otherwise, one might have had a bang at Winnipeg."

Admirable Breezy said that while he was warmly in favor of peace, he felt that a sea war between England and the United States would certainly make for good fellowship and mutual understanding between the two navies. "We don't know one another," he complained, "and under present circumstances I don't see how we can. But if our fellows could have a smack at your fellows, it would make for a good understanding of all round."

The Admiral is to speak in Carnegie Hall tonight on "What England Owes to the United States." A large attendance (of financial men) is expected.

DOCUMENT NO. 4

The New Chemical Terror

New York, July 26: Professor Gottlos Schwefeldampf, the distinguished German chemist, who is at the head of the German Kriegschemiefabrik at Stinken in Bavaria, arrived in New York yesterday on the *Hydrophobia* and is at the Belmore Hotel. The professor, who is a man somewhat below middle stature, is extremely short-sighted, and is at present confined to his room from the effects of a fall down the elevator. He speaks with the greatest optimism on the prospects of chemical warfare.

He considers that it has a wonderful future before it. "In the last war," he declared, sitting up in bed as much as a rheumatic infliction of long standing enabled him to do, "we were only beginning. We have developed now a gas which will easily obliterate the population of a whole town. It is a gas which is particularly destructive in the case of children, but which gives also very promising results with adults."

The professor spoke to the members of the press of the efficiency of this new discovery. Half a pint of the gas let loose in the room, he said, would easily have annihilated the eight representatives of the press who were present with him. He regretted that unfortunately he had none of the gas in a condition for instant use.

"But we shall not rely alone on gas," continued Professor Schwefeldampf. "In the Next War we expect to make a generous use of poison. Our poison factories are developing methods whereby we can poison the crops in the ground a hundred miles away. If our present efforts reach a happy conclusion, we shall be able to poison the livestock of an entire country. I need not dilate," he said, "on the favorable results of this—"

The Professor was interrupted by a violent fit of coughing, after which he sank back so exhausted that the members of the press were unable to prod any more copy out of him and left.

There! That's about the picture, not a bit exaggerated, of where we are letting this poor old world drift to. Can we manage, my dear people, to do something to stir up a little brotherly love all round? We ought to do it even if we have to send hundreds of people to jail to get it. As for me, I intend to start towards it right away. The very next time I see on the street a Russian Bolshevik with black whiskers like an eclipse of the sun, I shall go right up to him and kiss him and say, "Come, Clarence, let us forget the past and begin again."

International Amenities

Can We Wonder That It's Hard to Keep Friends?

I have been much impressed lately by the way in which the habit of "*scathing denunciation*," back and forward across the Atlantic, is growing in the press. Every time when international news gets a little slack somebody lands off a steamer and says something about British Education or about American women that sets the whole press into a flame. The people who say the things are of no possible importance. They are for the most part people of whom nobody ever heard before and never will again. But that doesn't matter. The newly arrived visitor stands up on the deck of his steamer, gets the reporters all grouped around him in a ring and then begins to "denounce." As a result next morning the newspapers of the entire continent carry news items such as the following, and the public seethes with indignation.

Denounces American Education

New York, April—:

"Mr. Farquhar McSquirt, who holds a high position in the Kindergarten Department of the Scottish Orphans Asylums at Dumfoolish, landed yesterday from the *Aquitania* on a tour of inspection of the American and

Canadian schools and at once uttered a scathing denunciation of education on this continent. He considers that the whole educational system of America is punk. He admits that a great many pupils attend school on this continent but denies that they learn a thing. He considers that the average boy of twelve in the Orkney Islands knows more than a graduate of Harvard and Yale. The American student, he says, has never learned to *think*; whereas the Scottish boy begins to think very soon after he learns to talk. Mr. McSquirt considers that the principal cause of the defect of American education is the utter lack of qualified teachers. He claims that the average American school teacher is a complete nut. Few of them stay more than ten years in the profession whereas in Scotland the average period is well over fifty years."

As soon as this kind of thing has been spilt all over the map of North America, the next thing to do is to mop it up. The newspapers send out enquiries to ten heads of ten great universities, and they all answer that while they have not the pleasure of knowing Mr. McSquirt personally—which means that they hope they never will know him—they emphatically deny his strictures on our education. They claim that the average American boy, while he may not have such long ears as a Scotch boy, is more receptive. He may not know as much as a Scottish student but what he knows he has digested, a thing the Scottish student has little chance to do. After this the public is soothed and the affair dies down.

Of course it must not be supposed that these "denunciations" are all in one direction. I don't mean for a moment that they are always directed against this continent. Not at all. That merely depends on which direction the traveller is going in. If he is headed the other way and is standing on British soil the denunciation is turned around and it runs something after this fashion.

Denounces Oxford

London, April—:

"Mr. Phineas Q. Cactus, T.Q., P.F., Principal of the Texas Normal Institute for Feeble Minded Navajo Indians, has just attracted wide attention here by a letter to the *Morning Post* in which he utters a scathing denunciation of the University of Oxford. He claims that at Oxford a student learns nothing. He admits that they go there and they stay there, but he says that during the whole time in Oxford no student ever thinks. In the schools of Texas no student is admitted unless he has passed an examination in thinking and during his entire course thinking is made compulsory at every step. Principal Cactus considers that Oxford dulls a man's mind. He says that after a course at Oxford the student is fit for nothing except the Church or the bar or the House of Lords. He claims that the average Oxford professor would make but a poor showing as a cowboy in Texas."

Education is a splendid topic for this kind of business. But perhaps an even better one is found in getting after our women and girls and denouncing them across the Atlantic. This is always good for ten days excitement. The sample press notice is as follows:

Denouncing American Girls

New York, April—:

"Lady Violet Longshanks, a direct descendant of Edward I, in the male line, landed yesterday morning in New York from the *Rule Britannia.* Lady Violet has at once excited widespread comment by an interview which she gave on the dock to a representative of the press. Her ladyship, who represents the *haut ton* of the oldest *noblesse* and who is absolutely *carte blanche*, gave expression to a scathing denunciation of the American girl. She declares that the American girl of to-day is without manners. No

American girl, the Countess claims, knows how to enter a room, still less how to get out of one. The American girl, according to Lady V. does not know how to use her voice, still less how to use her feet. At the same time the countess expressed herself fascinated with the size of the United States which she considers is undoubtedly a country of the future. Lady V. thinks it probable that many of the shortcomings of the American girl may be due to her habit of chewing tobacco."

And so, of course, as soon as Lady V. has said all this it has to be "mopped up" just like the other stuff. The press sends people to interview five heads of five women's colleges and they all declare that the American girl is as gentle as a lamb, and that if Lady V. really gets to know the American girl she will find that the American girl can use her feet, and will. As to the question of chewing tobacco they need only say that perhaps Lady V. is unaware that in all the first class women's colleges chewing tobacco is expressly forbidden not only on the campus, but in the bedrooms.

This reassures the public and gradually the trouble subsides and everybody cools off and the American girl gets right back to where she was. And then some American lady takes a trip over to England and starts the whole trouble again in a reversed direction, like this:

Denounces English Girls

London, April—:

"Mrs. Potter Pancake of Cedar Rapids, Iowa, President of the American Women's International Friendship League, has just jarred English society off its hinges by a sweeping condemnation, handed out from the window of her hotel, directed against English girls. Mrs. Pancake claims that the English girl is absolutely without grace and that her movements are inferior to those of a horse. Mrs. Pancake states further that the English girl moves like an alligator and is unable to sit down. She considers that these defects are mainly caused by drinking gin in inordinate quantities."

Whereupon trouble breaks out all over the British press from Cornwall to the Orkney Islands. The Archbishop of Canterbury is consulted and issues a statement to the effect that in his opinion the English girl is *more* graceful than a cow and that he has yet to see an English girl of the cultivated class take what *he* considers too much gin. This eases things up a bit, and the good effect is presently reinforced by a letter to the *Times* from the professor of Arthopedic Surgery at the Royal College of Physicians who says that he has made anthropometric measurements of over a thousand English girls and that their shapes suit *him* down to the ground. After that the trouble blows over and international friendship is just getting settled again and there is every prospect of the payment of the British debt and the scrapping of both navies and the rise of the pound sterling away over par, when someone starts it all off again with this:

Thinks Americans Crooked

"Mr. Joseph Squidge, M.P. Labor member for the mining district of Hiddaway-under-the-Sea, has just returned from a three weeks tour of America. Mr. Squidge, who visited the entire United States from New York to Yonkers, has just given an interview to the local paper at Hiddaway in which he says that public honesty is extinct in America. He considers that the entire population of the United States, not excepting the criminal classes, is crooked. He says that in America a man's word is never taken and that even in hotels a guest is required to sign his name."

This of course is too much—more than any decent people can stand, and as a consequence some one is at once sent over to England, either by accident or by design with the result that in a week or two the whole American press carries a despatch as follows:

Thinks British Dishonest

New York, April—:

"Edward Angle Eye, a journalist representing five thousand American Farmers Newspapers, has just cabled from London to Coffin Creek, Idaho, to say that the British are all liars. He says that with the possible exception of the Prince of Wales and Queen Mary, it is impossible to trust anybody in the British Isles. Public morality he claims has reached its lowest ebb and is washing away. He attributes the trouble to the large influx of Chinese in London."

And after that, can you wonder if we find it a little hard to keep peace and good will across the Atlantic.

French Politics for Beginners

As Explained in a Series of Cables from Our Own Special Correspondent in Paris

Paris, 10.30 a.m.

Nothing this morning intimated the imminence of a cabinet crisis. The sky was of spotless serenity, and the whole aspect of the city one of brightness and gayety. The hotels were full of tourists, the shops were crowded, the fountains were running, Punch and Judy was playing in the Champs Elysées, and the French franc which had shown signs of restlessness the day before had passed a quiet night.

The Chamber of Deputies, however, had hardly met at 10 o'clock in the Palais Bourbon when Mr. Painlevé rose in his seat and asked the premier if he knew what time it was. Mr. Briand replied that his watch had stopped. Mr. Painlevé rushing on to the floor in front of the tribune, demanded from the chamber whether a man whose watch had stopped was fit to be the premier of France. Instantly the chamber was in an uproar. Shouts of "*A Bas, Briand!*"—were mingled with cries of "Attaboy, Aristide!"

Mr. Briand, who preserved throughout the most complete calm, then asked for a vote of the chamber. The vote at once showed that not only was the whole of the Left side against Mr. Briand but also a bit of the Center and the East and South and some of the North-West. Mr. Briand immediately resigned and the great government which had presided over the destiny of France and weathered every storm for six days, went out of office.

Paris, 12.30 p.m.

It has now been learned that on the news of Mr. Briand's resignation the President of the Republic summoned Mr. Painlevé to the Palace of the Elysées and asked him if he could form a cabinet. On Mr. Painlevé asking for time the President said that he could have twenty minutes. Mr. Painlevé drove at once to the Chamber of Deputies and, crossing the floor of the house where Mr. Briand sat, kissed him on both cheeks and asked him if he would join his government. Mr. Briand, having thrown his arms around Mr. Painlevé, announced his willingness to join him. Within a few moments the chamber was informed of the formation of the Painlevé-Briand ministry, the news being greeted with acclamation.

The Painlevé-Briand Ministry

The president of the session having announced a ten minutes adjournment to allow the new ministry to make a budget, it became clear that the Painlevé-Briand ministry would find itself in a position of great strength. It will have the support of the whole radical bloc, together with a chunk of Socialists and about half a bloc of conservatives. No French government, for the last six months, has been in such a position of power. Briand, it is said with great satisfaction, will be virtually a dictator over the destinies of France. As soon as the news was disseminated on the Bourse the franc humped itself up two and a half points.

Paris, 11.45 a.m.

Mr. Briand and Mr. Painlevé, entering the chamber with their arms round one another's waists, read out their budget to a breathless house. The aim of the new government will be to put the finances of France on a basis of absolute stability. To do this they will at once borrow 4,000,000,000 francs. The loan, however, will be offset and made good by a credit with the Bank of France, which will then float a loan with the public, who will then be authorized, by a decree, to borrow from the bank. The entire credit thus created will be added up and declared extinguished. The announcement of the budget policy was received with a salvo of enthusiasm, the entire left embracing the whole of the right.

Fall of the Government

Paris, 12.30 p.m.

The Briand-Painlevé government has fallen. Entrenched in power as it seemed behind a solid parliamentary support, it fell suddenly and unexpectedly on an interpellation during the budget debate. Mr. Raymond Poincaré, who is generally regarded as the master mind of French politics, rose during the discussion of budget and asked whether the government intended to retain the tax on beer. On Mr. Briand's saying that it was proposed to keep this tax, Mr. Poincaré declared that the true national policy would be to let the Germans drink enough beer to pay taxes for both nations. If they couldn't do it they should be made to. The whole chamber seethed with enthusiasm, during which Mr. Briand and Mr. Painlevé announced that their government was at an end. The president of the chamber, calling for order amid the tumult, asked if there was any gentleman present who could form a new government. Mr. Poincaré offered to do so if the president would let him talk with Mr. Painlevé and Mr. Briand outside for a few minutes. The permission being given the three statesmen shortly afterward reentered the chamber and announced that they had succeeded in combining themselves into a ministry to be called the Poincaré-Painlevé-Briand Ministry.

Poincaré-Painlevé-Briand Ministry

Mr. Poincaré said, however, that they would only do this if they could be assured of a block behind them. If there was no block they wouldn't be a ministry. The enthusiasm of the Left together with part of the Right and a little bit of the Top, made it clear that the new ministry will receive an ample support. An adjournment was made with universal congratulations.

Fall of the French Ministry

Paris, 3.30 p.m.

The new French government, which was formed by Mr. Poincaré with the support of Mr. Painlevé and Mr. Briand fell right after lunch. Details are yet lacking. Apparently it came into the chamber after lunch and fell. There is a general consternation. The Bourse is wildly excited and all the exchanges reacted sharply. It is said that the Governor of the Bank of France will be arrested and perhaps the Archbishop of Paris. It is whispered that the fall of the ministry was occasioned by Mr. Joseph Caillaux, who seated himself in the chamber and looked at the ministry with that inscrutable look which he has, till it fell.

The Caillaux-Poincaré-Painlevé-Briand Ministry

Paris, 4.15 p.m.

A certain measure of calm has been restored in Paris by the announcement that an entirely new ministry has been formed by the union of Mr. Caillaux–Mr. Poincaré–Mr. Painlevé and Mr. Briand. In a statement to the press Mr. Briand said that the old government had outlived its usefulness and that he welcomed the addition of Mr. Caillaux. A new budget would be made at once and would constitute, he said, the best budget of the last three weeks. This budget, which will absolutely ensure the stability of French finance will be based on a vote of National Credit supported by a Universal Loan and guaranteed by a Public Debt. Mr. Caillaux, whose financial genius never shone more brightly, is working out a tax, to replace the proposed capital levy and the income tax, and to be called the Tax on Somebody Else.

It is said in well-informed circles that if the government can be widened to include a royalist element and to take in a few communists and a bloc of socialists, its success will be assured. If it can then pursue a policy which will be sufficiently clerical and conservative while at the same time strongly socialist, with a touch of opportunism, it may last till Saturday.

Meantime the theatres are all open, work is plentiful, everybody is happy, Paris is bright with spring flowers, the hotels are full of Americans dripping with money, the new fashions are said to be simply charming, the skirts don't reach anywhere, the watering places are wetter than ever—so what does a little thing like a government matter?

The Mother of Parliaments

But What Has Lately Gone Wrong with Mother?

"The House of Commons," says the well known *Guide Book to London of Today*, "not inaptly called the Mother of Parliaments, is undoubtedly the most august, as it is the most venerable, of the great representative assemblies of the world. It is with something like awe that we penetrate into the stillness of Westminster Palace, and find ourselves presently looking down from our privileged place in the gallery upon the earnest group of men whose measured tones and dignified formalities are deciding the fate of an empire."

That is what the Guide Book has been saying about the House of Commons for some two hundred years. But in reading over the press reports of the debates of the House within the last year or so as they come across the Atlantic, one is inclined to wonder whether the cold dignity of the dear old place is not getting a little thawed out in the warm times in which we live.

The proceedings in the later days sound a little too suggestive of the Cowboys Convention of Montana, or the meeting of the Literary Philosophical Society of Dawson City, Yukon.

Take in illustration the following report of the proceedings of one day some months ago, taken verbatim from the *London Times* and the

London Morning Post or the *Labor Herald*—I forget which. At any rate, those who read the debates of the house will recognize it at once as genuine.

"The House of Commons resumed its session yesterday at three o'clock. The Prime Minister in rising from the Treasury Benches to present his bill for the introduction of Buckwheat into the Tanganyika district of Uganda, stated that he would like first to refer to the fact that some member of the House had just thrown a banana at the Speaker. He would ask members to realize that throwing bananas at the Speaker impeded the business of the House. He would go so far as to say that it was bad manners.

"At the word 'manners' the House broke into an uproar. Cries arose from the labor benches, 'Manners! Yah! Manners!'

"Lady Luster at once leapt to her feet and said that there were members in the House whose manners were not fit for a stable.

"Joseph Dockside, M.P. for the Buckingham Palace district, asked if she meant him. Lady Luster called out that she did. The Speaker rose to a ruling against personal mention quoting a precedent under Henry VIII. But another banana hit him and he sat down.

"Mr. Dockside began to cry. He asked the House if it was fair to let an idle woman like Lady Luster tell him that he had no manners. He was only a poor man and had no schooling, and how could he even get a chance to pick up manners, even fit for a stable. Here he broke into sobs again while the labor benches resounded with the cries of 'Shame!' and the blowing of horns.

"Lady Luster then said that she had gone too far. She would take back the word stable. She meant 'Garage.'

"The Speaker, quoting a precedent from Edward the Confessor, said that the debate might go on—a pineapple hitting him in the waistcoat just before, and as, he sat down.

"The Prime Minister then said that as quiet had been restored (loud cries of '*Rah! Rah! Quiet!,*') he would resume his speech on the proposal of the government to subsidize the growing buckwheat—and, he would add, buckoats—in the Tanganyika district.

"At this point he was interrupted by Colonel MacAlpin MacFoozle, independent member for the East Riding of the West Hebrides. The Colonel wanted to know how the Prime Minister could speak of Tanganyika if he was fully aware of the condition of Scotland. Did he know of the present distress among the crofters? Was he aware of what was happening to the Scottish gillies, and the laddies and collies?

"Did he know that three more men had left the Hebrides? The Colonel, who spoke with violent passion, to the great delight of the House, said that he didn't give a curse for buckwheat or for Tanganyika and that personally he could lick the whole cabinet.

"At this, loud shouts of '*Attaboy! You're the hot stuff,*' were mingled with cries of '*Put him out!*' Lady Luster called out that if the Scots would quit drinking Scotch whiskey they would all save enough money to leave Scotland.

"For the moment, the transaction of public business was seriously threatened when Lord Pintop Daffodil rose and asked the Speaker's leave to tell a funny story. Lord Pintop, who is rapidly gaining the reputation of being the third funniest member of the House, was greeted with encouraging laughter and applause.

"The Speaker having ruled that a funny story had been told under Queen Anne, Lord Pintop then related a story of how a Pullman car passenger was put off at Buffalo by the porter. The House, which is easily moved from anger to merriment and which enjoys nothing (except its lunch) so much as a good joke, was convulsed with laughter.

"The Speaker, in thanking the honorable member for the story, said that he believed that it was the same story as was told under Queen Anne.

"The Prime Minister then said he would resume his speech on buckwheat. He was about to do so when Mr. Ilyitch Halfoff, member for the Russian district of Westminster, said that he would like first to rise and present a resolution for the immediate introduction of communism into England. The House was in a turmoil in a minute.

"Cries of '*Russia for ever!*' were mixed with the singing of the 'Marseillaise' and the countersinging of 'Scots Whoo Hoo!' It was said afterwards that the singing was the best ever heard in the House this month.

"At this point in the debate the yeoman usher of the Black Stick rushed into the House and called—'Hurry out, boys, there is a circus procession coming down Whitehall!' The whole House rushed out in a body, only the speaker remaining behind for one minute to adjourn the session."

New Light from New Minds

A Study in International Interviews

People who read the newspapers regularly must have noticed that the reported Interviews are getting to be much brighter and more interesting than they used to be. Till recently, when the press interviewed travellers, distinguished visitors and political emissaries, they talked to each of them about his own particular line of life and the things about which he was supposed to know something. The result was fearful dullness. A director of the Bank of England was interviewed about currency, an actor was interviewed about the stage and a bishop about religion. As a consequence every one of them got prosy and unintelligible.

Nowadays the thing is done in exactly the other way. Each distinguished visitor is asked questions about something that is outside of his own line of life. A vaudeville comedian gives his impressions of French politics and an English bishop gives his views of women's skirts. The result is a freshness and a charm which lends a new attraction to our newspapers on both sides of the Atlantic. Here are a few examples taken from the current press and drawn, as appears at once, indifferently from England and America.

Ball Player Visits St. Paul's

London, Friday: Ed Lanigan, star outfielder and manager of the Tuscaloosa Base Ball Nine, passed through London this morning and expressed himself as delighted with it. After he had had a run round town, Ed gave his views, on some of the things he had seen, to a crowd of assembled admirers at the Hotel Cecil. "What did you think of St. Paul's, Ed?" asked one of the boys. "It's certainly big stuff," said Ed, "and it gets me. Those old geysers certainly knew how to build. And I want to tell you boys that there's something about that building that you don't get every-day. I doubt if there are a dozen men in New York to-day who could duplicate it."

"How does the political situation in England strike you," he was next queried. "Fine!" answered the big man. "They've sure got a lot of taxes here. But then mind you there's a lot of wealth too. Of course things are pretty bad, but you've got to remember they were bad before, and anyway they're not so bad."

Movie Star Sees Riviera

Menton, Monday: Gus Phinn, the well-known movie star who is said to command a salary of anywhere from half a million dollars, was a recent visitor at Menton. Gus is enthusiastic over the Mediterranean sea. "I want to tell you right now," he said to a representative of the press, "that there is absolutely nothing wrong with the Mediterranean." "What did you specially notice about it, Gus?" asked the pressman. "Why, what gets me hardest is the colour of the water. Say, I don't think you can beat that blue anywhere. You might try but you can't do it." "Do you think," asked another of the group, "that the tone of English Social Life is deteriorating?" "No, I don't," Gus replied. "I think the tone is good. I think it A.1."

"What about the relations of England and France, Gus?" was another question. "They're all right," the star answered. "We met a lot of French boys on the boat and certainly nicer boys you wouldn't want to meet. Well, they're gentlemen that's what they are. The French are gentlemen."

"What about Germans, Gus?" one of the reporters ventured.

"All right!" answered the movie man heartily. "We had a German at our table in the hotel and they're all right. Mind you I think we were perfectly right in crushing them because they needed to be crushed. But they're all right."

Copper King Looks at Oxford

Oxford, Tuesday: E. J. Slagg, the multimillionaire owner of mines and president of Slagg Consolidated Copper, visited Oxford yesterday and was shown round the colleges. The big copper man whose quiet taciturnity and power of silence has made him the terror of the stock exchange, looked about him at everything with the same keen shrewdness with which he detects a vein of copper under a hundred feet of trap rock. Only now and then he darted a shrewd question or let fall a short comment.

"This place," he said, "is old." On the threshold of the Bodleian Library he paused a moment as if rapidly measuring the contents with his eye. "Mostly books?" he asked. The copper king also paused a moment before the monument erected to the memory of Latimer and Ridley. "What's the idea?" he asked.

But—as I said up above this new and brilliant flood of light is not only turned on Europe. By a similar process it is let loose on the American continent too.

British Lord Sees Jersey Tugs

New York, Wednesday: Lord Tinklepin who arrived from England on the *Aquitania* yesterday was taken for a trip up and down the harbor in a fast tug. His lordship expressed himself as amazed at the commerce of New York. "I had no idea of it," he said. Passing by one of the car ferries of the Erie Railway, Lord Tinklepin expressed the keenest interest. "What the devil is that?" he asked. On being told what it was, the distinguished visitor who is well known for his interest in physical science, at once asked "Why doesn't it upset?"

Lady Visitor Discusses American Banking

New York, Thursday: Lady Mary Messabout, President of the Women's Federation for Universal Mutual Understanding, was shown round financial New York yesterday as the guest of the Bankers Association. Lady Mary expressed the greatest wonder at the Sub-Treasury of the United States. "Is it possible" she said, "that it's full of money?" Lady Mary was questioned by representatives of the press as to her opinion of the American banking system. "It is really excellent," she answered, "so little delay and such civility everywhere." "Do you think,"—it was asked by a member of the press—"that the deflation of American currency would check the expansion of business?" "Oh, I hope not," Lady Mary answered warmly, "surely it would never do that."

French Baron Visits West

Saskatoon, Saskatchewan, Friday: The Baron de Vieux Chateau, who is visiting Saskatchewan with a view to seeing whether the richer parts of Canada would be suited for the poorer class of Frenchmen, was taken yesterday on a tour of inspection of the grain elevators of Saskatoon. "But they are marvellous!" the Baron said to a member of the press on his return to his hotel. "They seem to me absolutely—how shall I say it—enormous." In further discussion the Baron said the whole system of distributing the wheat seemed to him excellent. When asked what his impression of the Farmer's Cooperative movement was, the distinguished visitor again spoke with enthusiasm. "But your farmers," he said, "they are wonderful! What courage! What tenacity! To have come here and stayed here! It is wonderful."

An Advance Cable Service

International News a Month Ahead

It has recently become the habit to send out and circulate all sorts of special information in the form of "services." The schools of commerce send out "financial services" with a forecast of business conditions six months before they happen and some times even six months before they don't happen. The departments of agriculture send out crop reports even before the grain is planted. The meteorologists keep at least a fortnight ahead of the weather. Political forecasts are now ready for all the elections up to 1928. The hard winter that is going to begin about Xmas time has been definitely prophesied, in fact promised by the squirrels, the groundhogs and the makers of fur garments and by the West Indian Steamship agents.

It has occurred to me that a useful extension might be made to these "services" by adding an *Advance European Cable Service.* By this means all readers of newspapers, instead of having to read the cables day by day, could get them in a lump a month at a time. Anybody who has studied the newspapers of the last three or four years recognises at once that the cables run in a regular round, quite easy to prophesy. In the modest little attempt appended below, I have endeavoured to put in merely the ordinary routine of European public life for one month without prophesying anything of an exceptional or extreme character.

German Revolution Coming

Berlin, Monday 1: A monarchical wave is reported as having swept over Germany. The wildest excitement prevails. A hundred persons were trampled to death in Berlin the other day. The return of His Imperial Majesty the Kaiser is expected at any moment.

And Going

Berlin, Tuesday 2: A republican wave has swept over Germany in the place of the monarchical wave of yesterday. Another hundred people were trampled to death. William Hohenzollern is reported as still at Doorn in Holland.

And Has Gone

Berlin, Wednesday 3: Germany is quiet. Christmas shopping is beginning already. Everywhere there is cheerfulness and optimism. Nobody was trampled to death all day.

Frenzied Finance in France

Paris, Thursday 4: Following on the sensational statement of Monsieur Caillaux that France would pay her debts to the last penny, the wildest excitement prevailed on the Bourse. The franc which had been fairly steady all yesterday, rose to its feet, and staggered right across the street where it collapsed in a heap. Gloom prevails in financial circles.

Paris, Friday 5: Monsieur Caillaux has issued a supplementary statement to the effect that France will pay all her debts but it may take her a million years to do it. This assurance has restored universal confidence and Monsieur Caillaux is hailed everywhere as having redeemed the honor and credit of France. A tremendous ovation was given him today when eating a sandwich at the lunch counter. It is now said that Caillaux, who is recognised everywhere as the financial saviour of France, is working out a plan for wiping out the whole debt of France by borrowing it from England.

Home Life in England

London, Saturday 6: England is face to face with a coal strike of such magnitude that in twenty-four hours every fire in England will go out. If the transport workers and the public house keepers join the strike the whole industrial life of the nation will come to a full stop. Meantime the Archbishop of Canterbury says that if he can't get a satchelful of nut coal tonight he must close the cathedral.

London, Monday 8: The coal strike was called off at five minutes before midnight—one of the closest shaves of a total collapse of England that has been reported in the last six months. Meantime with cloudless skies and bright sunshine the whole attention of the nation today is riveted on the champion football game between the Huddersfield and Hopton-under-Lime. The Archbishop of Canterbury will kick off the ball.

Italian Upheaval Heaving Up

Rome Tuesday 9: The Italian Fascisti have broken loose again. Yesterday a man climbed up to the top of the Duomo at Milan and waved a black shirt, shouting EVIVA ITALIA! The whole nation is in a ferment. Anything may happen.

Rome, Wednesday 10: It is all right. It transpires that the shirt was not black, it was merely very dirty.

Austria in Chaos

Vienna, Thursday 11: Mr. Edward Edelstein, vice-president of the Canned Soup Company of Paterson, New Jersey who is making a ten day tour in central Europe to study business conditions, describes the situation of Austria as one of utter chaos. Trade is absolutely stagnant. Business is almost extinct while the currency is in entire confusion. In Vienna unemployment is everywhere, even the rich are eating in soup kitchens; the theatres are closed and social life is paralyzed.

Complete Revival of Austria

Vienna, Friday 12: Mr. John Smithers of Smitherstown, who is taking a five days vacation in Europe reports that the economic situation of Austria has been reestablished on a sound basis. The restoration of the currency this morning by the establishment of a new and easier mark, is working wonders. The factories are running on full time, the shops are crowded with visitors, the hotels are bursting with guests and the theatres are offering *Shakespeare*, *Grand Opera*, and *Uncle Tom's Cabin.*

Vienna, Saturday 5: Austria has collapsed again.

Dear Old Russia

Petrograd (otherwise Leningrad or Trotskiville), Monday 15: Reports from the Caucasus say that Red forces made a drive at the Caucasians yesterday. The latter just got out of the road in time.

Tuesday 16: Word has been received that the Reds made a fierce drive at Semipalatinsk. They only got half of it.

Wednesday 17: Wireless despatches say that the Reds are preparing for a drive against the Persians. Most of the Persians have already climbed up Mount Ararat.

Thursday 18: It is reported that the Council of Workmen's Soviets of Moscow have passed a resolution declaring that universal peace has come.

International Goodwill

Tokyo, Friday 19: Viscount Itch is reported in the Japanese *Daily Hootch* as saying that the time has come when Japan can not tolerate the existence of the United States on the other side of the Pacific. It will have to be moved. Wild excitement prevailed after the delivery of the speech. Enormous crowds paraded the streets of Tokyo, shouting "Down with America!" An American missionary was chased into a Chinese restaurant.

Tokyo, Saturday 20: Viscount Itch has issued a statement to the effect that Japan and the United States are sisters. Wild enthusiasm prevails. Great crowds are parading the streets, shouting "Attaboi Coolidji!" The missionary has come down again.

Yokohama, Monday 22: The business section of Yokohama was destroyed yesterday by an earthquake.

Yokohama, Tuesday 23: The business section of Yokohama has been propped up again and nailed into position.

From the Far Away South Seas

London, Wednesday 24: Cable advices received via Fiji and Melbourne report the Marquesas Islanders in a plebiscite have voted for prohibition, direct legislation, proportional representation and the abolition of cannibalism. Some more votes will be taken next week.

Back from Europe

The Reaction of Travel on the Human Mind

There comes a time every year when all the hundreds of thousands of people who have been over to Europe on a summer tour get back again. It is very generally supposed that a tour of this kind ought to have a broadening effect on the mind, and this idea is vigorously propagated by the hotel companies at Schlitz, Bitz, Biarritz, and picturesque places of that sort.

It is not for me to combat this idea. But I do know that in certain cases at least a trip to Europe sets up a distinct disturbance of the intellect. Some of these afflictions are so well defined that they could almost be definitely classified as diseases. I will quote only a few among the many examples that might be given.

I

Aristocropsis, or Weakening of the Brain from Contact with the British Aristocracy

There seems to be no doubt that a sudden contact with the titled classes disturbs the nerve cells or ganglions of the traveler from America, and brings on a temporary enfeeblement of mind. It is generally harmless, especially as it is usually accompanied by an extreme optimism and an exaggerated sense of importance.

Specimen Case. Winter conversation of Mr. John W. Axman, retired hardware millionaire of Fargo, Dakota, in regard to his visit to England.

"I don't know whether I told you that I saw a good deal of the Duke of Dumpshire while I was in England. In fact, I went to see him at his seat—all these dukes have seats, you know. You can say what you like about the British aristocrats, but when you meet one like the Duke of Dumpshire, they are all right. Why, he was just as simple as you or me, or simpler. When he met me, he said, 'How are you?' Just like that.

"And then he said, 'You must be hungry. Come along and let's see if we can find some cold beef.' Just as easy as that. And then he said to a butler or someone, 'Go and see if you can find some cold beef.' And presently the butler came back and said, 'There's some cold beef on the table, Sir,' and the Duke said, 'All right, let's go and eat it.' And he went and sat right down in front of the beef and ate it. Just as you or I would.

"All the time we were eating it, the Duke was talking and laughing. He's got a great sense of humor, the Duke has. After he'd finished the beef, he said, 'Well, that was a darn good piece of beef!' and of course we both roared. The Duke's keen on politics, too—right up to date about everything. 'Let's see,' he said, 'who's your President now?' In fact, he's just as keen as mustard, and looks far ahead too. 'France,' he said to me, 'is in for a hell of a time.'"

II

Nuttolingualism, or Loss of One's Own Language after Three Weeks across the Sea

Specimen No. 1. Verbatim statement of Mr. Phin Gulch, college student from Umskegee College, Oklahoma, made immediately on his return from a three weeks athletic tour in England with Oklahoma Olympic Aggregation. "England certainly is a ripping place. The chaps we met were simply topping. Of course here and there we met a bounder, but on the whole one was treated absolutely top hole."

Specimen No. 2. Information in regard to French restaurants supplied by Miss Phoebe McGinn, winner of the Beauty Contest Ticket to Europe and Back from Boom City, Montana. "The Paris restaurants are just charming and ever so cheap if you know where to go. There was one we used to go to in a little rue close to the gare where we got our dejeuner with croissants and cafe au lait for soixante-quinze centimes.

"Of course we used to give the garcon another quinze centimes as a pourboire. And after dejeuner we'd sit there half the matinee and read the journaux and watch the people go past in the rue. Always, when we left, the garcon would say, 'Au revoir.' Regular French, you know."

III

Megalogastria, or Desire to Talk about Food

Specimen Case. Mr. Hefty Undercut, of Saskatoon, Saskatchewan, retired hotel man, talks on European culture.

"I don't mind admitting that the English seem to me away ahead of us. They're further on. They know how to do things better. Now you take beefsteak. They cut it half as thick again as we do, and put it right on a grid over hot coals. They keep the juice in it. Or take a mutton chop. The way they cook them over there, you can eat two pounds to one that you eat here. You see they're an older people than we are.

"Or take sausages—when I travel I like to observe everything; it makes you broader;—and I've noticed their sausages are softer than ours, more flavoring to them. Or take one of those big deep meat pies—why, they eat those big pies at midnight. You can do it there. The climate's right for it.

"And, as I say, when I travel I go around noticing everything and sizing everything up—the meat, the lobsters, the kind of soup they have, everything. You see, over there there's very little sunlight and the air is heavy and you eat six times a day. It's a great place."

Introspexosis, or Seeing in Other People What Is Really in Yourself

It appears that many people when they travel really see nothing at all except the reflection of their own ideas. They think that what they are interested in is uppermost everywhere. They might just as well stay at home and use a looking glass. Take in witness:

The evidence of Mr. Soggie Spinnage, Secretary of the Vegetarian Society of North, Central, and South America, as given after his return from a propaganda tour in England:

"Oh, there's no doubt the vegetarian movement is spreading in England. We saw it everywhere. At Plymouth a man came right up to me and he said, 'Oh, my dear Brother, I wish we had a thousand men here like you. Go back,' he said, 'go back and bring over a thousand others.' And wherever I spoke I met with such enthusiasm.

"I spoke, I remember, in Tooting-on-the-Hump—it's within half an hour of London itself. And when I looked into their dear faces and told them about the celery in Kalamazoo, Michigan, and about the big cabbages in the South Chicago mud flats, they just came flocking about me! 'Go back,' they said, 'go back and send those over.'

"I heard a man in a restaurant one day say to the waiter, 'Just fetch me a boiled cabbage. I want nothing else.' I went right up to him, and I took his hand and I said, 'Oh, my dear friend, I have come all the way from America just to hear that.' And he said, 'Go back,' he said, 'go back and tell them that you've heard it.'

"Why, when you go to England you just see vegetables, vegetables, everywhere. I hardly seemed to see anything else. They say even the King eats vegetables now. And they say the Bishop of London only eats beans. I heard someone say that the Bishop seemed full of beans all the time.

"Really I felt that the cause was just gaining and growing all the time. When I came to leave, a little group of friends come down to the steamer to say good-bye. 'Go back,' they said, 'go back and send someone else.'

"That seemed to be the feeling everywhere."

III

Studies in the Newer Culture

A Little Study in Culture from Below Up

About fifteen years ago somebody invented the word *Attaboy*. At first it was used only by the urchins on the baseball bleachers. Presently it was used by the college students. After that it was taken up by business men, lawyers, judges and congressmen and it spread all over the world.

It was said that when King George of England welcomed home General Allenby after his conquest of Palestine, he put his hands on Allenby's shoulders and said with deep feeling, "Attaboy!"

The General, profoundly touched, was heard to murmur in return, "Some King, what!"

This story may or may not be true. It is possible that King George used merely some such dignified English phrase as "Not half bad at all!" But the story at any rate illustrates the tremendous change that has been creeping over our language.

I am not here referring to the use of slang. That of course is as old as language itself. The man who uses a slang word and, let us say, calls a man's hat his "*lid*" or calls a woman a "*skirt*," is unconscious of using a metaphor and of trying to be funny or peculiar. But the man who uses *attaboy* language in speech or writing is really trying to say something; he really thinks he is using English. It is not merely the words that he uses but the way in which he uses them.

Let me give you an instance—that is much quicker business than trying to explain the whole thing in a methodical fashion.

Attaboy Letter of Invitation

Here, for example—to illustrate the old style of writing and speaking—is a letter which I received almost thirty years ago inviting me to attend a gathering of my college class. In point of dignity and good form the letter speaks for itself.

TORONTO, Feb. 1st, 1896.

DEAR SIR:

I beg to inform you that a reunion of the graduating class of 1891 will be held on the 5th of February in the form of a dinner at the Queen's Hotel. The guest of honor on the occasion will be Professor Baxter, who has kindly consented to deliver an address to the class. It is confidently expected that all the members of the class will take this opportunity to renew old friendships. The price of the dinner, including wines, will be seventy-five cents. May I ask you to send a reply at your earliest convenience.

With sincere personal regards,
I have the honor to be
And to remain being,
Yours very faithfully,
JOHN SMITH.

Now it happened that just the other day I received a letter from the same old classmate inviting me to attend a similar gathering of the class—thirty years later. But here is how he has expressed the invitation—

Mr. He-Man from College!

This is You!

Say! what do you think? The real old He-Boys of 1891 are going to gather in for a feed at the Queen's on February 5th. Songs! Speeches!

Fireworks! And who do you think is going to be the main Big Talk! You'd never guess—why old Prof Baxter—old nutsey Baxter! Come and hear him. Come along right now! The whole feed—songs, fun and smokes included—is only six bucks. So get down in your pants and fork them out.

Yours, Attaboy! Hooroo!
Rev. John Smith,
(Canon of the Cathedral)

An Attaboy Dictionary

Let it be noted that the great point of the *Attaboy* system is the terrific desire for emphasis. A man is not called a man. He is called a *he-man.* Even that is not enough. He has to be 100 *per cent* he-man. And in extreme cases he must be called a "100 per cent, full blooded, bull-chested, big-headed, great-hearted man,"—all of this to replace the simple old-fashioned word *gentleman.*

Indeed, one could write quite a little dictionary of Attaboy terms like this—

Gentleman—(See above.)

Lady—a big-hearted, wide-eyed, warm-chested woman, a hundred per cent soul, and built square.

Friend—a he-man with a hand-grip and a jaw that means that as soon as you see him in front of you, you know that he is back of you.

Senator—far-sighted, frog-eyed, nation-making he-man.

Criminal—no such word. Try "hold-up man"—"yegg"—"thug"—"expert safe-cracker," etc., etc., etc.

In the same way when the *attaboy* language turns from the nouns to the verbs there has to be the same vital emphasis. The fatal step was taken when someone invented the word *punch.* Since then every form of action has to be described as if it occurred with a direct physical shock. A speaker has got to *hit* his audience with a *punch*, he must *lift* them, throw them, in short fairly *kick* them out of the room.

A book is said to be *arresting, gripping, compelling*. It has got to hold the reader down so that he can't get up. A preacher has got to be *vital, dynamic*; he must *put his sermon over*; he must pitch it at the audience; in short, preaching becomes a form of baseball with the clergyman in the box.

In other words the whole of our life and thought has got to be restated in terms of moving things, in terms of electricity, radio and all the crackling physical apparatus of the world in which we live.

Macaulay and Gibbon in Attaboy

It is quite clear that if this *attaboy* tendency goes on all the books of the past will have to be rewritten or nobody will understand them. Somebody will have to re-edit them so as to put into them the necessary "pep" and "punch" to make them readable by the next generation.

We can imagine how completely unintelligible will be the stately pages of such dignified writers as Macaulay or Gibbon. Here, for example, is a specimen of the way in which Gibbon's *Decline and Fall of the Roman Empire* will be revised. I take as an illustration a well-known passage describing the action of a heroic matron of Rome in rallying the wavering citizens after a retreat. It runs:

"A Roman matron of imposing appearance and striking countenance stepped forth before the hesitating citizens—"

Translation:

"A pre-war blonde who was evidently a real peach skipped out in front of the bunch—"

"At the sight of her the citizens paused—"

Translation:

"As soon as they put their lamps on her all the guys stood still—"

"Reluctant cries of admiration arose from the crowd—"

"'Some doll!' said the boys."

"'Cowards!' she exclaimed."

"'You big stiffs,' she snorted."

"'And would you leave the defense of your homes at such a time as this!'"

"'Do you mean to say that you are going to fly the coop?'"

"'To your posts all of you!' she cried."

"'Beat it,' she honked."

"Inspired by her courage the citizens with shouts of 'Long Live Sempronia!' rushed to the ramparts."

"Full of pep they all shouted, 'Attaboy, Lizzie!' and skipped up the ladders."

Rome was Saved

Epitaph on an Attaboy

Even the epitaphs on the grave stones will have to be altered. The old style used to run, "Here lies the body of John Smith, who was born on February 1, 1802 and departed this life on December 1, 1861. He was a loving son, a fond parent, a devoted husband and a patriotic citizen. This stone has been erected by his mourning widow to commemorate his many virtues and in the expectation of his resurrection."

But that kind of thing will have to be replaced by an epitaph with more "punch" in it, something more "gripping," more compelling. Try this:

"Mr. Passerby! Stop! This is for you—you careless HOG.

"Read it.

"Here lies a cuckoo, John Smith, one of the real boys. He opened his lamps first on February 1, 1802. He stepped off the big plank into the dark stuff on December 1, 1861—But when the big Horn. calls 'ALL UP,' *oh, say,* ATTABOY*!"*

The Crossword Puzzle Craze

"I beg your pardon," said a man sitting opposite to me in the smoking end of a Pullman car. "Do you happen to know the name of an Arabian Feudal Ruler in five letters?"

"Yes," I said, "a sheik."

He wrote down the word in a notebook that was spread out upon his knee. Then he said,

"And what's the Hottentot house on the move in five letters?"

"A Kraal," I answered.

"Oh—yes, Kraal!" he said. "I could only think of a bungalow; and here's another that's a regular bowler, what is an extinct graminiferous lizard in thirteen letters?"

"Ichthyosaurus," I said.

"How's that?" he asked. "My, I wish I'd had a college education—let me write it down—wait now—I-c-h-t-—say, I believe it's going to get it—yes, sir, it's getting it—By Gee! It's got it. It all fits in now except there's a dirty little hitch in this corner. Say, could there be any word in three letters that would be e-k-e?"

"Yes," I said, "'eke,' it means 'also.'"

"Then I've got the whole thing—just in time—here's my station. Say, I'm ever so much obliged. I guess I will have one on the wife when I show her this. That's a peach, that ichthy-what d'ye call it. Good-bye."

He left me and I knew that I had been dealing with another of the new victims of the crossword puzzle mania. I knew that as soon as he got into his house he would work the ichthyosaurus on his wife; indeed he would probably find her seated with a paper and pencil trying to figure out whether the Icelandish skol will fit in with a form of religion called "Tosh." The thing generally runs in families.

This crossword puzzle is said to have originated in Tibet. From there it was transferred to the Mongolians who introduced it to the Hairy Ainus of Japan, who were delighted with it, as they naturally would be. From them it crossed the ocean to the Siwash Indians who passed it on to the Dog Ribs and to the Flat Heads, and in this way it got to the American Colleges.

The mania has now assumed international dimensions. It is estimated that if the crossword puzzle solvers were stood up in line (either horizontally or vertically, they wouldn't care which), they would reach half way to Havana. Some might even get there.

But the greatest thing about the crossword puzzle is the way in which it is brightening up our language. Old words that had been forgotten for five hundred years are being polished up as bright as new. A man no longer says, "Good morning. How are you?" he says, "Good morn. How fare you?" And the other man answers that he feels yardly and eke his wife, especially as they expect eft soon to take a holy day and make a cast to Atlantic City.

Before this thing began there were lots of people so ignorant that they didn't know what "Yost" meant, or what a "farrago" is, or which part of a dog is its "withers." Now these are family words. Anyone would say quite naturally, "Just give that dog a kick in the farrago and put him out."

I notice especially the general improvement in exact knowledge for the names of animals and parts of animals. Who used to know what a *marsupial* was? Who could have told where the *dewlap* of an ox is? How many people had heard of the *carapace* of the mud turtle, or knew how to give a proper name to the east ear of an elephant?

Many crossword puzzle experts go further. When engaged in conversation they don't even need to use the very words they mean. They merely indicate them in crossword puzzle fashion and the expert listening to them can solve their conversation at once. Here is a sample of the new—

Crossword Puzzle Conversation

"Good morning, Short-for-Peter."

"Hullo, Diminutive-of-William. How do you experience-a-sensation in four letters this morning?"

"Worse than a word in four letters rhyming will *bell* and *tell*."

"Oh, I am sorry to hear it. What is the substance, body or cubic content of space in six letters with you?"

"Cold in the bronchial tunnels, passages, or English name for a subway."

"Possessing or exhibiting grace with the personal adjective! Who is treating you?"

"Only the woman in four letters bound to me by law for life!"

"Indeed! Surely you ought not to be an adverb in three letters in this weather."

"No, I ought to be a preposition in two. But I have to go to my effort, energy or mental or bodily exertion undertaken for gain in four letters."

"Well, take good care of yourself. Good remain with you as a form of exclamation used in parting in seven letters."

There are evidently large possibilities in this form of speech. I think that a lot of our literature could be brightened up with the words of romance and mystery by putting it into crossword puzzle language.

Crossword Poetry

Even our poetry would be none the worse for it. Here, for example, is a once familiar bit of Longfellow's verse turned into this kind of dialect:

> Under the spreading chestnut tree,
> The village smithy remains erect, upright or in a vertical position common to man and the apes but not seen in other animals,
> The smith, a mighty man, is a personal pronoun
> With large and sinuous extremities of his limbs in four letters,
> And the muscles of his brawny arms
> Are as strong as a company of musicians.

Admirable! Isn't it? It only needs a little industry and we can have the whole of our classical literature translated in this way.

But unfortunately the results of the new craze are not always so happy. I heard last week of a rather distressing case of the ill effects of puzzle solving. A man of my acquaintance was at an evening party where they were solving crossword puzzles and he was brought, with the rest of the company, to an absolute full stop by one item: what would you rather be out of than in, in twelve letters? The thing absolutely beat him.

He thought of it all night but with no result. He was still thinking of it as he drove his car down town next morning. In his absolute preoccupation he ran into a man on the street and shook him up quite badly. He was arrested and tried for criminal negligence.

The judge said to him: "I regret very much to have to impose a prison sentence on a man of your standing. But criminal negligence cannot be tolerated. I sentence you to six months in the penitentiary."

On this the puzzle-solver threw up his hands with an exclamation of joy and cried, "Penitentiary, of course, penitentiary! Now I've got it!"

He was scribbling on a little bit of paper when they led him away.

Information While You Eat

Some Reflections on the Joys of the Luncheon Clubs

Now that the bright tints of autumn are appearing on the trees, the season for the luncheon clubs is opening up again. Personally I think our luncheon clubs are one of the most agreeable features of modern city life. I have belonged to several luncheon clubs in our town ever since they started, and I never miss a lunch.

When I look back to the time when men used to be satisfied to sit down all alone in front of a beefsteak and a bottle of Budweiser with only just some apple pie and a cup of coffee and a cigar after it, and without singing a note all through—I don't see how we did it. Now, if I can't sing a little as I eat, and call "hear, hear" every now and then, I don't feel as if I could digest properly. So when I offer a few suggestions about our luncheon clubs, I don't want to be misunderstood. I am not criticizing but merely pointing out how we can make them brighter and better still.

Take the singing. After all, quite frankly, do we need to sing at lunch? Our clubs—and, I think, the clubs in most other towns, too—generally sing very slow, dragging melodies such as, "The... day... is... past,... the... sun is... set...." The effect of that kind of tune as intoned by a hundred men with a pound and a quarter beefsteak adjusted in each of them (125 lbs. total dead-weight of music) is, very frankly mournful. It sounds to me like the last of the Tasmanian Islanders leaving home.

Or else we sing Negro melodies. But why should we? Or we sing "Annie Laurie." Who was she, anyway? In fact, to be quite candid, I can eat lunch splendidly without asking to be carried back to Tennessee, or offering to lay down and die, either on the banks of the Doon or anywhere else.

Without the singing there could be a pleasant atmosphere of quiet which is now missing.

Take as another slight point of criticism the chairman's speech, introducing the speaker. There I do think a decided improvement could be made by cutting out the chairman's remarks altogether. They are misleading. He doesn't state things as they are. He always says:

"Today we are to have a rare treat in listening to Mr. Nut. I need not offer any introduction to this audience for a man like Mr. Nut. When we learned that Mr. Nut was to address us, we felt that the club was fortunate indeed."

Now if the man told the truth what he would say would be this:

"Gentlemen, I am sorry to announce that the only speaker we have been able to secure for today is this poor simp who is sitting beside me, Mr. Nut. You never heard of him before, gentlemen, but then neither did your committee. But we have hunted everywhere for a speaker, and we simply can't get any except this guy that you see here. He is going to talk to you on 'Our Trade Relations with Nicaragua.'

"I am well aware, gentlemen, that this subject seems utterly without interest. But it appears to be the only subject about which this poor shrimp knows anything. So I won't say any more—I'll let you judge for yourselves what you are going to get. Mr. Nut."

Then, of course, there is the vital question of whether, after all, a luncheon club needs to listen to speeches. Could it not perhaps fulfill its functions just as well if there was no address at all? The trouble is that one never gets time to study up the question beforehand and the recollection that is carried away by what the speaker said is too vague to be of any use.

I will give as an example my own recollection, as far as it goes, of the address that we had at our club last week, to which I have just referred, on the subject of our "Trade Relations with Nicaragua."

Let me say at the start that I am not quite clear whether it was Nicaragua or Nigeria. The chairman seemed to say Nicaragua, but I understood the speaker once or twice to say Nigeria.

I tried to find out afterwards from other members of the club whether it was Nigeria or Nicaragua. But they didn't seem to care. They hear so many people lecture on so many queer places that it runs off them like water. Only a few meetings before they had heard a man talk on "Six Weeks in Bangkok," and right after that another man on "Seven Weeks in Pongo Pongo" and the very next week after that the address was called "Eight Weeks in Itchi-Itchi."

But let it go at Nicaragua, because it is really just about the same. Before the speaker began to say anything about Nicaragua itself, or Nigeria itself as the case may be, he went through a sort of introduction. All the speakers seem to go over about the same ground in beginning. I tried to write this particular introduction down from memory but I am not sure that I have it correctly. It seemed to run as follows:

"I feel very much honored in being asked to address this club. It is an honor to address this club. And I feel that addressing this club is an honor. When I was invited to address this club I tried to think what I could address this club about. In fact I felt very much like the old darky. This old darky—" Here follows the story of an old darky, which has been told to our club already by six explorers, seven professors, and two clergymen.

It will just about stand repeating in print, but not quite. We always know that when the speaker looks round and says, "There was an old darky—" we are going to get it again. Some of the members can still laugh at it.

But even leaving out the introduction, there are other troubles. The addresses are, no doubt, full of information. But you can't get it. There's too much of it. You can't hold it. Here is what I got, listening as hard as I could, from the address of which I am speaking.

"Probably very few of us realize what a vast country Nicaragua, or Nigeria, is. It extends from latitude (I didn't catch it) to latitude—I'm not quite sure, and it contains a quarter of a million or half a billion square miles. The principal product is either logwood or dogwood—it may have been deadwood. Sugar either grows excellently or doesn't grow at all—I didn't quite catch which.

"The inhabitants are either the mildest or the wildest race known on the globe. They are polygamous and sell their wives freely to travelers for a few glass beads (we all heard that as plainly as anything). The whole of the interior of Nigeria or Nicaragua is dense mud. All that Nicaragua or Nigeria needs is richer soil, a better climate, a decent population, money, civilization, women, and enterprise."

So upon the whole, I am much inclined to doubt whether the speeches are worth while. It is so hard to carry away anything.

And anyway, having speeches means getting too big a crowd. A hundred men is too many. A group of fifty would be far better.

As a matter of fact, a more compact luncheon of, say, twenty would be better still. Twenty men around a table can all converse, they can feel themselves in actual personal contact with one another. With twenty men, or say, fifteen men, you feel you are among a group of friends. In fact, I am not sure but what ten, or eight, would be a cosier crowd still.

You get eight or six men together and you can really exchange ideas. You get a real mental friction with six men that you can't get with a large number. And moreover with six, or four, men sitting down like this day after day you get to know one another and in point of service and comfort there is no comparison.

You can have a luncheon served for four, or three, men that is really worth eating. As a matter of fact, if it comes to that, two is a better number still.

Indeed the more I think of it the better I like two—myself and a darned good waiter.

The Children's Column

As Brought Up to Date

I suppose that everybody who reads the newspapers is aware of the change that is coming over the thing called the Children's Column, or the Children's Corner, or the Children's Page. Forty years ago it was made up of such things as letters to little boys about how to keep white mice, and letters to little girls about making crochet work in six stitches. But now, what with the radio and progress and the general rapid movement of the age, it is quite different. Here are some samples that are meant to illustrate the change.

Anno Domini 1880

Letter to little Willie Weakhead telling him how to make a Rabbit Hutch.

DEAR WILLIE:
So you want to know how to make a rabbit hutch for your white rabbit? Well, it is not very difficult if you will follow the directions carefully. Get from the nearest joiner a large empty box and some boards about 4 inches wide. (You know what an inch is, do you not?) Then lay the boards across the open side of the box with a space of about two inches between

each and nail them in this position. Good nails can be bought in any drugstore but see that you are given ones with good points on them.

If you find it hard to nail on the boards, get your father or your uncle to help you. Be careful in using the hammer not to hit yourself on the thumb, as a blow with a hammer on the thumb is painful and is often followed by a blow on the fingers. Remember, if it starts to rain while you are working on your hutch, come in out of the wet.

Let us know how you get on and whether your bunnies like their new home.

Your's etc.
UNCLE TOBY (Editor:
Children's Column)

But contrast with this the modern thing which in these days of radio and modern science has taken the place of the rabbit hutch correspondence.

Anno Domini 1926

Letter from the Editor to little Willie Wisebean, grandson of the above, in regard to the difficulties which he is finding with his radio apparatus.

DEAR WILLIE:
You write that the other night in attempting to call up Arizona KQW on your radio, you found an inordinate amount of static on your antennae. We quite agree with you that the trouble was perhaps due to purely atmospheric conditions causing a fall in the potential. You can easily find out if this is the case by calculating the differential wave length shown by your variometer.

As you rightly say your apparatus may have been put out of order by your allowing your father and your grandfather into your workshop. If you are wise you will keep them out. As you say yourself, they are too old to learn and they may meet some injury in handling your machine. You say that your grandfather used to be very fond of carpentry and once made a rabbit hutch. Why not let him set to work now and make a rabbit hutch to put your father in?

By the way, if it turns out that your trouble is in your magnetic coils, we advise you not to try to remedy them but to buy new ones. You can get excellent coils from Messrs. Grabb and Gettit, for $100 a coil, or even more. On this your father might come in useful. With thanks for your interesting letter,

PROFESSOR I. KNOWIT, Ph.D.
T.K., D.F.
Oxon, Harvard, Oklahoma.

Or let us turn to another part of the same field—the feminine side. The change is even more striking. Compare the two following letters to the Lady Editor, making enquiries in each case about the way to arrange a children's party for little girls.

Anno Domini 1880

Letter to Dollie Dollhouse, aged 14, who has asked for advice about a party.

DEAR DOLLIE:
I am so glad to hear that you are going to give a party to your little girl friends for your fourteenth birthday. Of course you must have strawberries, great big luscious ones with lots of cream all over them. And of course you must have a lovely big cake, with icing all over the top of it, and you must put fourteen candles on it. Do you see the idea of the candles, dear? No, perhaps not at first, but if you will think a minute you will see it. It means that you are fourteen years old and that there is a candle

for every year. Isn't it a pretty thought, once you understand it? I got it out of an old Norwegian book of fairy stories and thought it so sweet.

You had better not try to light the candles yourself, but get your papa or your mama to come and do it, if they do not like to, then send for a man from the hardware store.

You say that after all the girls have eaten all they can you would like to have some games and ask what you can play. There are really such a lot of games that it is hard to advise, but among the best of the new games is one called *Hunt the Slipper*, which I am sure you would like. All that you need for playing it with is an old slipper, one without any tacks sticking out of it being the best. One of the girls sits on the slipper and then the player who is chosen to begin has to go round and roll over all the girls and see where the slipper is. You see it is quite a clever game and can easily be learned in half an hour. But remember that your play must never be rough. In rolling over the girls pick them up by the feet and roll them over in a ladylike way.

After the game if you can get your papa to come into the room and read a selection of poetry, such as a couple of cantos from *Paradise Lost*, the girls will go away delighted.

With best love and good
wishes for your party,
AUNT AGATHA
Lady Editor Children's
Column.

Here is the other sample which is the same thing, brought up to date.

Anno Domini 1926

Letter to Flossie Fitz Clippit, aged 14, granddaughter of Dollie Dollhouse, in answer to her request for advice about a party.

DEAR FLOSSIE:
The right number of covers for a luncheon to your girl friends is certainly eight. Ten, as you yourself seem to think, is too large a number to be cosy, while eight gives exactly the feeling of *camaraderie* without too much formality. Six, on the other hand, is a little too *intime*, while seven rather carries the idea of oddity, of something a little *louche*, or at least *gauche*, if not *hootch*.

For table decorations I find it hard to advise you, as I do not know the tinting of your room, nor the draperies or the shape and shade of your table and the complexion of your butler. But if not unsuitable for some special reason what do you say to great bunches of scarlet ilex thrown all over the table? Either that or large masses of wisteria and big bunches of Timothy hay?

I don't think that if I were you I would serve cocktails before lunch, as some of your friends might have views about it, but a delicious *coupe* can be made by mixing half a bottle of old rum with shredded wheat and then soaking it in gin.

For the menu, you will want something light and dainty, appealing rather by its exquisite taste than by sheer quantity. What do you say to beginning with a *canapé* of *paté de fois gras*, followed by a *puré* of mushrooms and leading up to a broiled lobster followed by a porterhouse beefsteak. I think that is the kind of thing your little friends would like. And if you have after it a *soufflé*, and a few quarts of ice cream with angel cake it will be found quite enough.

I quite sympathize with what you say about not wanting your mother. There is no doubt that the presence of a mother at any kind of entertainment gives a touch of coldness, a lack of affection. Your father, of course, is quite impossible; though I think it would be all right to let him shake hands with the girls as they pass out. At a recent luncheon where I was present I saw both the father and the mother brought into the drawing room for a few moments and introduced to the guests. The effect was really very sweet, with quite an old world touch to it. But I would not try to imitate it if I were you. Better be content with having the butler take up half a gallon of the *coupe* to your father in his library.

You will of course want to know about cigarettes. I should particularly recommend the new Egyptian *Dingos*, or, if you have not yet tried them, the new Peruvian *Guanos*. They seem to be the last word in tobacco.

With regards and good
wishes,
Man-Lady Editor
Children's Adult Column.

Old Proverbs Made New

It has occurred to me that somebody in one of the English departments of our colleges ought to get busy and re-write our national proverbs. They are all out of date. They don't fit any longer. Indeed, many of them are precisely the converse of existing facts.

Our proverbs have come down to us from the days of long ago; days when the world was very primitive and very simple and very different; when people never moved more than a mile and a half from home and were all afraid of the dark; and when wisdom was handed out by old men with white whiskers called *prophets*, every one of whom would be "retired" nowadays by any first class board of trustees as past the age-limit of common sense.

But in those days all the things that were said by these wise old men, who had never seen a motor car, were gathered up and called proverbs and repeated by all the common people as the last words of wisdom. The result is that even today we still go on repeating them, without realizing how hopelessly they are off the track.

Take as a first sample the proverb that is perhaps the best known in our language:

Birds of a Feather Flock Together

But they don't. Ask any first class naturalist. If the wise old men had taken another look they would have seen that the last thing birds ever want to do is to flock together. In ninety-nine cases out of a hundred they keep away from their own species, and only flock when it is absolutely necessary. So much for the birds. But the proverb is really supposed to refer to people and then it is wrong again. People "of a feather" do not flock together. Tall men fall in love with little women. A girl with a beautiful fair skin and red hair marries a man who looks like a reformed orang-outang. A clergyman makes a friend of an auctioneer and a banker would rather spend a day with an Adirondack fishing guide than with a whole vaultful of bankers. Burglars during the daytime go and swim in the Y.M.C.A. pool. Forgers in their off time sing in the choir, and choir-masters when they are not singing shoot craps.

In short, there is nothing in the proverb whatsoever. It ought to be revised under the modern conditions to read:

Birds of any particular feather and persons of any particular character or occupation show upon the whole a disposition rather to seek out something dissimilar to their own appearance and nature to consort with something homologous to their own essential entity.

In that shape one has a neat workable proverb. Try another:

A Rolling Stone Gathers No Moss

Entirely wrong again. This was supposed to show that a young man who wandered from home never got on in the world. In very ancient days it was true. The young man who stayed at home and worked hard and tilled the ground and goaded oxen with a long stick like a lance found himself as he grew old a man of property, owning four goats and a sow. The son who wandered forth in the world was either killed by the cannibals or crawled home years afterwards doubled up with rheumatism. So the old men made the proverb. But nowadays it is exactly wrong. It is the rolling stone that gathers the moss. It is the ambitious boy from Honkville, Indiana, who trudges off to the city leaving his elder brother in the barnyard and who later makes a fortune and founds a university. While his elder brother still has only the old farm with three cows and a couple of pigs, he has a whole department of agriculture with great sheds-full of Tamworth hogs and a professor to every six of them.

In short, in modern life it is the rolling stone that gathers the moss. And the geologists—outside of Tennessee—say that the moss on the actual stone was first started in exactly the same way. It was the rolling of the stone that smashed up the earth and made the moss grow.

Take another proverb:

All Is Not Gold That Glitters

How perfectly ridiculous! Everybody in the days in which we live knows—even a child knows—that all *is* gold that glitters. Put on clothes enough, appearance enough and you will be accepted anywhere. Just do a little glittering and everybody will think you are gold. Make a show, be a humbug, and you will succeed so fast that presently, being very wealthy and prominent, you will really think yourself a person of great merit and intellect. In other words, the glitter makes the gold. That is all there *is* to it. Gold is really one of the most useless of all material objects. Even now we have found no *real* use for it, except to fill our teeth. Any other employment of it is just *glitter*. So the proverb might be revised to read:

Every thing or person may be said to stand in high esteem and to pass at a high value provided that it or he makes a sufficient show, glitter, or appearance, the estimation being in inverse ratio to the true quantitative measurement of the reality of it, them or her. That makes a neat workable proverb, expressed with up-to-date accuracy.

Or here is another famous proverb that is exactly the contrary of truth:

People Who Live in Glass Houses Ought Not to Throw Stones

Not at all. *They are the very people who ought to throw stones and to keep on throwing them all the time. They ought to keep up such a fusillade of stones from their glass house that no one can get near it.*

Or if the proverb is taken to mean that people who have faults of their own ought not to talk of other people's faults, it is equally mistaken. They ought to talk of other people's faults all the time so as to keep attention away from their own.

But the list of proverbs is so long that it is impossible to do more than make a casual mention of a few others.

One Swallow Does Not Make a Summer

Perhaps not. But there are ever so many occasions when one swallow—just one single swallow—is better than nothing to drink at all. And if you get enough of them they *do* make a summer.

Charity Begins at Home

Perfectly ridiculous. Watch any modern city householder when a beggar comes to his door. *Charity begins with the Federated Charities Office, or with the Out of Work Mission, or with the City Hall, or if need be, with the*

Police Court—in short, anywhere *but at home. Our whole effort is now to keep charity as far from home as possible.*

It Is a Wise Child That Knows Its Own Father

Not at all. Alter this and make it read: *It is a very silly boy who isn't on to his old man.*

Even a Worm Will Turn At Last

Wrong. *It turns at once, immediately. It never waits.*

A Bird in the Hand Is Worth Two in the Bush

Yes, but a bird in a good restaurant is worth ten of either of them.

There—that's enough. Any reader of this book may go on having fun with the other proverbs. I give them to him.

IV

In the Good Old Summertime

The Merry Month of May

As Treated in the Bye-Gone Almanacs

The part of the year known in ballad poetry as the Good Old Summer Time begins with what is popularly called the Merry Month of May. The winter is then over except in the City of Quebec, in Butte, Montana, and in the Back Bay regions of Boston. The gathering warmth of the sun calls all nature to life.

The Heavens in May

In the older almanacs of the kind that used to be made for farmers, the first items under this month always dealt with the aspect of the heavens. The farmer was told that in May the sun, passing out of the sign of Taurus, moved into the constellation of Gemini; that the apparent declination of the sun was 15 degrees and 4 minutes and that the neap tides fell on the thirteenth and twenty-seventh of the month. He was also informed that Mars and Mercury during May are both in opposition and that Sirius is the dog star.

In the city this information is now useless. Nobody can see the heavens even if he wants to; the open space between the skyscrapers formerly called the sky is now filled with electric lights, pictures of motor wheels turning round, and men eating breakfast food with a moving spoon.

We doubt also if the up-to-date farmer is really concerned with the Zodiac. We will therefore only say that in this month if the farmer will on any clear night ascend to the cupola of his pergola with his binoculars and with his radio plug in his ears and his insulators on his feet and view the heavens from midnight till three in the morning, he will run a first class chance of getting pneumonia.

The Garden in May

For those to whom gardening—even in the limited restrictions of a city back yard—is a hobby and a passion, the month of May is the most enticing month of the year. It seems strange to think that so many men with a back yard at their disposal—a back yard let us say, twenty feet by fifteen—should nevertheless spend the long evenings and the Saturday afternoons of the month of May striding up and down the golf links or wandering along a trout stream. How much better to be out in the back yard with a spade and hoe, pickaxe and sledge hammer and a little dynamite preparing the exuberant soil for the luxuriant crop.

In the amateur garden in the back yard no great technical knowledge is needed. Our citizen gardener who wishes to begin should go out into his back yard and having stripped himself to his waist, all but his undershirt, should proceed first to dig out his ground.

He must excavate a hole ten by fifteen, by ten by two; of course, the hole won't be as big as that, but it will *seem* to be. He must carefully remove on his back all large boulders, volcanic rocks, and other accumulated debris. These if he likes he may fashion tastefully into a rockery or a rookery, or also, if he likes, he may throw them over the fence into his neighbor's back yard. He must then proceed to fill the hole half full of sweet-smelling fertilizer.

This will almost complete his first evening's work. In fact, he will be just about filling in his stuff when the other men, come past on their way home from golf. He will then finish his task by putting back a fourth of the soil, which he will carefully pulverize by laying down and rolling in it. After this he can then take a bath (or two baths) and go to bed.

The ground thus carefully prepared, the amateur gardener should wait a day or so and then, proceeding to his back yard, should draw on his overalls up to his neck and proceed to plant his bulbs and seeds.

The tulip is a favorite flower for early planting owing to its fine raucous appearance. Excellent tulip bulbs may be had of any florist for one dollar, which with proper care will turn into a flower worth thirty cents. The dahlia, the most handsome of the ganglions, almost repays cultivation, presenting a splendid carboniferous appearance with unsurpassed efflorescence. The potato is not bad, either.

When the garden plot is all filled up with buried bulbs and seeds, the gardener should roll the dirt down flat, by rolling it, and then for the rest of the month of May, sit and look at it.

A Cool Drink for May

The month of May is the time of year when dandelion wine, owing to the presence of dandelions, is perhaps easier to make than at any other time. An excellent recipe is as follows:

1. Pluck, or pick, a small basketful of dandelion heads.
2. Add to them a quart of water and leave the mixture to stand for five minutes.
3. Pour off the water, remove the dandelions, and add as flavoring a quart of 1872 champagne.
4. Drink it.

The Countryside in May

It is in the month of May that the countryside, for the true lover of nature, is at its best. For one who knows by name and can distinguish and classify the flora of the lanes and fields, a country walk among the opening buds is a scene of unalloyed joy. The tiny hibiscus is seen peeping out from under the grass while everywhere in the spring air is the sweet scent of the ornithorhyncus and the megalotherium. One should watch in this month for the first shoots of the spiggot, while the trained eye will easily distinguish the lambswart, the dogsfoot, and the cowslip.

Nor are the birds, for anyone who knows the names, less interesting than the flowers. The corvex americanus is building its nest in the tall timber. The sharp whistling notes of the ilex and the pulex and the index are heard in the meadows, while the marshes are loud with the song of the ranunculus. But of course for those who do not know these names nothing is happening except that a lot of birds are singing and the grass is growing. That, of course, is quite worthless and uninteresting.

Great Events in May

May 1. Birth of Shakespeare.
May 5. End of the Trojan war.
May 10. Beginning of the Trojan war.
May 15. Birth of Shakespeare.
May 20. Shakespeare born.
May 25. Trojan war ends again.
May 30. Death of Shakespeare and beginning of the Trojan war.

How We Kept Mother's Birthday

As Related by a Member of the Family

Of all the different ideas that have been started lately, I think that the very best is the notion of celebrating once a year "Mother's Day." I don't wonder that May the eleventh is becoming such a popular date all over America and I am sure the idea will spread to England too.

It is especially in a big family like ours that such an idea takes hold. So we decided to have a special celebration of Mother's Day. We thought it a fine idea. It made us all realize how much Mother had done for us for years, and all the efforts and sacrifice that she had made for our sake.

So we decided that we'd make it a great day, a holiday for all the family, and do everything we could to make Mother happy. Father decided to take a holiday from his office, so as to help in celebrating the day, and my sister Anne and I stayed home from college classes, and Mary and my brother Will stayed home from High School.

It was our plan to make it a day just like Xmas or any big holiday, and so we decided to decorate the house with flowers and with mottoes over the mantelpieces, and all that kind of thing. We got Mother to make mottoes and arrange the decorations, because she always does it at Xmas.

The two girls thought it would be a nice thing to dress in our very best for such a big occasion, and so they both got new hats. Mother trimmed both the hats, and they looked fine, and Father had bought four-in-hand silk ties for himself and us boys as a souvenir of the day to remember Mother by. We were going to get Mother a new hat too, but it turned out that she seemed to really like her old grey bonnet better than a new one, and both the girls said that it was awfully becoming to her.

Well, after breakfast we had it arranged as a surprise for Mother that we would hire a motor car and take her for a beautiful drive away into the country. Mother is hardly ever able to have a treat like that, because we can only afford to keep one maid, and so Mother is busy in the house nearly all the time. And of course the country is so lovely now that it would be just grand for her to have a lovely morning, driving for miles and miles.

But on the very morning of the day we changed the plan a little bit, because it occurred to Father that a thing it would be better to do even than to take Mother for a motor drive would be to take her fishing. Father said that as the car was hired and paid for, we might just as well use it for a drive up into hills where the streams are. As Father said, if you just go out driving without any object, you have a sense of aimlessness, if you are going to fish, there is a definite purpose in front of you to heighten the enjoyment.

So we all felt it would be nicer for Mother to have a definite purpose; and anyway, it turned out that Father had just got a new rod the day before, which made the idea of fishing all the more appropriate, and he said that Mother could use it if she wanted to; in fact, he said it was practically for her, only Mother said she would much rather watch him fish and not to try to fish herself.

So we got everything arranged for the trip, and we got Mother to cut up some sandwiches and make a sort of lunch in case we got hungry, though of course we were to come back home again to a big dinner in the middle of the day, just like Xmas or New Year's Day. Mother packed it all up in a basket for us ready to go in the motor.

Well, when the car came to the door, it turned out that there hardly seemed as much room in it as we had supposed, because we hadn't reckoned on Father's fishing basket and the rods and the lunch, and it was plain enough that we couldn't all get in.

Father said not to mind him, he said that he could just as well stay at home, and that he was sure that he could put in the time working in the garden; he said that there was a lot of rough dirty work that he could do, like digging a trench for the garbage, that would save hiring a man, and so he said he'd stay home; he said that we were not to let the fact of his not having had a real holiday for three years stand in our way; he wanted us to go right ahead and be happy and have a big day, and not to mind him. He said that he could plug away all day, and in fact he said he'd been a fool to think there'd be any holiday for him.

But of course we all felt that it would never do to let Father stay home, especially as we knew he would make trouble if he did. The two girls Anna and Mary, would gladly have stayed and helped the maid get dinner, only it seemed such a pity to, on a lovely day like this, having their new hats. But they both said that Mother had only to say the word, and they'd gladly stay home and work. Will and I would have dropped out, but unfortunately we wouldn't have been any use in getting the dinner.

So in the end it was decided that Mother would stay home and just have a lovely restful day round the house, and get the dinner. It turned out anyway that Mother doesn't care for fishing, and also it was just a little bit cold and fresh out of doors, though it was lovely and sunny, and Father was rather afraid that Mother might take cold if she came.

He said he would never forgive himself if he dragged Mother round the country and let her take a severe cold at a time when she might be having a beautiful rest. He said it was our duty to try and let Mother get all the rest and quiet that she could, after all that she had done for all of us, and he said that that was principally why he had fallen in with this idea of a fishing trip, so as to give Mother a little quiet. He said that young people seldom realize how much quiet means, to people who are getting old. As to himself, he could still stand the racket, but he was glad to shelter Mother from it.

So we all drove away with three cheers for Mother, and Mother stood and watched us from the verandah for as long as she could see us, and Father waved his hand back to her every few minutes till he hit his hand on the back edge of the car, and then said that he didn't think that Mother could see us any longer.

Well—we had the loveliest day up among the hills that you could possibly imagine, and Father caught such big specimens that he felt sure that Mother couldn't have landed them anyway, if she had been fishing for them, and Will and I fished too, though we didn't get so many as Father, and the two girls met quite a lot of people that they knew as we drove along, and there were some young men friends of theirs that they met along the stream and talked to, and so we all had a splendid time.

It was quite late when we got back, nearly seven o'clock in the evening, but Mother had guessed that we would be late, so she had kept back the dinner so as to have it just nicely ready and hot for us. Only first she had to get towels and soap for Father and clean things for him to put on, because he always gets so messed up with fishing, and that kept Mother busy for a little while, that and helping the girls get ready.

But at last everything was ready, and we sat down to the grandest kind of dinner—roast turkey and all sorts of things like on Xmas Day. Mother had to get up and down a good bit during the meal fetching things back and forward, but at the end Father noticed it and said she simply mustn't do it, that he wanted her to spare herself, and he got up and fetched the walnuts over from the sideboard himself.

The dinner lasted a long while, and was great fun, and when it was over all of us wanted to help clear the things up and wash the dishes, only Mother said that she would really much rather do it, and so we let her, because we wanted just for once to humor her.

It was quite late when it was all over, and when we all kissed Mother before going to bed, she said it had been the most wonderful day in her life, and I think there were tears in her eyes. So we all felt awfully repaid for all that we had done.

Summer Sorrows of the Super-rich

In the course of each summer it is my privilege to do some visiting in the class of the super-rich. By this I mean the class of people who have huge estates at such fashionable places as Nagahucket, and Dogblastit, and up near Lake Owatawetness, where the country is so beautifully wild that it costs a thousand dollars an acre.

Even people who had never had the opportunity of moving about way up in this class know more or less the sort of establishment I mean. When you visit one of these houses you always pass a "lodge" with a bright bed of flowers in front of it, which is a sign that the house itself is now only three miles away.

Later on the symptoms begin to multiply. You see a log cabin summer-house made to imitate a settler's home and built out of cedar imported from the Fiji Islands. Then presently there is a dear little waterfall and a dam of great slabs of rock, built for only a hundred and fifty thousand dollars and supplying electric light worth forty cents an evening.

After that you pass Scotch gardeners planting out little fir trees and go through a zone of woodsmen cutting birch billets for open fires, and chauffeurs, resting, and there you are all of a sudden in front of Dogblastit House, standing beside its own lake, with its own mountains and ten thousand acres of the finest natural woods ever staged by land-scape gardeners.

Now would you think that the people who live in these great places are happy? They are not. They have troubles of which you and I and the ordinary people never dream. They come out of the wilderness to rough it, and to snatch a brief four months' vacation between the strain of the Riviera and the pressure of New York, and then right in the happiest season of the summer, they come up against desperate problems.

The particular ones that follow were related to me at Dogblastit. But I gather that the same difficulties are met in all establishments of the sort. They are discussed in all the conversation among hosts and guests, just as we discussed them last summer around the birch fires in the lounge at Dogblastit.

Problem No. 1:

What to do to amuse the butler in the evening? It seems that he doesn't play bridge. The butler who was here last year was always quite content if he could be provided with a game of bridge, and except for a run to New York now and then and a trip to see his brother in Vancouver in the middle of the summer, he stayed on the place without a break and seemed quite satisfied.

But the new man Jennings doesn't care for cards. He says quite frankly that it is not a matter of conscience and that he doesn't mind cards in the house, but they simply don't interest him. So what can one do?

Problem No. 2:

How to get the chauffeur's collars starched? It appears that there have been very great difficulties at Dogblastit about this. It is very hard to get the kind of gloss that Ransome likes on his collars. There is, of course, an electric laundry in the basement of Dogblastit itself, but unfortunately the laundry maids who do all the work in it will not undertake any collars over eleven inches long. They say they simply won't undertake them.

The experiment was made of bringing up a laundress from Boston, but it was found that she wouldn't undertake to starch anything at such a high altitude. She can only do her work at from 500 to 800 feet above sea level. Beyond that, she said, she could do nothing.

They tried also sending Ransome's collars by express to New York, but this was quite unsatisfactory, because the express people threw them about so roughly. More than once they were seen actually throwing the packet of Ransome's collars right from the platform of Dogblastit station into the express car. The only feasible thing up to now has been to have Ransome take one of the cars and drive his collars either to New York or to Philadelphia. The objection is that it takes up so much of his time, especially as he always likes to drive his boots over to Burlington, Vermont, once a week, where he can get them properly treated.

Problem No. 3:

What to get for the cook to read on Sunday? The trouble is, she doesn't care for fiction. She evidently is a woman of literary culture, because she said one day that she had read the whole of Shakespeare and thought it very good. In the library of Dogblastit itself, which is a really beautiful room done in Japanese oak with leaded windows to represent the reading room of a settler's cabin, there are practically no books that suit the cook. In fact, there is nothing but the Blue Book (one needs that to look up people in) and the Pink Book and the Red Book, and of course the Automobile Road Book and then some Guide Books such as *The Perfect Bartender*, and the *Gentleman's Cellar* and *Cocktails for all Occasions.*

Beyond that there are, of course, all the new books—the new fiction—because there is a standing order with Spentano to send up fifty pounds of new fiction by express once a week. None of the guests of the house ever care to read any book more than three weeks old, as they are quite worthless for conversation.

An order was sent to Boston for the Harvard Classics but the cook says she doesn't care for the way they are selected. The only compromise so far is to get her books about the South Seas. She says she is just crazy over the South Sea literature. So we have given her *Six Weeks in the Marquesas Islands* and *Four Days in Fiji, Half Hours in Hoo-Poo.* But all that will only last her less than seven weeks, and after that we don't know what to do.

Problem No. 4:

What to do with the governess when she is not working? This has proved up to the present a quite insoluble problem. It is so hard to know just what to do with Mademoiselle after she has finished governing the children. We can't, so it is felt, have her in the drawing room and yet what can one do with her? We have tried shutting her up in the garage, but that is dull. In open weather we can lock her out on the piazza, but she is apt to get from there into the billiard room where the guests are. The only plan seems to be to give her somewhere a cosy, little wee room for herself, either at the back of the ash-house, or else underneath the laundry.

The problems I have named are the principal ones—the ones that always recur in any large house of real class and standing. But there are a lot of others as well that I need not treat in detail. For example, there is the difficult question of how to keep Robert, the under-gardener, out of the kitchen. Robert would never have been engaged if it had been known that he was a dangerous man. But this was only reported by the housekeeper after Robert had been brought up and had been in the house a week. When you bring a man up you can't bring him down.

And who is it that is stealing all the jewelry? We don't like to make any fuss or disturbance. But another diamond ring went last night and one feels that something ought to be done.

My visits with my fashionable friends have been so much disturbed by perpetual conversation on these problems that I have decided to give them up altogether and to get back into my own class of society. I have some friends, real ones, who have a wooden house on an island where there is no electric light within twenty miles and where they use rain-water out of a barrel.

They have coal-oil lanterns to see by; they wear flannel collars and they pass the soap from one room to another as it is needed. The men cut the firewood, as required, and never keep more than half an hour's supply on hand, and the girls do all the work because help can't be got and they know ten different ways of cooking canned salmon.

I am going back there. For me that is the only real old summer stuff that is worth while. I was brought up on it and have never grown out of it. Anybody who likes may have my room and my tiled bath at Dogblastit.

How My Wife and I Built Our Home for $4.90

Related in the Manner of the Best Models in the Magazines

I was leaning up against the mantelpiece in a lounge suit which I had made out of old ice bags, and Beryl, my wife, was seated at my feet on a low Louis Quinze tabouret which she had made out of a Finnan Haddie fishbox, when the idea of a bungalow came to both of us at the same time.

"It would be just lovely if we could do it!" exclaimed Beryl, coiling herself around my knee.

"Why not!" I replied, lifting her up a little by the ear. "With your exquisite taste—"

"And with your knowledge of material," added Beryl, giving me a tiny pinch on the leg—"Oh, I am sure we could do it! One reads so much in all the magazines about people making summer bungalows and furnishing them for next to nothing. Oh, do let us try, Dogyard!"

We talked over our project all night, and the next morning we sallied forth to try to find a site for our new home. As Beryl (who was brimming over with fun as the result of talking all night) put it, "The first thing is to get the ground."

Here fortune favored us. We had hardly got to the edge of the town when Beryl suddenly exclaimed, "Oh look, Dogyard, look, there's exactly the site!" It was a piece of wasteland on the edge of a gully with a brickyard on one side of it and a gravel pit on the other. It had no trees on it, and it was covered with ragged heaps of tin cans, old newspapers, and stones, and a litter of broken lumber.

Beryl's quick eye saw the possibilities of the situation at once. "Oh, Dogyard!" she exclaimed, "isn't it just sweet? We can clear away all this litter and plant a catalpa tree to hide the brickyard and a hedge of copernicus or nux vomica to hide the gravel pit, and some bright flowers to hide the hedge. I wish I had brought some catalpa seed. They grow so quickly."

"We'd better at least wait," I said, "till we have bought the ground."

And here a sudden piece of good fortune awaited us. It so happened that the owner of the lot was on the spot at the time—he was seated on a stone whittling a stick while we were talking, and presented himself to us. After a short discussion he agreed to sell us the ground for one dollar in cash and fifty cents on a three years' mortgage. The deed of sale was written out on the spot and stamped with a two-cent stamp, and the owner of the lot took his departure with every expression of good will. And the magic sense of being owners of our own ground rendered us both jubilant.

That evening Beryl, seated on her little stool at my feet, took a pencil and paper and set down triumphantly a statement of the cost of our bungalow up to date. I introduce it here as a help to readers who may hope to follow in our footsteps:

Ground site	$1.50
Stamp for mortgage	.02
Car fare	.10
Total	$1.62

I checked over Beryl's arithmetic twice and found it strictly correct.

Next morning we commenced work in earnest. While Beryl cleared away the cans and litter, I set to work with spade and shovel excavating our cellar and digging out the foundations. And here I must admit that I had no light task. I can only warn those who wish to follow in our footsteps that they must be prepared to face hard work.

Owing perhaps to my inexperience, it took me the whole of the morning to dig out a cellar forty feet long and twenty feet wide. Beryl, who had meantime cleaned up the lot, stacked the lumber, lifted away the stones and planted fifty yards of hedge, was inclined to be a little impatient. But I reminded her that a contractor working with a gang of men and two or three teams of horses would have taken a whole week to do what I did in one morning.

I admitted that my work was not equal to the best records as related in the weekly home journals, where I have often computed that they move 100,000 cubic feet of earth in one paragraph, but at least I was doing my best. Beryl, whose disappointment never lasts, was all smiles again in a moment, and rewarded me by throwing herself around my neck and giving me a hug.

That afternoon I gathered up all the big stones and built them into walls around the cellar with partition walls across it, dividing it into rooms and compartments. I leveled the floor and packed it tight with sand and gravel and dug a drain ten feet deep from the cellar to the gully about thirty feet away.

There being still a good hour or so of daylight left, I dug a cistern four feet wide and twenty feet deep. I was looking round for something more to dig by moonlight, but Beryl put her foot down (on my head while I was in the drain) and forbade me to work any more for fear I might be fatigued.

Next morning we were able to begin our building in good earnest. On our way we stopped at the fifteen-cent store for necessary supplies, and bought one hammer, fifteen cents; a saw, fifteen cents; half a gallon of nails, fifteen cents; a crane, fifteen cents; a derrick for hoisting, fifteen cents; and a needle and thread, for sewing on the roof, fifteen cents.

As an advice to young builders, I may say that I doubt if we were quite wise in all our purchases. The fifteen-cent derrick is too light for the work, and the extra expenditure for the heavier kind (the twenty-five-cent crane) would have been justified. The difference in cost is only approximately) ten cents, and the efficiency of the big crane is far greater.

On arriving at our ground we were delighted to find that our masonry was well set and the walls firm and solid, while the catalpa trees were well above the ground and growing rapidly. We set to work at once to build in earnest.

We had already decided to utilize for our bungalow the waste material which lay on our lot. I drew Beryl's attention to the fact that if a proper use were made of the material wasted in building there would be no need to buy any material at all. "The elimination of waste," I explained, "by the utilization of all by-products before they have time to go by, is the central principle of modern industrial organization."

But observing that Beryl had ceased to listen to me, I drew on my carpenter's apron which I had made out of a piece of tar-paper, and set to work. My first care was to gather up all the loose lumber that lay upon and around our ground site, and saw it up into neatly squared pieces about twenty feet long. Out of these I made the joints, the studding, the partitions, rafters, and so on, which formed the frame of the house.

Putting up the house took practically the whole morning. Beryl, who had slipped on a potato bag over her dress, assisted me by holding up the side of the house while I nailed on the top.

By the end of the afternoon we had completed the sides of our house, which we made out of old newspaper soaked in glue and rolled flat. The next day we put on the roof, which was made of tin cans cut open and pounded flat.

For our hardwood floors, mantels, etc., we were fortunate in finding a pile of hardwood on a neighboring lot which had apparently been overlooked, and which we carried over proudly to our bungalow after dark. That same night we carried over jubilantly some rustic furniture which we had found, quite neglected, lying in a nearby cottage, the lock of which oddly enough, was opened quite easily with the key of Beryl's suitcase.

The rest of our furniture—plain tables, dressers, etc.—I was able to make from ordinary pine lumber which I obtained by knocking down a board fence upon an adjacent lot. In short, the reader is able to picture our bungalow after a week of labor, complete in every respect and only awaiting our occupation on the next day.

Seated that evening in our boarding house, with Beryl coiled around me, I calculated the entire cost of our enterprise—including ground site, lumber, derricks, cranes, glue, string, tin-tacks and other materials—as four dollars and ninety cents.

In return for it we had a pretty seven-roomed house, artistic in every respect, with living-room, bed-rooms, a boudoir, a den, a snuggery, a doggery—in short, the bungalow of which so many young people have dreamed.

Seated together that evening, Beryl and I were full of plans for the future. We both have a passionate love of animals and, like all country-bred people, a longing for the life of a farm. So we had long since decided to keep poultry. We planned to begin in a small way, and had brought home that evening from the fifteen-cent store a day-old chicken, such as are now so widely sold.

We put him in a basket beside the radiator in a little flannel coat that Beryl had made for him, and we fed him with a warm mash made of breakfast food and gravel. Our printed directions that we got with him told us that a fowl eats two ounces of grain per day and on that should lay five eggs in a week. I was easily able to prove to Beryl by a little plain arithmetic that if we fed this fellow 4 ounces a day he would lay 10 eggs in a week, or at 8 ounces per day he would lay 29 eggs in a week.

Beryl, who was seized at once with a characteristic fit of enthusiasm, suggested that we stick 16 ounces a day into him and begin right now. I had to remind her laughingly that at 8 ounces a day the fellow would probably be working up to a capacity, and carrying what we call in business his peak load. "The essential factor in modern business," I told her, "is to load yourself up to the peak and stay there."

In short, there was no end to our rosy dreams. In our fancy we saw ourselves in our bungalow, surrounded by hens, bees, cows and dogs, with hogs and goats nestling against our feet. Unfortunately our dreams were destined to be shattered. Up to this point our experience with building our bungalow had followed along after all the best models, and had even eclipsed them. But from now on we met a series of disasters of which we had had no warning. It is a pity that I cannot leave our story at this point.

On arriving at our bungalow next day we found notices posted up forbidding all trespassers, and two sour-looking men in possession. We learned that our title to the ground site was worthless, as the man from whom we had bought it had been apparently a mere passer-by. It appeared also that a neighboring contractor was making serious difficulties about our use of his material. It was divulged further that we had been mistaken in thinking that we had taken our rustic furniture from an empty cottage. There were people living in it, but they happened to be asleep when Beryl moved the furniture.

As for our hen—there is no doubt that keeping fowls is enormously profitable. It must be so, when one considers the millions of eggs consumed every day. But it demands an unremitting attention and above all—memory. If you own a hen you must never forget it—you must keep on saying to yourself—"How is my hen?" This was our trouble. Beryl and I were so preoccupied with our accumulated disaster, that we left our one-day-old chick behind the radiator and never thought of him for three weeks. He was then gone. We prefer to think he flew away.

The Everlasting Angler

The fishing season is now well under way. Will soon be with us. For lovers of fishing this remark is true all the year round. It has seemed to me that it might be of use to set down a few of the more familiar fish stories that are needed by any one wanting to qualify as an angler. There is no copyright on these stories, since Methuselah first told them, and anybody who wishes may learn them by heart and make free use of them.

I will begin with the simplest and best known. Everybody who goes fishing has heard it, and told it a thousand times. It is called:

I

The Story of the Fish That Was Lost

The circumstances under which the story is best told are these. The fisherman returns after his day's outing with his two friends whom he has taken out for the day, to his summer cottage. They carry with them their rods, their landing net and the paraphernalia of their profession. The fisherman carries also on a string a dirty looking collection of little fish, called by courtesy the "Catch." None of these little fish really measures more than about seven and a half inches long and four inches round the chest. The fisherman's wife and his wife's sister and the young lady who is staying with them come running to meet the fishing party, giving cries of admiration as they get a sight of the catch. In reality they would refuse to buy those fish from a butcher at a cent and a half a pound. But they fall into ecstasies and they cry, "Oh aren't they beauties! Look at this big one!" The "big one" is about eight inches long. It looked good when they caught it but it has been shrinking ever since and it looks now as if it had died of consumption. Then it is that the fisherman says, in a voice in which regret is mingled with animation:

"Yes, but say, you ought to have seen the one that we lost. We had hardly let down our lines—"

It may be interjected here that all fishermen ought to realize that the moment of danger is just when you let down your line. That is the moment when the fish will put up all kinds of games on you, such as rushing at you in a compact mass so fast that you can't take them in, or selecting the largest of their number to snatch away one of your rods.

"We had hardly let down our lines," says the fishermen—"when Tom got a perfect monster. That fish would have weighed five pounds—wouldn't it, Tom—"

"Easily," says Tom.

"Well, Tom started to haul him in and he yelled to Ted and me to get the landing net ready and we had him right up to the boat," "Right up to the very boat," repeat Tom and Edward sadly. "When the damn line broke and biff! away he went. Say! he must have been two feet long, easily two feet!"

"Did you see him?" asks the young lady who is staying with them. This of course she has no right to ask. It's not a fair question. Among people who go fishing it is ruled out. You may ask if a fish pulled hard, and how much it weighed but you must not ask whether anybody *saw* the fish.

"We could see where he was," says Tom.

Then they go on up to the house carrying the "string" or "catch" and all three saying at intervals—"Say! if we had only landed that big fellow!"

By the time this anecdote has ripened for winter use, the fish will have been drawn actually into the boat (thus settling all questions of seeing it) and will there have knocked Edward senseless, and then leaped over the gunwale.

II

Story of the Extraordinary Bait

This is a more advanced form of fishing story. It is told by fishermen for fishermen. It is the sort of thing they relate to one another when fishing out of a motor boat on a lake, when there has been a slight pause in their activity and when the fish for a little while—say for two hours, have stopped biting. So the fishermen talk and discuss the ways and means of their craft. Somebody says that grasshoppers make good bait: and somebody else asks whether any of them have ever tried Lake Erie soft shell crabs as bait, and then one—whoever is lucky enough to get in first—tells the good old bait story.

"The queerest bait I ever saw used," he says, shifting his pipe to the other side of his mouth, "was one day when I was fishing up in one of the lakes back in Maine. We'd got to the spot and got all ready when we suddenly discovered that we'd forgotten the bait—"

At this point any one of the listeners is entitled by custom to put in the old joke about not forgetting the whiskey—

"Well there was no use going ashore. We couldn't have got any worms. It was too early for frogs, and it was ten miles to row back home. We tried chunks of meat from our lunch, but nothing doing! Well, then, just for fun I cut a white bone button off my pants and put it on the hook. Say! you ought to have seen those fish go for it. We caught, oh, easily twenty, yes thirty—in half an hour. We only quit after we'd cut off all our buttons and our pants were falling off us! Say, hold on boys, I believe I've got a nibble! Sit steady!"

Getting a nibble of course will set up an excitement in any fishing party that puts an end to all story telling. After they have got straight again and the nibble has turned out to be "the bottom" as all nibbles are—the moment would be fitting for anyone of them to tell the famous story called:

III

Beginner's Luck, or the Wonderful Catch Made by the Narrators Wife's Lady Friend

"Talking of that big catch that you made with the pants button," says another of the anglers, who really means that he is going to talk of something else—"reminds me of a queer thing I saw myself. We'd gone out fishing for pickerel, 'dorés,' they call them up there in the lake of Two Mountains. We had a couple of big row boats and we'd taken my wife and the ladies along—I think there were eight of us, or nine perhaps. Anyway it doesn't matter. Well, there was a young lady there from Dayton, Ohio, and she'd never fished before. In fact she'd never been in a boat before. I don't believe she'd ever been near the water before."

All experienced listeners know now what is coming. They realize the geographical position of Dayton, Ohio, far from the water and shut in everywhere by land. Any prudent fish would make a sneak for shelter if he knew that a young lady from Dayton, Ohio, was after him.

"Well, this girl got an idea that she'd like to fish and we'd rigged up a line for her, just tied on to a cedar pole that we'd cut in the bush. Do you know you'd hardly believe that that girl had hardly got her line into the water when she got a monster. We yelled to her to play it or she'd lose it, but she just heaved it up into the air and right into the boat. She caught seventeen, or twenty-seven, I forget which, one after the other, while the rest of us got nothing. And the fun of it was she didn't know anything about fishing; she just threw the fish up into the air and into the boat. Next day we got her a decent rod with a reel and gave her a lesson or two and then she didn't catch any."

I may say with truth that I have heard this particular story told not only about a girl from Dayton, Ohio, but about a girl from Kansas, a young lady just out from England, about a girl fresh from Paris, and about another girl, not fresh—the daughter of a minister. In fact if I wished to make sure of a real catch, I would select a girl fresh from Paris or New York and cut off some of my buttons, or hers, and start to fish.

IV

The Story of What Was Found in the Fish

The stories however do not end with the mere catching of the fish. There is another familiar line of anecdote that comes in when the fish are to be cleaned and cooked. The fishermen have landed on the rocky shore beside the rushing waterfall and are cleaning their fish to cook them for the midday meal. There is an obstinate superstition that fish cooked thus taste better than first class kippered herring put up in a tin in Aberdeen where they know how. They don't, but it is an honourable fiction and reflects credit on humanity. What is more, all the fishing party compete eagerly for the job of cutting the inside out of the dead fish. In a restaurant they are content to leave that to anybody sunk low enough and unhappy enough to have to do it. But in the woods they fight for the job.

So it happens that presently one of the workers holds up some filthy specimen of something in his hand and says "Look at that! See what I took out of the trout! Unless I mistake it is part of a deer's ear. The deer must have stooped over the stream to drink and the trout bit his ear off."

At which somebody says—whoever gets it in first—says,

"It's amazing what you find in fish. I remember once trolling for trout, the big trout, up in Lake Simcoe and just off Eight Mile Point we caught a regular whopper. We had no scales but he weighed easily twenty pounds. We cut him open on the shore afterwards, and say, would you believe it, that fish had inside him a brass buckle—the whole of it—and part of a tennis shoe, and a rain check from a baseball game, and seventy-five cents in change. It seems hard to account for it, unless perhaps he'd been swimming round some summer hotel."

These stories, I repeat, may now be properly narrated in the summer fishing season. But of course, as all fishermen know, the true time to tell them is round the winter fire, with a glass of something warm within easy reach, at a time when statements cannot be checked, when weights and measures must not be challenged and when fish grow to their full size and their true beauty. It is such stories as these, whether told in summer or in winter, that the immemorial craft of the angler owes something of its continued charm.

Have We Got the Year Backwards? Is Not Autumn Spring?

Once a year with unfailing regularity there comes round a season known as Autumn. For a good many hundred years the poets have been busy with this season as they have with all the others. Around each of them they have created a legend. And the legends are mostly untrue and need correcting.

For example, in spring there is supposed to be a tremendous gayety let loose. The young lamb is said to skip and play; and the young man's fancy is supposed to turn towards thoughts of love. Anybody who has seen a young lamb humped up and shivering in April rain for want of an overcoat knows just how false this lamb idea is; and anybody who has seen a young man of today getting smoothed up for a winter evening party knows just when the real season of the lovers comes.

There are hawthorns in blossom in the lanes in the spring, and in the winter there are rubber trees in the restaurants with no blossoms at all. But the rubber tree sees more of love in one evening than the hawthorn does in its whole life.

The same kind of myth has gathered round the summer. The poets have described it as rich, luscious, glorious, crowned with flowers and drowsy with the hum of the bee. In reality, summer is the dead time. It is the time of the sweltering heat and the breathless nights, when people sleep upside-down with their feet on the rail of the bed; when there is no one in the city but the farmers and no one on the farms but the city people; in short when life is all disturbed, deranged, and out of sorts; when it is too hot to think, too late to begin anything, and too early to start something; when intellect dies, oratory is dumb, and national problems slumber. At such a time there is nothing of current interest except the expeditions to the North Pole and the rescue parties sent out to drag away the explorers.

Then comes autumn. The poet describes it as the decline of the year. The leaf withers. The russet woods shiver in the moaning wind. The poet on his lonely autumn walk talks with the shepherd on the mutability of life and all is sadness.

Now it occurs to me all this stuff about Autumn, as applied here and now, is nonsense. No doubt it was all true when men lived in woods and caves, shivered in the rain, and counted the days until the return of the sun. But in our own time the thing doesn't fit at all. Autumn is the real beginning of the year, the new start after the dead season. Witness, in illustration, some of the glad signs that mark the oncoming of the Autumn season.

The Return of the Oyster:

I can imagine no more pleasing sight to the true lover of nature than the first oyster peeping out of its half shell. How dainty is its coloring! How softly it seems to lie upon its little dish! All through the dull, dead summer it has been asleep in its bed of mud, but now Nature has burst forth again and the oyster is back with us.

The Young Lamb:

And alongside of the oyster, look who is here too! The lamb, not the poor ungainly thing that humped up itself in the springtime in a feeble attempt to jump, but the true lamb, valued at a dollar a portion, and eaten along with autumn cauliflowers, Jerusalem artichokes, and October asparagus. With what eager eyes it is regarded by the people who have spent the summer in the country where there are no fresh meat and no vegetables. For the true aspect of the bounty of Nature, give me every time the sight of a butcher shop in autumn, with the pink lobsters nestling in the white celery, pure as snow. When the poet wanted inspiration he went and talked with a shepherd. I'd rather talk with a chef.

And the flowers! Ah, there now is something worth seeing. Look at these autumn chrysanthemums right out of the hothouses, and the gladioluses, or the gladiolalula—if that is the right plural. Even the beautiful big blue violets will soon be with us, at five dollars a bunch.

And no wonder we need the flowers, for with autumn the glad season of happiness is beginning again. Witness as the principal sign of it—

The Re-opening of the Vaudeville Season:

All through the dull dead summer we have not seen a single "act." We were away from town, or it was too hot, or the theatres in our vicinity were closed.

But now we are all back in our seats again watching The Seven Sisters—can they really be sisters—pounding out music from wine glasses, from sticks of wood, from cowbells—from anything they have handy. Here are again the two wonderful trapeze performers who hurl themselves through the air. So far we have never seen them break their necks. But, courage, a new season is beginning.

Here is the Magician with his cards, and the Strong Man with his dumb-bells, and the Trained Dog that actually sits on a stool. They are all back with us for the opening of another happy season.

The only trouble is to find time to go to see them. So many things are starting up into life all at once in this glad moment of the year. Not only Vaudeville is beginning but Football has opened up again. Here we are crowded into the stadiums—or rather, the stadiora—in tens of thousands, covered with college colors and chrysanthemums, in the bright autumn sunshine, with splendid seats only a quarter of a mile from the game.

Football having started means, of course, that the colleges are all reopening and when that happens we can feel our intellectual life that has been dormant in the dead heat of summer, come back again with a throb. Soon we shall be going again to popular lectures on Social Dynamics, and Intellectual Hydraulics—the kind of thing that brings learning right to the people and leaves it there.

And not only the colleges. The clubs—culture and brotherhood clubs—are all beginning a new season. There are the men's luncheon and speaking clubs and the Ladies Fortnightly, and the Morning Musical, all starting in at once. All through the summer we have never heard a single address. Now in one week we can hear a talk on *Mexican Folk Music*, or on *Two Weeks in Mongolia*, or *Ten Years in Sing Sing*.

The new life is on the move. The dead leaves have been swept up and burnt. The trees no longer spoil the view. The motoring is fine. If the poet on his Autumn walk, sunk in reverie, gets in the way, let him look out or we'll sink him where he'll never come back.

Autumn, crowned with its wreath of celery and lobsters, is with us again!

Our Summer Convention

As Described by One of Its Members

Our summer convention—the first annual convention of Peanut Men—has just been concluded and has been such a success that I feel I'd like to set down a little account of it in print.

The way it began was that a few of us—all peanut men—got talking together about every other business except ours having conventions and ours not being represented in this way at all. Everybody knows there are now conventions of the electrical men and the pulp and paper men, and even of professors and psychologists and chiropodists. And as everybody knows, too, these conventions are not merely for business and social purposes, but they are educative as well. People who go to a convention and listen to the papers that are read will learn things about their own business that they never would have thought of.

Anyway, we got together and formed an association and elected officers—a Grandmaster of the Nuts, and a Grand Kernel, and seven Chief Shucks and a lot of lesser ones—and decided to hold a convention. We restricted the membership—because that is always found best in conventions—and made it open only to sellers, roasters, buyers, importers and consumers of peanuts. Others might come as friends but they couldn't appear as Nuts. To make the thing social it was agreed that members might bring their wives, as many as they liked.

We thought first of New York or Chicago as the place for us, but they always seemed too crowded. Then we thought of Montreal and a whole lot of members were all for it, partly because of the beautiful summer climate. But our final choice was Lake Owatawetness in the mountains.

It was a great sight the day we opened up the convention. We had flags across the street and big streamers with *Welcome to the Nuts* and things like that on them and all the delegates rode in open hacks and pinned on each was a big badge with the words *I Am a Complete Nut.* Underneath this motto was his name and his town and his height and weight and his religion and his age.

Well, we all went to the town hall and we had an address of welcome from the Grand Master. They said that it was one of the best addresses ever heard in the town hall and lasted just over two hours. Personally I can't speak for it because I slipped out of the hall a little after it began. I had an idea that I would just ease off a little the first morning and wait till the afternoon to begin the real educative stuff in earnest. There were two other fellows who slipped out about the same time that I did and so we went down to the lake and decided we'd hire a boat and go down the lake fishing so as to be ready for the solid work of the afternoon. One of the fellows was from Wichita, Kansas, and was a Presbyterian and weighed 168 pounds, and the other was from Owen Sound, Ontario, not classified, and weighed 178 pounds and was five feet, nine and a half inches high.

We took some lunch with us so as not to need to get back till two, when the first big conference opened. We had a printed program with us and it showed that at the two o'clock session there was to be a paper read on *The Application of Thermodynamics to the Roasting of Peanuts* and we all agreed that we wouldn't miss it for anything.

Well, we went clear down the lake to where we understood the best fishing was and it was a longer row than we thought. We didn't really start fishing till noon—not counting one or two spots where we just fished for twenty minutes or so to see if any fish were there but there weren't. After we got to the right place we didn't get a bite at all, which made us want to stay on a while, though it was getting near the time to go back, because it seemed a shame to quit before the fish began to bite, and we were just thinking of leaving when a Methodist from Oshkosh, Wisconsin, who was nearby, caught a black bass, a real peach. There seemed to be a good many other boats coming down, too, and quite near us there was a Catholic delegate from Syracuse (five feet, eight inches) who caught a catfish and two Episcopalians (150 pounds each) from Burlington, Vermont, who seemed to be getting bites all the time.

So we decided to stay. We didn't get so many fish but we all agreed that an afternoon on the water for health's sake was a fine thing to put a man into shape for the convention work. We knew that in the evening Professor Pip of the State Agricultural College was to read a paper on *The Embryology of the Nut* and we wanted to be right on deck for that.

Rowing back just before supper time some one of us happened to mention cards, just casually, and the delegate from Owen Sound who was unclassified asked me if I ever played poker. I told him that I *had* played it, once or twice, not so much for any money that might be in it, but just for the game itself, as you might say. The man from Wichita said that he had played it that way, too, and that if you took it like that it was a fine game: in fact for a quiet evening's amusement there was nothing like it. We all three agreed that if it hadn't been for wanting to hear Professor Pip's talk on The Embryology of the Peanut we could have had quite a little game, a three-handed game, or, perhaps, get in one or two of the other boys after supper in one of the rooms.

Anyway, after supper we went upstairs and began throwing down hands just to see what would turn up while we were waiting for the lecture time and the first thing we knew we got seated round the table and started playing and it seemed a pity to quit and go to the lecture. For my part I didn't care so much because I am not so much interested in The Embryology of the Nut as in the selling of it.

Later on I saw a delegate (from Saskatoon, Saskatchewan, a Universal Christian, six feet high) who said that he had spoken with a man who had heard the lecture and that it was fine. It appears there was only a small turn-out, smaller even than in the afternoon, but those who were there and stayed—some couldn't stay—said that it was all right. They said it was too long—a lecture is apt to be too long, and that the professor spoke pretty low, in fact you couldn't exactly hear him, and that you couldn't understand the subject matter but the lecture itself was good. It was all right.

By the next morning we had the convention pretty well in full swing and you could see that the crowd were getting to know one another. This second morning was to be the big morning of the convention because the state governor was to give an address and everybody felt that it was a great honor to have him come. They had put up a sort of arch for him to drive under, with a motto *Welcome You Big Nut.* They say the governor was awfully pleased with it and still more when they made him a Chief Grand Nut at the morning ceremony.

I didn't hear his address myself, not more than a few sentences. I couldn't stay. He had just begun a survey of the history of the development of the arable land of the state (he had it all in his hand and was reading it) when I had to go. I had said something to some of the boys the night before about golf—and it appeared that the privileges of Watawetness Golf Club had been extended to us—and I felt that I mustn't go back on it. It was disappointing, but there was no use worrying over it.

They said the governor's address was great. It was too long, everybody admitted, and a few took exception to it because it was not exactly connected with the convention, and some criticized it because it was the same address that he had given to the Skiers and Snowshoemen Convention last February. But still it was good.

Playing golf cut me clean out of the afternoon session, too, as I didn't get back till it must have been started. In this session the programme was to divide the convention up into little groups for intensive study of the peanuts, organized by Miss Mutt of the Botany Section of the State Teachers Association. Each study group was to take some topic under a special speaker and exhaust it. But quite a lot of the delegates had gone fishing, and some were playing pool and some were scattered round. It seems they couldn't make up the groups except just the speaker in each group and Miss Mutt herself of course. So Miss Mutt gave them a talk on the Botany of Selling Peanuts. They said it was fine. It was too long, they thought, and would have been much better, ever so much better, if it had been shorter—quite short; but it was good.

That night was the big banquet. The governor stayed for it, and there was to be his speech and the Secretary of Agriculture and speeches from the Grand Master, and from Clergymen, and Teachers. In fact it looked pretty good and from all I heard it was considered a big success. The only thing against it was that some of the delegates had brought in some stuff into the hotel (I don't know where they got it from), and a lot of them were slipping out of the banquet room and slipping up to the rooms where they had this stuff.

Some didn't come down. They said quite a lot didn't come down. I went up there for a while but I didn't stay long, or not so very long, and when I got back to the door of the banquet room, one of the guests, a minister, was talking on the moral aspect of Importing Peanuts. So I didn't stay, as I am more interested in the selling aspect.

The next morning I left early. There was to be another whole day and some mighty interesting papers to be read. But I felt I would be needed badly in my business at this time; in fact I felt pretty keen to get back to it. I saw many other delegates come away on the same train, a lot of them. They had taken off their badges, so I couldn't tell their names and their religions but they all agreed that the convention had been a wonderful success and a great educative influence in our business.

V

Travel and Movement

All Aboard for Europe

Some Humble Advice for Travellers

Every summer thousands and thousands of our people in America go across to Europe. They say that about fifty thousand people leave on the steamers every week. It's either fifty thousand or five hundred thousand, or five thousand—I forget which. Anyway, there are a great many people travelling every year.

Some of them go because they need a change of air; some to improve their minds; some because they were tired of making money, and others because they were tired of not making money. And some again go to see Europe, before it all falls to pieces: and others go simply and plainly for a vacation because they want for a few weeks to be really happy.

It is especially for this last class that these few words of advice are written. If you want to be happy when you start off on a sea voyage you have got to be prepared to face a lot of disillusionment. You are going to find all through the trip the most striking difference between travel as it is pictured in the Guide Book and travel as it is in fact.

The difference begins at the very moment of embarkation. Here is what is said in the attractive Steamship Guide Book—done up in colors with a picture of two girls walking on a promenade deck, and swaying in the wind like rushes, while a young man goes past in flannels and a straw hat.

"What," asks the Guide Book, "is more delightful than the embarkation on an Atlantic voyage? The size of the great steamer, its spotless decks, its commodious cabins, its luxurious saloon and its cozy library, thrill us with a sense of pleasure to come. As we step on board and look about us at the dancing waters of the harbor ruffled under the breeze from the open sea beyond, we feel that now at least we are entering on the realization of our dreams."

Yes. Exactly. Only unfortunately, my dear reader, it is just at the very moment of embarkation that you are certain to discover that your black valise is missing. Your steamer trunk is there all right in your stateroom and the brown valise and the paper parcel that your aunt has asked you to deliver in Aberdeen when you land at Liverpool. But the black valise apparently is clean gone.

You certainly had it in the Pullman car and your sister remembers seeing it in the taxicab—but where is it? Talk about embarkation on the ruffled harbor and the unrealized dream! Who can think of these things with a valise missing and the huge whistle of the steamer booming out the time of departure?

No use asking that man in uniform; apparently he's only one of the officers. Don't try to fight your way up to the bridge and challenge the captain. He doesn't know. Round the purser there are twenty people in the same condition as yourself, over one thing or another, all trying to get at him and bite him. There seem to be lots of stewards running up and down, but all they can do is ask you what number is your stateroom and say that the valise ought to be there. A conspiracy, evidently, the whole thing.

The result is that you are fussing up and down for half an hour and when at last the valise is found (in the next stateroom, owing to the simple fact that you wrote the wrong number on it), you are already far out at sea and have never seen the embarkation at all.

Never mind, there's lots of the trip left yet. After all, listen to what the Guide Book says about our first morning at sea—

"There is an extraordinary exhilaration," it prattles on, "about the first day at sea. From the lofty deck of the great liner our eye sweeps the limitless expanse. All about is the blue of the Atlantic, ruffled with the zephyrs of a summer morning. We walk the deck with a sense of resilience, a fullness of life unknown to the dweller upon terra firma, or stand gazing in dreamy reverie at the eternal ocean."

Oh, we do, do we? But I guess not. On our first morning at sea we have too much else to think of, even in the calmest weather, than mere reverie on the ocean. What is troubling us, is the question of deck chairs—how do we get one?—are they free, or do we have to pay?—and if we pay now, do we have to tip the man?—and which man is it that gives out our chairs?—and if we want to get our chairs next to Mr. Snyder from Pittsburgh, whom do we see about it?

There is room enough in this problem to keep us busy all morning; and even when we have got it straight, we start all over again with the question of what we do to get the seat that we want at the table. We would like to get ourselves and Mr. Snyder and Mr. and Mrs. Hopkins from Alberta all at the same table. Somebody has said to somebody that there's a steward giving out seats or going to give out seats somewhere in one of the saloons or somewhere. That's enough for us. That keeps us hot and busy all morning.

And you will find, alas my dear reader, that no matter what the Guide Book says about it, that kind of worry is going to haunt you all the way. When you have done with the valises and the deck chairs and the seats at the table you still have plenty of other problems to fret over, such as—

The English customs officers—what do they do? Do they examine everything? Will they say anything about those canvas slippers that your aunt has asked you to deliver to her cousin in Nottingham (close to London)? If you explain that she made the slippers, does that make any difference? Or, at any rate, can you say to the man, "Oh very well, I'll send them back to America rather than pay a cent on them?" In short, the English customs officers—what do they do? Travelers lie awake at night and think of that.

And along with that—

At what hour will you land at Liverpool and will you be able to get the 11.30 train to London or will you have to wait for the 12.30? That's an excellent one. Many travellers have thought so hard about that and talked so much about it on deck, that they never even noticed the blue of the sea, and the rush of the flying fish or the great dolphins that flopped up beside the ship.

But even allowing that you can perhaps get a train—some train—from Liverpool, more intense worries set in as we near the other side.

The question of letters, telegrams and marconigrams. When the purser says that he has no messages for you and no letters for you, is he not perhaps getting your name wrong. He may have made a mistake. Might it not be better to go to him again (the fourth time) and ask him whether he has got your name quite right? By all means, and let Mr. Snyder go too, and you can both stand in line at the purser's window and fret it out together and thus never see the Norwegian sailing ship under full canvas two hundred yards away.

But there is worse yet—

The ocean is crossed, the trials are over and the land is in sight. And again the little Guide Book breaks out in ingenuous joy!

"Land in sight! With what a thrill we go forward to the front of the ship and look ahead to catch a glimpse of the white cliffs of old England rising from the sea. All the romance of history and of exploration rises to the mind with this first view of the old land. We stand gazing forward, as might have stood a Columbus or a Cabot filled with the mystery of the New Land."

Do we? No, we don't. We've no time for it. As a matter of fact, we don't get any such first glimpse at all. We are down below, wrestling with the problem of how much we ought to tip the bath room steward. Is eight shillings what he gets, or is six enough? We feel we need information, light, knowledge. We must try to find Mr. Snyder and learn what he thinks the bathroom steward ought to get.

And then, somehow, before we know it, and while we are still worrying and fretting over stewards and tips and baggage, our voyage is all over—the time is gone—and we are saying goodbye to the passengers and Mr. Snyder and Mr. and Mrs. Hopkins of Alberta, and the stewards and the purser—noble fellows they all seem now. But we have a queer sense of loss and disillusionment as if our voyage had not yet begun, and a strange longing that we might have it all over again and this time know enough not to spoil it with our poor meaningless worries.

My friend, this is a parable. As is the Atlantic voyage, so is our little pilgrimage in life, a brief transit in the sunshine from shore to shore, whose short days are all too often marred by the mean disputes and the poor worries that in the end signify nothing. While there is still time, let us look about us to the horizon.

The Gasoline Goodbye

And What Would Have Happened to the Big Moments of History If the Motor Had Taken a Hand in Them

In the days before the motor car, when a man said goodbye he shook hands and he was gone. If he was to ride on horseback, he made a brief farewell to each person present, shook hands, leaped upon his horse and was off.

Now that the motor car has come into use as the general instrument of visiting, this no longer happens. The people say goodbye, get into their motor car, and are *not* gone. They make an affectionate farewell and then sit looking out of their glass windows, while the car goes "Phut, phut—bang,"—and sticks there.

The more dramatic the goodbye, the more touching the farewell, the more determined the car always is to say "Phut, phut—bang," and refuse to move.

Witness the familiar scene of the goodbye of the Joneses to the Smiths at 6 P.M. on any Sunday evening at any rural place where city people spend their vacation. The Joneses have motored over in their own car—a real peach, tin all over—and have spent Sunday afternoon with the Smiths, who have a cottage for the summer which they call OPEN HOUSE, and where they take care that nobody gets in at meal times.

When the time has come for the Joneses to go, they all mingle up in a group with the Smiths and everybody says goodbye to everybody else, and shakes hands with each one, and they all say, "Well, we certainly had a grand time." Then they all climb into the car with Mr. Jones himself at the wheel and they put their heads out of the windows and they say, "Well, goodbye, goodbye!" and wave their hands.

And then the car goes—

"Whr-r-r-r-r-r-r-r-r-r-r-r-—phut, bang!"

A wisp of thin blue smoke rolls away and when it has gone the Joneses are seen sitting there, absolutely still. The car hasn't moved an inch.

Jones at the wheel sticks his head down among the grips and clutches and says—"I guess she is a little cold," and the Smiths say—"Yes, it often takes a little time to start them." Then there's a pause and nothing seems to be happening and then very suddenly and cheerfully the engine of the car starts making a loud—

"Pur-r-r-r-r-r-r-r-r-r-r-r-r-r!"

On this, all the Joneses and all the Smiths break out into goodbyes again. All talking together:

"Well, come back soon—We certainly will—We sure had a great time—Remember us all to Alf—We certainly will—You certainly have a nice cottage here—We certainly enjoyed that lemonade—well—goodbye, goodbye, goodbye!"

And then the car goes—

"Whir-r-r-r-r-r-r-r-r-r-r-r—phut, bang!"

And there is another puff of blue smoke, and when it clears away, what is behind it? Why, the Joneses, right there in their car.

When the machine goes "bang!" all the Joneses in the car and all the Smiths standing beside the road are knocked into silence for a few seconds. Then Jones mutters—"Seems to be something wrong with the ignition"—and somebody else says—"She doesn't seem to be feeding right"—and there's a little chorus of—"Oh, she is just a little cold, they take a little warming up"—"she'll start in a minute."

And then again the machine begins, this time at a terrific speed, about a million revolutions to the minute—

"Whir-r-r-r-r-r-r-r-r-r-r-r-r-r-r-r-r-r-r-r-r-R-R!"

At this happy sound the goodbyes break out all over again in a chorus.

"Goodbye—Look after yourselves—Tell Min we'll see her Friday—goodbye—We certainly had a—"

"Bang!"

All stopped again.

This time Jones is determined that when the engine starts he'll keep it started. There shall be no false alarms this time. "Let her get going good," some of them advise him. And so when the engine next starts Jones doesn't throw in his clutch but just lets her go on humming and roaring till everybody feels assured that this time the start is actually going to happen and the goodbyes erupt all over again.

The noise gets louder and louder, the conversation rises into shouts mixed with the "phut, phut, phut" of the machine, and then all of a sudden there's a tremendous "bang!" and a volume of blue smoke and when it clears away—where are the Joneses?

Gone—clean gone, they seem to have vanished off the earth! At last you catch a glimpse of their car already two hundred yards away, disappearing in a cloud of smoke.

"They're off!" murmur the Smiths, and the painful scene is over...

Thinking over all this, I cannot but reflect how fortunate it has been for mankind that the motor car was not invented earlier in our history. So many of the great dramas of history have turned upon farewells and departures that some of the most romantic pages of the past would have been spoiled if there had been any gasoline in them.

Take for example the familiar case of Napoleon saying goodbye to his officers and soldiers at Fontainebleau before going into exile. The fallen emperor stood beside the steed he was about to mount, turned a moment and addressed to his devoted comrades words that still echo in the ears of France. But suppose that he had said the same thing while seated in a little one-seater car with his head stuck out of the window. How inadequate it would have sounded:—

"Farewell, my brave comrades—phut, phut—together we shared the labor and the burden of a hundred campaigns—phut, bang, phut—we must forget that we have conquered Europe—whir-r-r, phut—that our eagles have flown over every capital—bang—I leave you now for exile, but my heart forever will remain—whir-r-r, phut—buried in the soil of France, bang!"

Or take as a similar case in point the famous farewell to the nation spoken by George Washington as his last service to the republic that he had created.

General Washington, supposing there had been gasoline in those days, would have been reported as leaning out from the window of his sedan car and speaking as follows:—

"Let America cultivate and preserve the friendship of the world—phut, phut—let us have peace and friendship with all whir-r-r—and entangling alliances with none—bang! I have grown old in the service of this country and there is something wrong with my ignition. To each and all of you I bid now a last farewell—

"Whir-r-r—

"Farewell!

"Phut, phut, phut, phut.

"Farewell!

"Bang!"

Complete Guide and History of the South

Based on the Best Models of Traveler's Impressions—

In setting down here my impression of Southern life, Southern character, Southern industry, and what I am led to call the soul of the Southern people, I am compelled to admit that these impressions are necessarily incomplete. The time at my disposal—twenty-four hours less fifteen minutes while I was shaving—was, as I myself felt, inadequate for the purpose.

I could have spent double, nay treble, nay quadruple the time in the South with profit, and could have secured twice, nay three times, nay four times as many impressions. At the same time I may say in apology that my impressions, such as they are, are based on the very best models of travelers' impressions which are published in such floods by visitors to this continent.

To one who has the eye to see it, the journey south from New York to Washington, which may be called the capital of the United States, is filled with interest. The broad farm lands of New Jersey, the view of the city of Philadelphia, and the crossing of the spacious waters of the Susquehanna, offer a picture well worth carrying away. Unfortunately I did not see it. It was night when I went through. But I read about it in the railroad folder next morning.

After passing Washington the traveler finds himself in the country of the Civil War, where the landscape recalls at every turn the great struggle of sixty years ago. Here is the Acquia Creek and here is Fredericksburg, the scene of one of the most disastrous defeats of the northern armies. I missed it, I am sorry to say. I was eating lunch and didn't see it. But the porter told me that we had passed Fredericksburg.

It is however with a certain thrill that one finds oneself passing Richmond, the home of the Lost Cause, where there still lingers all the romance and glory that once was. Unluckily our train didn't go by Richmond but straight south via Lynchburg Junction. But if it had I might have seen it.

As one continues the journey southward, one realizes that one is in the South. The conviction was gradually borne in on me as I kept going south that I was getting South. It is an impression, I believe, which all travelers have noted in proportion as they proceed south.

I could not help saying to myself, "I am now in the South." It is a feeling I have never had in the North. As I looked from the train window I could not resist remarking, "So this is the South." I have every reason to believe that it was.

One becomes conscious of a difference of life, of atmosphere, of the character of the people. The typical Southerner is courteous, chivalrous, with an old-world air about him. I noted that on asking one of my fellow travelers for a match he responded, "I am deeply sorry, I fear I have none. I had a match in my other pants yesterday, but I left them at home. Perhaps I could go back and get them."

Another gentleman in the smoking room of whom I ventured to ask the time replied, "I am deeply sorry, I have no watch. But if you will wait till we get to the next station, I will get out and buy a clock and let you know." I thanked him, but thought it the part of good taste to refuse his offer.

Every day one hears everywhere reminiscences and talk of the Civil War. Nearly everybody with whom I fell into conversation—and I kept falling into it—had something to say or to recall about the days of Lee and Jackson and of what I may call the Southern Confederacy.

One old gentleman told me that he remembered the war as if it were yesterday, having participated in a number of the great episodes of the struggle. He told me that after General Lee had been killed at Gettysburg, Andrew Jackson was almost in despair; and yet had the Southerners only known it, there was at the time only a thin screen of two hundred thousand union troops between them and Washington.

In the light of these conversations and reminiscences it was interesting presently to find oneself in Georgia and to realize that one was traversing the ground of Sherman's famous march to the sea. Unluckily for me, it was night when we went through, but I knew where we were because during a temporary stoppage of the train, I put my head out of the curtains and said to the porter, "Where are we?" and he answered "Georgia." As I looked out into the profound darkness that enveloped us, I realized as never before the difficulty of Sherman's task.

At this point, perhaps it may be well to say something of the women of the South, a topic without which no impression would be worth publishing. The Southern women, one finds, are distinguished everywhere by their dignity and reserve. (Two women came into the Pullman car where I was, and when I offered one of them an apple she wouldn't take it.) But they possess at the same time a charm and graciousness that is all their own. (When I said to the other woman that it was a good deal warmer than it had been she smiled and said that it certainly was.)

The Southern woman is essentially womanly and yet entirely able to look after herself. (These two went right into the dining car by themselves without waiting for me or seeming to want me.) Of the beauty of the Southern type there can be no doubt. (I saw a girl with bobbed hair on the platform at Danville, but when I waved to her even her hair would not wave.)

On the morning following we found ourselves approaching Birmingham, Alabama. On looking at it out of the car window, I saw at once that Birmingham contains a population of 200,000 inhabitants, having grown greatly in the last decade; that the town boasts not less than sixteen churches and several large hotels of the modern type.

I saw also that it is rapidly becoming a seat of manufacture, possessing in 1921 not less than 14,000 spindles, while its blast furnaces bid fair to rival those of Pittsburgh, Pennsylvania and Hangkow, China; I noticed that the leading denomination is Methodist, both white and colored, but the Roman Catholic, the Episcopalian and other churches are also represented. The town, as I saw at a glance, enjoys exceptional educational opportunities, the enrollment of pupils in the high schools numbering half a million.

The impression which I carried away from Birmingham enabled me to form some idea (that is all I ever get) of the new economic growth of the South. Everywhere one sees evidence of the fertility of the soil and the relative ease of sustenance. (I saw a man buy a whole bunch of bananas and eat them right in the car.) The growth of wealth is remarkable. (I noticed a man hand out a fifty-dollar bill in the dining car and get change as if it were nothing.)

I had originally intended to devote my time after leaving Birmingham to the investigation and analysis of the soul of the South, for which I had reserved four hours. Unfortunately I was not able to do so. I got called in to join a poker game in the drawing room and it lasted all the way to New Orleans.

But even in the imperfect form in which I have been able to put together these memoirs of travel I feel on looking over them that they are all right, or at least as good as the sort of stuff that is handed out every month in the magazines.

The Give and Take of Travel

A Study in Petty Larceny, Pro and Con

I have recently noted among my possessions a narrow black comb and a flat brown hairbrush. I imagine they must belong to the Pullman Car Company. As I have three of the Company's brushes and combs already, I shall be glad to hand these back at any time when the company cares to send for them.

I have also a copy of the New Testament in plain good print which is marked "put here by the Gibbons" and which I believe I got from either the Ritz-Carlton Hotel in Montreal or the Biltmore in New York. I do not know any of the Gibbons. But the hotel may have the book at anytime, as I have finished with it. I will bring it to them.

On the other hand, I shall be very greatly obliged if the man who has my winter overshoes (left on the Twentieth Century Limited) will let me have them back again. As the winter is soon coming I shall need them. If he will leave them at any agreed spot three miles from a town I will undertake not to prosecute him.

I mention these matters not so much for their own sake as because they form a part of the system of give and take which plays a considerable part in my existence.

Like many people who have to travel a great deal I get absent-minded about it. I move to and fro among trains and hotels shepherded by redcaps and escorted by bell boys. I have been in so many hotels that they all look alike. If there is a difference in the faces of the hotel clerks I can't see it. If there is any way of distinguishing one waiter from another I don't know it. There is the same underground barber surrounded by white marble and carrying on the same conversation all the way from Halifax to Los Angeles. In short I have been in so many towns that I never know where I am.

Under these circumstances a man of careless disposition and absent mind easily annexes and easily loses small items of property. In a Pullman car there is no difficulty whatever, if one has the disposition for it, in saying to a man sitting beside you, "Good morning, sir. It looks like a beautiful day," and then reaching over and packing his hair brush into your valise. If he is the right kind of man he will never notice it, or at best he will say in return, "A beautiful morning," and then take away your necktie.

There is, let it be noticed, all the difference in the world between this process and petty larceny.

The thing I mean couldn't possibly be done by a thief. He wouldn't have the nerve, the quiet assurance, the manner. It is the absolute innocence of the thing that does it. For example, if a man offers me a cigarette I find that I take his cigarette case and put it in my pocket. When I rise from my hotel dinner I carry away the napkin. When I leave my hotel room I always take away the key.

There is no real sense in this: I have more hotel keys than I can use as it is. But the fault is partly with our hotels. So many of them put up a little notice beside the door that reads, "Have You Forgotten Anything?" When ever I see this I stand in thought a minute and then it occurs to me, "Why of course, the Key!" and I take it with me.

I am aware that there is a class of persons—women mostly—who carry away spoons and other things deliberately as souvenirs. But I disclaim all connection with that kind of thing. That is not what I meant at all.

I would never take a valuable spoon, unless I happened to be using it at the table to open the back of my watch, or something of the sort. But when I sign my name on the hotel book I keep the pen. Similarly and in all fairness, I give up my own fountain pen to the telegraph clerk. The theory works both ways.

As a rule, there is nothing more in all this than a harmless give and take, a sort of profit and loss account to which any traveler easily becomes accustomed. But at the same time one should be careful. The theory may go a little too far. I remember not long ago coming home from a theatre in Trenton, New Jersey, with a lady's white silk scarf about my neck.

I had no notion how it got to be there. Whether the woman had carelessly wrapped it about my neck in mistake for her own, or whether I had unwound it off her, I cannot say. But I regret the incident and will gladly put the scarf back on her neck at any time. I will also take this occasion to express my regret for the pair of boots which I put on in a Pullman car in Syracuse in the dark of a winter morning.

There is a special arrangement on the New York Central whereby at Syracuse passengers making connections for the South are allowed to get up at four and dress while the others are still asleep. There are signs put up adjuring everybody to keep as quiet as possible. Naturally, these passengers get the best of everything and, within limits, it is fair enough as they have to get up so early. But the boots of which I speak outclass anything I ever bought for myself and I am sorry about them.

Our American railways have very wisely taken firm grounds on this problem of property mislaid or exchanged or lost on the Pullman cars. As everybody knows when one of our trains reaches a depot the passengers leave it with as mad a haste as if it were full of smallpox. In fact, they are all lined up at the door like cattle in a pen ready to break loose before the train stops. What happens to the car itself afterwards they don't care. It is only known to those who have left a hair brush in the car and tried to find it.

But in reality, the car is instantly rushed off to a siding, its number-placard taken out of the window so that it cannot be distinguished, after which a vacuum cleaner is turned on and sucks up any loose property that is left in it. Meantime the porter has avoided all detection by an instantaneous change of costume in which he appears disguised as a member of the Pittsburgh Yacht Club. If he could be caught at this time his pockets would be found to be full of fountain pens, rings and current magazines.

I do not mean to imply for a moment that our railways are acting in a dishonest way in the matter. On the contrary, they have no intention of keeping or annexing their passengers' property. But very naturally they do not want a lot of random people rummaging through their cars. They endeavor, however, through their central offices to make as fair a division of the lost-and-found property as they can. Anyone applying in the proper way can have some of it. I have always found in this respect the greatest readiness to give me a fair share of everything.

A few months ago for example I had occasion to send to the Canadian National Railway a telegram which read, "Have left gray fedora hat with black band on your Toronto-Chicago train." Within an hour I got back a message, "Your gray fedora hat being sent you from Windsor, Ontario." And a little later on the same day I received another message which read, "Sending gray hat from Chicago," and an hour after that "Gray hat found at Sheboygan, Michigan."

Indeed, I think I am not exaggerating when I say that any of our great Canadian and American Railways will send you anything of that sort if you telegraph for it. In my own case the theory has become a regular practice. I telegraph to the New York Central, "Please forward me spring overcoat in a light gray or fawn," and they send it immediately; or I call up the Canadian Pacific on the telephone and ask them if they can let me have a pair of tan boots and if possible a suit of golf clothes.

I have found that our leading hotels are even more punctilious in respect to their things than the railways. It is now hardly safe to attempt to leave in their rooms anything that one doesn't want. Last month, having cut my razor strop so badly that it was of no further use, I was foolish enough to leave it hanging in a room in the Biltmore Hotel in New

York. On my return home I got a letter which read: "Dear Sir: We beg to inform you that you have left your razor strop in room 2216. We have had your strop packed in excelsior packing and await your instructions in regard to it."

I telegraphed back, "Please keep razor strop. You may have it." After which in due course I got a further letter which said, "We are pleased to inform you that the razor strop which you so generously gave to this Company has been laid before our board of directors who have directed us to express their delight and appreciation at your generous gift. Any time you want a room and bath let us know."

VI

Great National Problems

The Laundry Problem

A Yearning for the Good Old Days of the Humble Washerwoman

A long time ago, thirty or forty years ago, there used to exist a humble being called a Washerwoman. It was her simple function to appear at intervals with a huge basket, carry away soiled clothes, and bring them back as snow-white linen.

The washerwoman is gone now. Her place is taken by the Amalgamated Laundry Company. She is gone but I want her back.

The washerwoman, in fact and fiction, was supposed to represent the bottom of everything. She could just manage to exist. She was the last word. Now the Amalgamated Laundry Company uses hydro-electric power, has an office like a bank, and delivers its goods out of a huge hearse driven by a chauffeur in livery. But I want that humble woman back.

In the old days any woman deserted and abandoned in the world took in washing. When all else failed there was at least that. Any woman who wanted to show her independent spirit and force of character threatened to take in washing. It was the last resort of a noble mind. In many of the great works of fiction the heroine's mother almost took in washing.

Women whose ancestry went back to the crusades *very nearly*, although never quite, started to wash when the discovery of the missing will saved them from the suds. But nowadays if a woman exclaimed, "What shall I do? I am alone in the world! I will open an Amalgamated Laundry!"—it would not sound the same.

The operation of the old system—as I recall it from the days of forty years ago—was very simple. The washerwoman used to call and take away my shirt and my collar and while she washed them I wore my other shirt and my other collar. When she came back we changed over. She always had one and I had one. In those days any young man in a fair position needed two shirts.

Where the poor washerwoman was hopelessly simple was that she never destroyed or injured the shirt. She never even thought to bite a piece out with her teeth. When she brought it back it looked softer and better than ever. It never occurred to her to tear out one of the sleeves. If she broke out a button in washing, she humbly sewed it on again.

When she ironed the shirt it never occurred to the simple soul to burn a brown mark right across it. The woman lacked imagination. In other words, modern industrialism was in its infancy.

I have never witnessed at first hand the processes of a modern incorporated laundry company using up-to-date machinery. But I can easily construct in my imagination a vision of what is done when a package of washing is received. The shirts are first sorted out and taken to an expert who rapidly sprinkles them with sulphuric acid.

Then they go to the coloring room where they are dipped in a solution of yellow stain. From this they pass to the machine-gun room where holes are shot in them and from there by an automatic carrier to the hydraulic tearing room where the sleeves are torn out. After that they are squeezed absolutely flat under enormous pressure which puts them into such a shape that the buttons can all be ripped up at a single scrape by an expert button ripper.

The last process is altogether handwork and accounts, I am informed, for the heavy cost. A good button-ripper with an expert knowledge of the breaking strain of material, easily earns fifty dollars a day. But the work is very exacting, as not a single button is expected to escape his eye. Of late the big laundries are employing new chemical methods, such as mustard gas, tear bombs, and star shells.

Collars, I understand, are treated in the same way, though the process varies a little according as the aim is to produce the Fuzzled Edge Finish or the Split Side Slit. The general idea, of course, in any first class laundry, is to see that no shirt or collar ever comes back twice. If it should happen to do so, it is sent at once to the Final Destruction Department, who put gun cotton under it and blow it into six bits. It is then labelled "*damaged*" and sent home in a special conveyance with an attendant in the morning.

Had the poor washerwoman kept a machine-gun and a little dynamite, she could have made a fortune. But she didn't know it. In the old days a washerwoman washed a shirt for ten-twelfths of a cent—or ten cents a dozen pieces. The best laundries, those which deny all admission to their offices and send back their laundry under an armed guard, now charge one dollar to wash a shirt, with a special rate of twelve dollars a dozen.

On the same scale the washerwoman's wages would be multiplied by a hundred and twenty. She really represented in value an income of fifty dollars a year. Had it been known, she could have been incorporated and dividends picked off her like huckleberries.

Now that I think of it, she was worth even more than that. With the modern laundry a shirt may be worn twice, for one day each time. After that it is blown up. And it costs four dollars to buy a new one. In the old days a shirt lasted till a man outgrew it. As a man approached middle life he found, with a certain satisfaction, that he had outgrown his shirt. He had to spend seventy-five cents on a new one, and that one lasted till he was buried in it.

Had some poor woman only known enough to pick up one of these shirts and bite the neck out of it, she might have started something really big.

But even when all this has been said there remains more yet. In the old days if you had a complaint to make to the washerwoman you said it to her straight out. She was there. And she heard the complaint and sneaked away with tears in her eyes to her humble home where she read the Bible and drank gin.

But now if you have a complaint to make to an Amalgamated Laundry Corporation, you can't find it. There is no use complaining to the chauffeur in livery. He never saw a shirt in his life.

There is no use going to the office. All you find there are groups of lady employees sheltered behind a cast-iron grating. They never saw your shirt. Don't ask them. They have their office work and in the evening they take extension lectures on the modern drama. They wouldn't know a shirt if they saw it.

Nor can you write to the company. I speak here of what I know for I have tried to lay a complaint before a laundry company in writing, and I know the futility of it. Here is the letter I wrote:

To the Board of Directors,
The Amalgamated Universal Laundry Company
Gentlemen:
I wish you would try to be a little more careful with my shirt. I mean the pink one. I think you put a little more starch in the neck the last time than you intended and it all seems stuck together.

Very faithfully yours,——

But the only answer I got was a communication in the following terms:

Dear Sir,
Folio 110,615. Department 0412. Received February 19th, 9.26 A.M. Read March 19th, 8.23 A.M. Sent down April 19th 4.01 A.M. Sent up May 19th 2 A.M.

We beg to inform you that your communication as above will be laid before the shareholders at the next general meeting. In answering kindly indicate folio, department, street, age and occupation. No complaints received under names or in words.

Yours,
Folio 0016.

After that I felt it was hopeless to go on. My only chance for the future is that I may get to know some beautiful rich woman and perhaps her husband will run away and leave her weeping and penniless and drinking gin, and then I will appear in the doorway and will say, "Dry your tears, dear, dear friend; there is prosperity for you yet; you shall wash my shirt."

The Questionnaire Nuisance

A Plan to Curb Zealous Investigators in Their Thirst for Knowledge

Everybody who manages an office or carries on a profession or teaches in a college, is getting to be familiar with the thing called "questionnaire." It is a sheet of questions or inquiries sent round broadcast and supposed to deal with some kind of social investigation. Some of these questions come direct from the insane asylums, but others purport to come from students, investigators, and social workers. But wherever they come from, they are rapidly developing into a first class national nuisance.

Here for example on my desk is a letter which reads:

"I am a graduate of the Myopia Woman's College of Agricultural Technology, and I am making a special investigation of the government ownership of cold storage plants. Will you please write me the history of any three governments which you know to possess cold storage plants? Will you also let me have your opinion on coldness, on storage, and on plants?"

Here is another one that came in by the same mail:

"I am a social worker in Nut College, Nutwood on the Hum, and am making out a chart or diagram to show whether the length of the human ear is receding or going right ahead. Will you kindly measure your ears and let me know about their growth? Keep me advised if they start."

Along with these are letters asking me to give my opinion, with reasons, whether or not elected aldermen are more crooked than aldermen not even fit to be elected; asking where I stand on the short ballot and what I think of prison reform and the union of the Presbyterian churches.

I have come to the conclusion that something decisive has got to be done about these questionnaires; so I have decided in the interests of myself and other sufferers to write out a model answer for one of them and afterwards to let that answer suffice for all the others. Here is the one that I have selected for answering. I didn't make it up. It is the genuine article, as anyone used to these things will recognize at once.

It runs as follows:

"Dear Sir:

"I am an American college student and I have been selected along with Mr. John Q. Beanhead of the class of 1926, of whom you may have heard, to represent the Bohunk Agriculture College in the forthcoming debate against Skidoo Academy. Our subject of debate is to be on the question: Resolved, that the United States should adopt a parliamentary system of government. Knowing that you have the knowledge of these problems, and trusting that you will be pleased to answer at once, I have selected the following questions which I hope will not take too much of your valuable time to answer:

"1. How does the efficiency of the British government compare with that of the United States?

"2. Do you think the minority has too much power in the United States?

"3. What is your opinion of a democracy?

"4. What is a responsible government?

"5. How would the adoption of the British system affect our Supreme Court?

"I will sincerely appreciate any further suggestions which you may care to make in answer to these questions or concerning any advantage or defect of either system, or any other system.

"Yours truly,
"O. Y. KNOTT."

The answer which I prepared for Mr. Knott reads as follows:

"Dear Sir:

"As soon as I heard from your letter that the big debate is on between Bohunk and Skidoo, I was thrilled with excitement. Can we win it? Can we put enough international energy behind you and Mr. Beanhead (Do I know of him? How *can* you ask it?) to drive the thing through? I want to say at once that in this business you are to regard my own time as absolutely valueless. I may tell you frankly that from now until the big debate is pulled off I purpose to lay aside every other concern in life and devote myself to your service. I couldn't possibly answer your question in any other way.

"So now let turn to your actual questions. You ask first, 'How does the efficiency of the British government compare with that of the United States?'

"Here is a nice, straightforward, manly question. You won't object if my answer is of rather extended length, and you must not mind if it takes me a week to get it ready for you. I shall not only have to handle a good deal of historical material, but I also propose to cable to Mr. Stanley Baldwin and ask him how the efficiency of his government is standing right now.

"Your next question asks whether the minority has too much power in the United States. Again a wonderfully shrewd inquiry. How *do* you manage to think of these things? Has it too much power? Let me think a little. In order to answer your question, I'm afraid I shall have to read over the history of the United States from the Declaration of Independence.

"You ask next, What is my opinion of a democracy? This I can answer briefly. It is the form of government under which you are permitted to live.

"Your next question is, 'What is a responsible government?' I admit the keenness of the inquiry. It is amazing the way you get to the center of things. But I am not prepared. Give me a month on this, if you possibly can.

"Your last question (for the present) reads 'How would the adoption of the British System affect our Supreme Court?' Here again I can hardly answer without perhaps fatiguing you with details. But I will write to Justice Taft and to Lord Reading and while we are waiting for their answers perhaps you would care to send me along a few more questions. I can be working on them in my spare time."

I had written the above letter and then on second thoughts I decided not to send it. What would be the use? The kind of young man who sends out the questionnaires is quite impervious to satire.

The only thing to do is to try to form a league of grown-up people who refuse to be investigated. I propose to be the first in it. Henceforth I will answer no questions except to the census taker and the income tax man.

If any college girl is investigating the upward trend of mortality among mules or the downward movement of morality among humans, she need not come to me. If any young man is making a chart or diagram or a graph to show the per capita increase of crime let him go to the penitentiary. My door henceforth is closed.

This Expiring World

I have just been reading in the press the agonizing statement that there are only 4,000,000,000,000 cords of pulp wood left in the world, and that in another fifty years it will be all gone. After that there will be no pulp. Who is it that is consuming all this pulp, I do not know. I am sure that in my own home, apart from a little at breakfast, we don't use any.

But the main point is that in fifty years it will all be finished. In fifty years from now, where there used to be great forests of pulp-trees reaching to the furthest horizon, there will be nothing but a sweep of bare rolling rocks, lifeless and untenanted, where nothing will be heard except the mournful cry of the waterfowl circling in the empty sky over what was once the forests of North America.

Or no—I forgot. It seems that there will be no waterfowl either. In the very same newspaper I read that the waterfowl of America are disappearing so fast that in another forty years they will be extinct. Parts of the country that only a few years ago were literally black with black duck, teal, ptarmigan, and pemmican now scarcely support one flamingo to the square mile. In another generation the whole continent will have turned into farms, fields, motor roads, and the motor cars will have penetrated everywhere.

Motor cars, did I say? I fear I am in error there again. In forty years there will be no motor cars. Gasoline, it is certain, is running out. Professor Glumb of Midnight, Alaska, has just made a calculation to show that at the rate at which we are using up the world's gasoline, the supply will end in forty years.

He warns us that even now there are only 4,000,000,000,000,000 gallons in sight. There may be just a little more, he thinks, under the Red Sea; he has not been down, but he doubts if there are more than a couple of million billion gallons. In a little time it will be all gone. The motor cars will stand packed in rows and it won't be possible to move them an inch.

And what is worse, it won't be any use trying to substitute coal. There won't be any. It is to run out the year before gasoline. Our reckless use of it all through the nineteenth century has brought us to the point where there are only 10,000,000,000,000 tons left. Assuming that we go on consuming it, even at our present rate, the last clinkers will be raked out of the last furnace in 1964. After that the furnace man will simply draw his salary and sit in the cellar: there won't be a thing for him to do.

At first some of the scientists—such as Professor Hoopitup of Joy College—were inclined to think that electricity might take the place of coal as a source of power, heat, light, and food. But it appears not. The electricity is nearly all gone. Already the Chicago drainage canal has lowered Niagara Falls the tenth of an inch, and in places where there was once the white foaming cataract leaping in a sheet of water a foot thick, there is now only eleven inches and nine-tenths.

We may perhaps last on a little longer if we dam the St. Lawrence, and dam the drainage canal, and dam the Hudson—in short, if we dam the whole continent up and down. But the end is in sight. In another forty years the last kilowatt of electricity will have been consumed, and the electric apparatus will be put in a museum, and exhibited as a relic of the past to the children of the future.

Children? No, no, I forgot. It is hardly likely there will be any, forty years hence. The children are disappearing as rapidly as the gasoline and the waterfowl. It is estimated that the increase of the birth rate on this continent is steadily falling. A few years ago it was 40 per thousand, then it sank to 20, then it passed to 10, and now it is down to decimal four something. If this means anything it means that today we have an average of a thousand adults to decimal four something of a child. The human race on this continent is coming to a full stop.

Moreover, the same fate that is happening to gasoline and coal seems to be overtaking the things of the mind. It is, for example, a subject of universal remark that statesmen seem to be dying out. There may be a few very old statesmen still staggering round, but as a class they are done. In the same way there are no orators: they're gone. And everybody knows that there is hardly such a thing left now as a gentleman of the old school. I think that one was seen a month or so ago somewhere in a marsh in Virginia. But that's about the last. In short, civility is dead, polite culture is gone, and manners are almost extinct.

On the other side of the account I can find nothing conspicuous except the very notable increase of the criminal class. It has recently been calculated by Professor Crook (graduate of Harvard and Sing Sing) that within forty years every other man will belong to the criminal class; and even the man who isn't the other man will be pretty tough himself.

In other words, the outlook is bad. As I see it, there is nothing for it but to enjoy ourselves while we can. The wise man will go out, while it is still possible, and get some pulp and a pint of gasoline and a chunk of coal and have a big time.

Are We Fascinated with Crime?

Most readers will agree with me that of late the newspapers have been fine reading. First there was the account of the new murder in Cleveland where the body was sent away by express. Then there was the story of the bob-haired bandit—it didn't say whether man or woman—who held up an entire subway station and got clean away with the iron ticket office. There was the man who killed his mother-in-law and refused to give any reason, and the high-school girl of fifteen who shot the teacher because he tried to teach her algebra. Along with this there were two kidnappings, three disappearances of reputable citizens, two degeneracies and a little sprinkling of bank robberies and train wrecking in Arkansas. Take it all in all it made the morning paper well worth reading. With a sheet of news like that the trip on the street car to one's work passes like a moment.

There were of course the foreign murders, too. But I generally keep them for my lunch hour. I find it hard to get up the same interest when they murder Turks and Finns and Letts as when you have the thing right at home. One body packed in a trunk in Cleveland and sent by express is better to me than a whole car-load lot of Letts. I get more out of it. But taking them all together and adding up the home and foreign crimes I found that yesterday's paper was thirty per cent straight criminality. That

I think is about a record and will compare very favorably with Soviet Russia or with the Dark Ages. Indeed I doubt if the Dark Ages, even in equatorial Africa, had anything on us in point of interest in crime.

My first feeling over this record was one of pride. But afterwards on reflection I began to feel a little bit disturbed about it, and to wonder whether as a race and a generation we are not getting morbidly fascinated with crime, and liable to suffer for it!

Our newspapers are filled with bandits, safe breakers, home wreckers, crooks, policemen and penitentiaries. The stories that sell best are stories in which there is murder right straight off on the first page. The sneaking fascination of the daring criminal has put the soldier and the patriot nowhere. Stories of brave men who give their lives for their country are now written only for children. Grown up people read about daring criminals, who talk worse English than the first year class at a college and call a trust company a "crib" and a bank manager a "stiff." That is the kind of literature that is making Shakespeare and Milton and Emerson sound like a lecture on anthropology.

If a rich man is killed by his chauffeur in Tampa, Florida, and his body hidden in the gasoline tank, why should you and I worry? We don't live in Tampa and we have no chauffeur and gasoline is too expensive for us to waste like that.

Yet a whole continent will have to sit up and read a column of news about such a simple little event as that.

I suppose that in a sense this hideous interest in crime and its punishment is as old as humanity. It must have created quite a stir when Cain killed Abel. On our own continent our oldest knowledge of manners and customs is the story of the Indian's delight in torture, feebly paralleled by the Puritan's pleasure in throwing rotten eggs at a sinner in the stocks. In what are now called the "good old times" in England, say about the time of the Tudors, people used to tramp long distances with a "lunch" in their pockets to go and see a man burnt in a sheet of white flame. One reads stories of people taking little children to executions and holding them up to see. Even when the days of the burning were over people still gathered in crowds of a morning round Newgate jail in London to see the hangings. Rare sport it must have been. For a specially good show they were there the night before, sitting up all night to hold the good places.

In what we call the civilized countries mankind has forbidden itself the pleasure of inflicting tortures and watching executions. But we are breaking out in a new spot. The same evil instinct finds another vent. Since we are not allowed any longer to go to executions and to take a personal part in crimes we like to read about them. And the vast apparatus of our press and our telegraph can give us opportunities in this direction of which our ancestors never dreamed. Think what could have been made by a first class New York newspaper organization, and by the moving picture people, of the burning of Latimer and Ridley? It seems like a lost opportunity.

Under our conditions we don't have to confine ourselves, as the man of two centuries ago did, to the crimes of our own neighbourhood. We can gather them in from all the world. He had to be content with a hanging every now and then. We can have a dozen or two every day, and if we care to count Finns and Letts, easily a hundred.

But the moralist—that's me—is bound to ask where is it leading us? What is the result of it on our minds and characters, this everlasting dwelling on crime. Somebody wrote long ago that—

Vice is a monster of such hideous mien,
That to be hated needs but to be seen,
But too oft seen, familiar with her face
We first endure, then pity, then embrace.

The same is true of crime. The everlasting depiction and perusal of it corrupts the mind—not yours of course, my dear reader, because you are strong minded. But it corrupts the feeble mind. Personally I admit that I found myself reflecting on the man that killed his mother-in-law and gave no reason and wondering perhaps—but let it go.

Everybody knows that this North American Continent—the people of the United States, the Canadians, the Mexicans and the Eskimos—is undergoing a wave of crime such as was never known before. Some people attribute this to one thing, some to another. Some say it is because of the decline of Presbyterianism, and some say it is an effect of motor cars. But my own idea is that the chief cause of it is crime literature, crime news and universal outbreak of crime interest.

One naturally asks what are we going to do about it? Many people would immediately suggest that the first thing to be done is to amend the federal constitution of the United States so as to forbid all morbid interest in crime; and then to pass a series of state statutes for hanging anybody who takes too much interest in hanging.

I don't think that the evil can be cured that way. That is a method of doing things that has worn pretty thin. In the United States and Canada we have got so many prohibitive and preventive statutes already that we are in danger of all being in jail before we are done with it. The only remedy is the slow but efficacious force of public opinion of what used to be called, in days before legislatures made statutes, the working of the spirit.

For social evils the first remedy is a social consciousness of the evil. If the community becomes conscious of its unwholesome morbid interest in crime, that already will start the cure. Sensible persons here and there will begin to take the mote—or the motor—out of their own eye—as a first step toward taking the beam out of their neighbors. Newspapers and magazine makers and moving picture makers have no innate desire to foist crime news on the public. They are probably sick of it. Left to themselves they would rather go fishing or dig in the garden. The notion that a newspaper reporter is half brother to the criminal is erroneous. In point of news, and amusements and pictures, the public always gets what the public wants. This is a pity, but it is so.

There is no need for anybody to start a "national movement" in this matter. Personally I refuse to join in it. I have been dragged into too many already—swatting flies, and going to see mother on May 11th, and never spitting except at home—my time is all taken up with them.

But anybody can start a movement by beginning with himself. That's what I mean to do. Henceforth it is of no use for a newspaper editor to hand me out stories of crime and violence. I'm done with them. I want to read the quiet stuff—about how the autumn hoe crop is looking, and about the latest lectures on paleontology and how cold it has turned at Nome in Alaska. That kind of thing improves the human mind and does nothing but good.

But before I do start, I'd just like to have one little peep at that news I see in today's paper about the man who murdered the barber in Evansville because he was too slow in shaving him. That sounds good, but after that I'm done.

VII

Round Our City

At the Ladies' Culture Club

A Lecture on the Fourth Dimension

It has become a fixed understanding that with each approaching winter there begins the open season for the various Ladies' Culture Clubs. I suppose that this kind of club exists in everybody else's town just as it does in mine. We have one in my town that meets at eleven (every other Tuesday), has just a small cup of coffee and just a tiny sandwich, hears an hour's talk, usually on music or art, and then goes home.

Then there's one that meets at lunch, every second Thursday and every third Tuesday, quite informally, just eats a tiny beefsteak with a nice dish of apple pie after it and listens to a speech on national affairs, excluding of course all reference to political parties or politics, or public opinion, and all references to actual individuals or actual facts.

After that there's a club, mostly of older women, which meets at three (without refreshments till after) and discusses social problems such as how to keep younger women in hand. This club meets every first Monday in the month unless it falls at the beginning of a week.

But the club that has most interested me recently is the Ladies' Culture Club because I had the honor of visiting it a little while ago. The club was founded two winters ago—as was explained to me over the ice cream by the president—with the idea that it is a pity that women know so little of science and that nowadays science is really becoming a quite important thing, and when you think of radio and electrons and atoms and things like that one ought to know something about them for fear of your feeling ignorant.

So when the club was founded it was made absolutely and exclusively a woman's club, men taking no part in it whatever, except that men are invited to be the speakers and to sit on the platform and attend the meetings.

The day I was there the meeting was held in the ballroom of the new Grand Palaver hotel, because that is a simple place suitable for science. There were no decorations except flowers and no music except a Hungarian orchestra which stopped the moment the lecture began. This is a rule of the club.

The attendance was so large that several of the ladies remarked with pride that it would hardly have been possible to get an equal number of men to come at three o'clock in the afternoon to listen to a lecture on Four Dimensional Space.

The great mass of members were seated in chairs on the floor of the ballroom with a certain number of men here and there among them; but they were a peculiar kind of men. The president and a group of ladies were on a raised platform and they had in the middle of them Professor Droon who was to lecture on Four Dimensional Space. In front of him they had put a little table with a glass and water, enough water to last a camel for a four days' trip. Behind Professor Droon was a barricade of chairs and plants with spikes. He couldn't escape.

The President rose and made the regulation announcement that there were a good many members who had not yet paid their fees this season and it was desirable that they should do so owing to the high cost of bringing lecturers to the club.

She then picked up a piece of paper and read from it as follows:

"The Pythagorean philosophers as well as Philolans and Hicetus of Syracuse conceived of space as immaterial. The Alexandrine geometers substituted a conception of rigid coordinates which has dominated all scientific thinking until our own day. I will now introduce Professor Droon who will address the members on Four Dimensional Space if the ladies near the doorway will kindly occupy the chairs which are still empty at the front."

Professor Droon, rising behind the water jug, requested the audience in a low voice to dismiss from their minds all preconceived notions of the spatial content of the universe. When they had done this, he asked them in a whisper to disregard the familiar postulate in regard to parallel lines. Indeed, it would be far better, he murmured, if they dismissed all thought of lines as such and substituted the idea of motion through a series of loci conceived as instantaneous in time.

After this he drank half the water and started.

In the address which followed and which lasted for one hour and forty minutes, it was clear that the audience were held in rapt attention. They never removed their eyes from the lecturer's face and remained soundless except that there was a certain amount of interested whispering each time he drank water.

When he mentioned that Euclid, the geometrician, was married four times there were distinct signs of amusement. There was a sigh of commiseration when he said that Archimedes was killed by a Roman soldier just as he was solving a problem in mechanics. And when he mentioned the name of Christopher Columbus there was obvious and general satisfaction.

In fact, the audience followed the lecture word for word. And when at length the professor asked in a whisper whether we could any longer maintain the conception of a discrete universe absolute in time and drank the rest of the water and sat down, the audience knew that it was the end of the lecture and there was a distinct wave of applause.

The comments of the audience as they flowed out of the hall showed how interested they had been. I heard one lady remark that Professor Droon had what she would call a sympathetic face; another said, yes, except that his ears stuck out too far.

Another said that she had heard that he was a very difficult man to live with; and another said that she imagined that all scientists must be because she had a friend who knew a lady who had lived in the same house all one winter with the Marconis and very often Marconi wouldn't eat. There was a good deal of comment on the way the professor's tie was up near his ear and a general feeling that he probably needed looking after.

There was a notice at the door where we went out which said that the next lecture would be by Professor Floyd of the college department of botany on The Morphology of Gymnosperms. They say there will be a big attendance again.

Our Own Business Barometer

For Use in Stock Exchanges and Stock Yards

Recently, with the assistance of a group of experts, I have been going into the statistical forecast business.

I have been led to do this by noticing how popular this kind of thing has come to be. All over the country there are banks and trust companies, and statistical bureaus and college departments that send out surveys of business conditions and prophecies of what good business is going to do. In any good high school the senior commercial class the prepared to work out a chart showing what "world conditions" are going to be next month.

I note that this kind of literature is having a wonderful popularity. Many people are so busy nowadays that they have hardly time to read even the latest crime news, such as how the bob-eared bandit held up the Grand Central Station and got away with the entire Information Stand. But they can always find a few leisure moments for reading about the probable effect of the failure of the Siamese rice crop on the motor car industry.

In other words, this kind of literature has come to stay. There is henceforth a regular demand for a wide-eyed, clear-sighted survey of the business field. It is for this reason that I have been led to go into it and with the aid of experts am prepared to offer for the use of business men a brief survey of the prospects of the globe for next month.

We decided, naturally, to begin with the discussion of export wheat. It is the custom of all survey makers to start with the wheat situation and we follow their example. We find that advices from Argentine, from Turkestan and from Simcoe County, Ontario, indicate that the wheat situation is easier than it was. My experts place the Russian output at about half a billion poods while the Egyptian crop is not likely to fall below two hundred million quids. Add to this a Chinese autumn production of at least a million chunks and a first impression is one of exuberance if not hilarity.

But other factors are less reassuring.

There is a visible supply of 10,000,000 bushels of wheat in the elevators at the head of the Great Lakes and 10,000,000 bushels in transit to Liverpool, but on the other hand the Japanese consumption of wheat bread has fallen 3.6 per cent in the last month and the Chinese will hardly touch it.

Disturbed political conditions in the Argentine republic may result in the cessation of Argentine export but on the other hand improved conditions in Soviet Russia may result in the liberation of the Russian supply. The wheat crop in Hindoostan is said to be in serious danger of destruction from rust but as against that the wheat crop in Persia looks great. Speculative buying on the European exchanges may force the price up but on the other hand speculative selling may force it down. Our expert opinion therefore is that we don't know. Wheat may go up in price; but it may not.

General business conditions, in our opinion, show distinct signs of improvement but they also show unmistakable signs of getting worse. There were 2,100 business failures reported last month in the United States and Canada. But in a way that's nothing. There are a great many people who deserve to fail. Bank deposits, however, increased from $21,161,482,936.84 to $22,668,931,056.48, or something like that; we are speaking only from memory.

Sterling exchange in New York opened for the month at $4.84, rose sharply to $4.84 $^{26}/_{32}$, reacted to $4.83 and then moved steadily up to $4.89. Why it did this we have been unable to find out.

Meantime the Brazilian revolution has focused financial attention on the milreis. As far as we can understand what the milreis did, it seems to have risen upwards, fallen down, lain flat, tried to get up, failed, raised itself again and then flopped. Our experts are not prepared to give any opinion as to what the milreis will do next. Some people think this is a good time to buy it, but if it was ours we should sell it. We wouldn't want it round the place.

The movement of prices has been in various directions, some up, some down and some sideways. There was a five per cent drop in Portland cement, and a ten per cent fall in pig iron. But we ourselves are not using any just now and were more affected by the rise of 2 cents a gallon in gasoline which hit us hard and shortened our investigations by about ten miles a day.

During the same period under consideration there have been strikes, lockouts, earthquakes, cloudbursts, insurrections and other disturbing conditions beyond even the power of a senior commercial class to calculate.

Taking all these factors into consideration our conclusion upon the whole is that we don't know what business is going to do next month, and we don't believe that anyone else does. It is our humble opinion that a problem which contains among its factors the weather, earthquakes, snowstorms, revolutions, insurrections, labor, the tariff, the wishes and desires of one and three quarter billions of human beings and the legislation of over a thousand legislatures is a little beyond us.

We will go a little further. We incline to believe, and our experts agree with us (they are paid to), that all this business barometer, statistical forecast stuff means nothing more than the age-long desire of the human race for prophecies. There is no doubt people like to listen to a good prophecy. Children have their fortunes read in the leaves of tea-cups. Servant girls pay a quarter to have a Negress do it with a pack of cards.

And cultivated people pay five dollars to get a divination from a Persian astrologer hailing from East Thirteenth Street, New York.

And so the business man has started up his own particular form of divination in his new statistical forecast. Our advice to our business clients (as we do not propose to stay in the forecast business) is this. If you want a really good forecast don't bother with all the statistics and the index numbers and the averages. Go and get your fortune told in the good old-fashioned way in words of this sort:

"There is a fair woman coming into your life and there is also a dark woman. One of them will bring you great happiness but beware of the other. You are going to strike a great opportunity of getting rich; but you are also in danger of getting poor. You have nerve but you lack confidence, but if you will cherish your belief in yourself you will never know what a boob you really are. One dollar."

That is the kind of forecast that has been going since the days of the Pharaohs and is still the best known. Stick to it.

My Pink Suit

A Study in the New Fashions for Men

This morning I put on my pink suit for the first time, and I must say it looked too cute for anything. I felt of course that it was an innovation and a great change, but I was glad to be in it.

I suppose everybody has been reading all about the new fashions for men and how over in London and Paris all the men are wearing suits of pink and sky blue and chrome yellow. All the London and Paris papers that I have seen say that the new suits are a great success and that the idea is all the rage. But, as I say, everybody knows about that and I don't need to explain it. I only wanted to talk about my own suit.

I had it made out of pink georgette undershot with a deep magenta and crossed with au invisible slate blue so that the material shimmers in the light with different colors, and when I walk up and down in front of a long mirror (I bought the mirror at the same time as the suit), the colors run up and down my back in ripples of moving light. The magenta color seems to suit my figure, though several of my very best friends say that personally they think that they prefer the slate.

I had two or three men over in the morning to sit up in my room and watch me walk up and down in front of the glass. Of course, ordinarily at that time of the day they would be at their business, but I just telephoned over to them and told them that my new suit was such a darling that they simply *must* come over and see it. So they came over and we just sat around while I put on one part of the suit after another and showed it off in the long glass.

They all agreed that the color was lovely and they said they were just crazy to get a suit like mine. One said that he thought that for himself the color might be a little young and that for his age he would rather have a bottle green or a peacock blue—something a little older, but I told him that I was quite sure he could wear anything just as young as anybody. In fact, I know a man who is past sixty, who can wear pink for evening wear, and who looks just as young in it as anybody else would.

Perhaps I should explain, as I know a lot of my friends would like to know about it, just how I had my suit cut. The coat is made rather full at the chest and then brought in at the waist line and cut out again very full about the hips with gores and with ruffled insertions of pleated chiffon at the point where the back falls to the hips.

It has a ruching round the neck and is wattled around the collar with an accordion frill brought round just below the ears and then thrown back so as to show the back of the neck. Some of my friends thought that instead of a ruching they would rather have had a little frill of lace so cut as to show the throat. But I doubt whether, with my throat, this would be so good.

The buttons are in a large size of mother-of-pearl and are carried in a bold line edgeways from the shoulder to the waist with two more buttons larger still, behind at the place where the back dips in above the hips.

Everybody agreed that the buttons are very bold, but they thought that they would be quieter on the street than in the house.

The waistcoat is cut very simply and snugly so as to show the curve of the stomach as far as possible. It has just one little pink bow at the bottom, but beyond that it is quite plain. One or two of my friends thought that it might be a little too severe, but most of us agreed that though it might seem severe indoors it wouldn't be so at all out of doors, especially on high ground.

The trousers are cut very snug around the line of the hips with gored insertion at each side so as to give free play for leaping or jumping and then are flared out to the knee where they are quite full and wide. They end, absolutely, only a little way below the knee and of course they need to be worn over clocked stockings or else I have to have my legs tattooed. They seem terribly short when I put them on, but everybody says that it is the length they are wearing in Paris and in London and that some of the men are even cutting off their trousers half way between the waistcoat and the knee.

I must say that I felt a little strange in my pink suit when I went out presently on the street in it. One of the men asked me to lunch with him, so I went out in my suit with just a little straw hat, half-size, and a bunch of violets in the lapel of my coat. I felt quite shy at first and quite different from my usual self, and I think I even blushed when some one came across to my table at lunch and told me he had never seen me look so well.

I went over to my office in the afternoon and the very first person who came in to do business with me said he was delighted with my suit, and so we sat and talked about it for a long time and he told me of an awfully good shirtmaker that he could recommend if I wanted to get some of the shirts they are wearing. He said that over in London they are all going in for fancy shirts to match the new suits and that the colors they wear are the most daring you can imagine. He told me that a friend of his, quite an elderly man, had just got back from the other side wearing a canary-colored shirt with pussy willow tassels round his neck, and that it was really quite becoming.

Other people came into my office later in the day and we did nothing but talk about the new styles and how delicious it is going to be for men to dress in all the colors they like to wear.

On my way home in the street car which was rather crowded, a man got up and gave me his seat, and of course I thanked him with a smile that showed all my teeth, but I didn't speak to him because I wasn't sure whether I ought to speak to strangers in my pink suit.

Well, when I got home I first stood and looked at myself in the long glass for quite a while. And then—I don't know just why—I went and took off my new pink costume and put on the old gray suit that I had worn the day before. It was made, as far as I remember, about two and a half, or else four and a half, years ago.

It has no ruching, crocheting, or insertions in it, and it isn't flared or gored or pleated, and it doesn't sweep boldly round the hips or the neck or anywhere. It has a bulge here and there where I have sat on it or knelt in it or hung it on the electric light. The pockets of it stick out a good deal from having been filled up with pipes and tins of tobacco and fishing tackle. There is more or less ink on it, but nothing that really injures it for use.

Somehow I think I'll go back to it.

Why I Left Our Social Workers' Guild

We recently started in our town—as I suppose most people would have started in most towns—an organization called the Social Workers' Guild. Our idea was that we would try to do good in the community around us. We would send children from the slums down to the sea, and bring children up from the sea to go to college. Wherever we find a poor widow living in a basement with a string of children and a new baby appearing every year, we would turn up on the threshold with a great basketful of toys. If the plumber was out of work and nearly in despair, just then one of our agents would drop a broken furnace in his lap. Anybody who has ever felt the fascination of that kind of thing, knows just what I mean.

And the best of it all was that all the cost of doing good was to be met by the proceeds of entertainments and amusements organized by the Guild, so that really we gave our money without knowing it and had all the fun thrown in.

I don't want to say a single word against the general idea of such Social Guilds as ours. They are certainly very noble in intention. But as I have been led to terminate absolutely and forever my own membership of the Guild, I will explain the reason for my doing so by publishing my correspondence with Mr. J. Brazil Nut, the secretary of the league, or rather the series of letters sent by Mr. Brazil Nut to me.

Letter No. 1

Dear Sir,

I beg to inform you that the Committee of the Guild has discovered a very distressing case of a family who came here from Cyprus two years ago and are anxious to return home but are unable to do so. At the present time they are living in a small apartment of which we need only to say that not a single window faces the south, that there is no elevator although the place is three stories high, and that the condition of the front steps is deplorable and the door bell apparently *permanently out of order.* The landlord, we regret to say, stubbornly refuses to knock the place down.

The father of the family is a good workman and only too willing to work. His trade is that of a camel driver and hitherto he has been unable to find a camel. But he says that if money could be found he would go back to Cyprus where he knows of a camel.

Our Committee considering the case a deserving one, has decided to hold a dance in the Social Workers' Hall on Saturday evening next. It is proposed to engage Bimbasti's orchestra and, in view of the distressing nature of the case, to serve a light supper for which tables may be reserved by telephone. The price of the tickets, of which I am venturing to send you two, will be $10.00 each, the ticket carrying with it the privilege of eating supper, or of leaving without eating it, as may be preferred.

Yours very faithfully,
J. Brazil Nut
Secretary of the S.W.G.

Letter No. 2

Dear Sir,

I have much pleasure in thanking you for your very generous subscription for two tickets for the dance and supper given last week by the Guild in aid of a distressed family from Cyprus, and informing you that the affair was organized and carried through with great success and with great enjoyment by all concerned. Some fifty couples participated in the dancing, and the whole, or at least seventy-five per cent, of the supper was eaten on the spot.

Unfortunately the expenses of the affair proved more heavy than was expected. Taking into account the fee for Bimbasti's orchestra and the cost of bunting, flowers and supper, our Committee is faced with a deficit of about five hundred dollars. Some of the ladies of the Committee have proposed that we give the entire deficit to the family from Cyprus, or perhaps try to buy them a camel with it.

But the general feeling is in favor of carrying the deficit forward and wiping it out by an informal vaudeville entertainment to be held in the Hall of the Guild next Saturday evening. In view of the high cost of the talent to be engaged we have decided to place the tickets at $25.00 or three for $100.00. I am venturing to send you five, which you are at entire liberty to keep, and send me the money, or, if you prefer to do so, you may return the tickets with the money.

Meantime I regret to say that our field committee has reported one or two more very distressing cases. We have on our hands the case of a man, a master mechanic, by trade a maker of blow torches, who appears hopelessly addicted to drink. The man himself confesses that he is quite unable to get along without alcohol. Our workers find it extremely difficult, under present conditions, to get him any. But they think, and the man himself agrees, that if they could give this man a sea trip to South America he would need no alcohol at least until his return. Our Committee are also anxious to obtain funds to buy a wooden leg, for a professional beggar who needs it in his business. It seems that he has inadvertently lost the leg he had. A week ago after his work he put his leg into his valise and carried it home as usual. But there in some way it disappeared.

It is now proposed that all these cases shall be collectively disposed of by our special vaudeville entertainment, and I trust that you will undertake to take at least five tickets.

Very faithfully,
J. Brazil Nut
Secretary of the S.W.G.

Letter No. 3

Dear Sir,
In thanking you for your very generous subscription for five tickets for the Guild Vaudeville entertainment of last Saturday which you were not able to attend, I desire to inform you that the performance was an unqualified success. Although slightly delayed in starting and not beginning until a quarter to eleven and briefly interrupted later on by the going out of the electric lights for half an hour, the whole affair was most enjoyable. The amateur performance of our treasurer Mr. Jones with the dumb-bells—quite as heavy as anything seen on the stage—was voted extraordinary and the Social Guild Girls Christian Chorus might have been mistaken for regular music hall work.

Unfortunately the paid numbers cost us heavily and out of all proportion to our receipts. I regret to say that we are face to face with a deficit of some two thousand dollars.

In order to avoid the heavy personal assessment represented by this sum, our committee now proposes to hold, three weeks from today, an indoor Kermesse or Bazaar to last for three days. It is suggested that we engage the armories building and have the floor divided up into booths with little streets in between, with a restaurant and dance floor. The Kermesse will undertake the sale of a great variety of goods which will be purchased in advance by funds advanced by various members of the Guild who have been elected Patrons and Associate Patrons. It is understood that any Associate Patron may advance $1,000, receiving it back out of the profits, while a Patron has the privilege of advancing

$2,000. I am glad to inform you that you have been elected unanimously to be a Patron.

Our needs of the profits of this Kermesse are all the greater insomuch as the cases reported by our field workers increase in numbers and in gravity. We have before us the cast of a family from Honolulu who have recently arrived here and are sorry that they came. They think they would like to go to Tugugigalpa in Honduras—either there or Winnipeg. We have also a skilled mechanic, very deserving, whose trade was making eye-pieces for the periscopes of German submarines and who is unable to find work.

But we look confidently to the success of our forthcoming Kermesse to put everything on a new footing.

Very faithfully yours,
J. Brazil Nut

Letter No. 4

Dear Sir,
In writing to inform you of the disastrous failure of the Kermesse, held by this Guild, for which your name was put down as a Patron, we feel it only proper to say that the failure was due to no lack of interest or enthusiasm on the part of our members. The careful revision of our accounts by experts seems to show that the financial failure arose very largely from the fact that the articles disposed of were sold at a much lower price than what was paid for them. Some of our best experts agree that this would involve a loss of money. But others note that we lost money also from the fact that we had to pay for rent, for heat, for light as well as for illumination and warmth.

But all agree that there need have been no loss if the premises had been bigger, the restaurant larger, the music louder, the crowds greater and the deficit heavier. I am now laying before our committee a plan for holding a Winter Festival which is to last one month. It will be held in one of the larger hotels, the entire building being taken over for our purpose. We shall also take over one of the railway stations and probably one of the abattoirs and two or three of the larger provision houses.

As before we are nominating patrons who are entitled to underwrite, or subscribe, or guarantee, any sum over $50,000 which they feel disposed to offer. All such sums will be paid back on the last day of the festival.

Yours very faithfully,
J. Brazil Nut

Letter No. 5

(This time from the Honorary President of the Society—Mr. Tridout Solidhead, one of our leading business men.)

Dear Sir,
In refusing to accept your very generous resignation from the Social Workers' Guild, I beg to inform you that we have decided to suspend for the present the plan of a winter festival proposed by Mr. Brazil Nut. Instead of this we are accepting the resignation of Mr. Nut from his position of secretary and we are proposing to give him a gold watch with a chain and padlock as a mark of our esteem. The presentation will be made at a dinner which will be given to Mr. Nut before he is taken away to where he is going. I am sure that you will be delighted to subscribe to the dinner (25 cents) and to the cost of the watch (10 cents per member).

Our new committee have looked into some of our urgent field cases and disposed of them. It appears that the family from Cyprus were alluding to Cyprus, Ohio, and we have invited them to walk there. The man from Honolulu we are having taught by a Negro to play the Hawaiian ukelele, and we have got for the man with the wooden leg a situation as a timber cruiser with a lumber company. We have meantime put the question of the back deficit into the hands of a group of business men. They propose to wipe it out by holding a small entertainment at which (by a special license from the municipality) they will operate a roulette table, and a faro bank, with the sale of cold drinks, selected by a business committee, on the side. They are now looking for a suitable place, about twelve by fifteen, to hold this entertainment in.

Meantime we trust you will reconsider your resignation. We are having this matter of a public charity looked into by some of our best business men. Already they incline to the idea that if it is carried on in the right spirit and with proper energy and self-sacrifice, there may be money in it.

Very sincerely,
A. Tridout Solidhead

VIII

The Christmas Ghost

The Christmas Ghost

Unemployment in One of our Oldest Industries

The other night I was sitting up late—away after nine o'clock—thinking about Christmas because it was getting near at hand. And, like everybody else who muses on that subject, I was thinking of the great changes that have taken place in regard to Christmas. I was contrasting Christmas in the old country house of a century ago, with the fires roaring up the chimneys, and Christmas in the modern apartment on the ninth floor with the gasoline generator turned on for the maid's bath.

I was thinking of the old stage coach on the snowy road with its roof piled high with Christmas turkeys and a rosy-faced "guard" blowing on a keybugle and the passengers getting down every mile or so at a crooked inn to drink hot spiced ale—and I was comparing all that with the upper berth No. 6, car 220, train No. 53.

I was thinking of the Christmas landscape of long ago when night settled down upon it with the twinkle of light from the houses miles apart among the spruce trees, and contrasting the scene with the glare of motor lights upon the highways of today. I was thinking of the lonely highwayman shivering round with his clumsy pistols, and comparing the poor fellow's efforts with the high class bandits of today blowing up a steel express car with nitroglycerine and disappearing in a roar of gasoline explosions.

In other words I was contrasting yesterday and today. And on the whole yesterday seemed all to the good.

Nor was it only the warmth and romance and snugness of the old Christmas that seemed superior to our days, but Christmas carried with it then a special kind of thrill with its queer terrors, its empty heaths, its lonely graveyards, and its house that stood alone in a wood, haunted.

And thinking of that it occurred to me how completely the ghost business seems to be dying out of our Christmas literature. Not so very long ago there couldn't be a decent Christmas story or Christmas adventure without a ghost in it, whereas nowadays—

And just at that moment I looked and saw that there was a ghost in the room.

I can't imagine how he got in, but there he was, sitting in the other easy chair in the dark corner away from the firelight. He had on my own dressing gown and one saw but little of his face.

"Are you a ghost?" I asked. "Yes," he said, "worse luck, I am."

I noticed as he spoke that he seemed to wave and shiver as if he were made of smoke. I couldn't help but pity the poor fellow, he seemed so immaterial.

"Do you mind," he went on, in the same dejected tone, "if I sit here and haunt you for a while?"

"By all means," I said, "please do."

"Thanks," he answered, "I haven't had anything decent to work on for years and years. This is Christmas eve, isn't it?"

"Yes," I said, "Christmas Eve."

"Used to be my busiest night," the ghost complained, "best night of the whole year—and now—say," he said, "would you believe it! I went down this evening to that dinner dance they have at the Ritz Carlton and I thought I'd haunt it—thought I'd stand behind one of the tables as a silent spectre, the way I used to in King George III's time—"

"Well?" I said.

"They put me out!" groaned the ghost, "the head waiter came up to me and said that he didn't allow silent spectres in the dining room. I was put out."

He groaned again.

"You seem," I said, "rather down on your luck?"

"Can you wonder?" said the ghost, and another shiver rippled up and down him. "I can't get anything to do. Talk of the unemployed—listen!" he went on, speaking with something like animation, "let me tell you the story of my life—"

"Can you make it short?" I said.

"I'll try. A hundred years ago—"

"Oh, I say!" I protested.

"I committed a terrible crime, a murder on the highway—"

"You'd get six months for that nowadays," I said.

"I was never detected. An innocent man was hanged. I died but I couldn't rest. I haunted the house beside the highway where the murder had been done. It had happened on Christmas Eve, and so, every year on that night—"

"I know," I interrupted, "you were heard dragging round a chain and moaning and that sort of thing; I've often read about it."

"Precisely," said the ghost, "and for about eighty years it worked out admirably. People became afraid, the house was deserted, trees and shrubs grew thick around it, the wind whistled through its empty chimneys and its broken windows, and at night the lonely wayfarer went shuddering past and heard with terror the sound of a cry scarce human, while a cold sweat—"

"Quite so," I said, "a cold sweat. And what next?"

"The days of the motor car came and they paved the highways and knocked down the house and built a big garage there, with electricity as bright as day. You can't haunt a garage, can you? I tried to stick on and do a little groaning, but nobody seemed to pay attention; and anyway, I got nervous about the gasoline. I'm too immaterial to be round where there's gasoline. A fellow would blow up, wouldn't he?"

"He might," I said, "so what happened?"

"Well, one day somebody in the garage actually saw me and he threw a monkey wrench at me and told me to get to hell out of the garage. So I went."

"And after that?"

"I haunted round; I've kept on haunting round, but it's no good, there's nothing in it. Houses, hotels, I've tried it all. Once I thought that if I couldn't make a hit any other way, at least I could haunt children. You remember how little children used to live in terror of ghosts and see them in the dark corners of their bedrooms? Well, I admit it was a low down thing to do, but I tried that."

"And it didn't work?"

"Work! I should say not. I went one night to a bedroom where a couple of little boys were sleeping and I started in with a few groans and then half materialized myself, so that I could just be seen. One of the kids sat up in bed and nudged the other and said, 'Say! I do believe there's a ghost in the room!' And the other said, 'Hold on; don't scare him. Let's get the radio set and see if it'll go right through him.'

"They both hopped out of bed as brisk as bees and one called downstairs, 'Dad, we've got a ghost up here! We don't know whether he's just an emanation or partially material. We're going to stick the radio into him—' Believe me," continued the ghost, "that was all I waited to hear. Electricity just knocks me edgeways."

He shuddered. Then he went on.

"Well it's been like that ever since—nowhere to go and nothing to haunt. I've tried all the big hotels, railway stations, everywhere. Once I tried to haunt a Pullman car, but I had hardly started before I observed a notice, '*Quiet is requested for those already retired*,' and I had to quit."

"Well, then," I said, "why don't you just get immaterial or dematerial or whatever you call it, and keep so? Why not go away wherever you belong and stay there?"

"That's the worst of it," answered the ghost, "they won't let us. They haul us back. These spiritualists have learned the trick of it and they just summon us up any time they like. They get a dollar apiece for each materialization, but what do we get?"

The ghost paused and a sort of spasm went all through him. "Gol darn it," he exclaimed, "they're at me now. There's a group of fools somewhere sitting round a table at a Christmas Eve party and they're calling up a ghost just for fun—a darned poor notion of fun, I call it—I'd like to—like to—"

But his voice trailed off. He seemed to collapse as he sat and my dressing gown fell on the floor. And at that moment I heard the ringing of the bells that meant that it was Christmas midnight, and I knew that the poor fellow had been dragged off to work.

finis